Development and Physiology

The Biology of You

Preliminary Edition

By Barbara Kuemerle, Ph. D.
Case Western Reserve University

cognella®
academic publishing

Bassim Hamadeh, CEO and Publisher
Michael Simpson, Vice President of Acquisitions
Jamie Giganti, Senior Managing Editor
Jess Busch, Senior Graphic Designer
Amy Stone, Acquisitions Editor
Mirasol Enriquez, Project Editor
Luiz Ferreira, Senior Licensing Specialist

First published in the United States of America in 2016 by Cognella, Inc.

Printed in the United States of America

ISBN: 978-1-62131-813-2 (pbk)/ 978-1-62131-812-5 (br)

www.cognella.com   800-200-3908

Contents

"If I had an hour to solve a problem, and my life depended on the solution, I would spend the first 55 minutes determining the proper question to ask, for once I know the proper question, I could solve the problem in less than 5 minutes"

Albert Einstein

Preface

"Necessity is the mother of invention." [Franck, R., 1821]

The students were complaining, "You have WAY too many slides!" Time and time again, students consistently gave very low ratings (in the range of 2 out of 5) to the statement, "The textbook and/ or supplementary materials are useful" when evaluating my course:, Development and Physiology. This course is the third in a series of core courses that all biology majors must complete. The students are required to purchase a general biology text to be used in our first and third core courses. But this voluminous and cumbersome general text, which has over 1,300 pages and costs over $200, just wasn't ideal for my course, as much of the information was too generalized. My other option was to require that the students purchase an advanced textbook, but I simply could not find one that was a good fit for the needs of my course. So, I chose to supplement, and supplement I did! (Hence the persistent mantra: "You have WAY too many slides!"). The course of college academics was also undergoing a profound paradigm shift. The time-honored practice of passive learning, where professors flip through seemingly endless PowerPoint slides and students sit placidly in a large lecture hall, was no longer viewed as an adequate instructional method. Academics at the college level should prepare students to be active learners and critical thinkers and not regard them as empty vessels to be filled with facts in the lecture hall.

It was time for a change … for a new plan, a new strategy. I decided to start with what I knew. I had spent most of my adult life as a scientific researcher with little formal training in educational instruction. I asked myself, "How would a researcher propose to evaluate and design a new methodology?" Being a researcher necessitated being frugal. I decided the best way to proceed was not to try to "reinvent the wheel," but rather to use any existing resources that would apply to my course. Outstanding *free* educational resources, such as animations, short films, 3-D figures, review questions, case studies, videos of short talks by well-respected thought leaders in the field, etc. were already readily accessible online. Sharing a short presentation (posted on the Howard Hughes Medical Institute HHMI website) by the renowned Nobel Prize Laureate, Eric Kandel, about the molecular basis of long-term potentiation was incredibly engaging to the students. Showing a colorful animation of the multiple processes of the cardiac cycle as they occur simultaneously in real time (such as the movement of the electric current and blood through the components of heart as it corresponds to an electrocardiogram, EKG, trace) was much more instructional and compelling than any rudimentary drawings I could make on the overhead projector.

Next, just as a good researcher would, I wanted to utilize the best technology available. Directing students to the vibrant, precise images on the Human Connectome website provided a clear description of verified connections in the human brain, as well as comprehensible explanations of the current technology utilized to obtain this exciting data. To supplement my instruction, I endeavored to identify those innovative resources that were most applicable to my course and direct the students to them. The internet provides a superb tool box, and in this day in age, when technology is progressing at such a rapid pace, trustworthy websites that would keep up with that pace could effectively supplement the foundational information provided by a textbook.

Another objective was to convince my students of the value and the significance of what they were learning, so they would devote treasured time and effort to this course. In addition to engaging them in the subject matter, I endeavored to challenge their thought processes and enhance their analytical skills. I asked myself, "Are there any instructional tools already available that deal with course topics that students would find interesting and applicable and, thus, cultivate their enthusiasm, while also honing their critical thinking skills?" The answer is a categorical "Yes!" One example is The National Center for Case Study Teaching in Science (NCCSTS). Its primary goal is "to promote the nationwide application of active learning techniques to the teaching of science, with a particular emphasis on case studies and problem-based learning." This valuable resource can be accessed at: http://sciencecases.lib.buffalo.edu/cs/

Researchers are also required to be concise. Massive, general biology texts had too much overall information, whereas advanced textbooks had too much detail for the course. I did not want my course to be a mile wide and an inch deep (nor a mile deep and an inch wide); I wanted to design a course where the material was challenging, yet manageable; and the course learning goals/outcomes were obvious to students, rather than a speculative labyrinth. Thus, I had to do it myself … to write comprehensible text with a succinct message that provided the necessary foundation for the topics to be mastered. Nothing more, nothing less. By design, I endeavored to keep the written text to a minimum and use illustrations to illuminate key topics, while supplementing with easily accessible and first-rate animations available on the internet. Why? Because "A picture speaks a thousand words," and a moving picture (animation, film) speaks 10,000 words.

I do have some support for this notion (albeit anecdotal). It all began when my daughter enrolled in Honors Biology in her freshman year in high school. I became the official tutor to a cohort of animated fifteen-year-olds, holding regular review sessions in my basement (gratis, of course). In our sessions, I often showed them short videos of complex biological processes that are often difficult for a novice to comprehend by just viewing a static illustration, such as DNA replication, transcription, translation, the Avery McCloud Experiment, the lac operon in action, RNA interference, etc. These clear, simple videos enlivened these processes and brought new-found clarity. There was a resounding, "That makes soooo much more sense now. NOW we get it! You should tell our teacher about these!"

My new course design would not necessarily be considered a "flipped" course, but, rather, a "blended" course with the goal of implementing tangible, achievable tasks that could be incorporated immediately and regularly to bring about improvement in student development, academic achievement and continued education. This effort is inspired by the Kolb Learning Cycle (Kolb, 1984) which emphasizes experience, reflection, hypothesis generation, and active testing; and has been developed in the day-to-day classroom. It utilizes the resources outlined above: a concise, manageable text (to provide foundational information to prepare the student for the classroom experience), teaching aids that incorporate advanced technology, show relevance, generate enthusiasm, and require critical thinking skills. The course design challenges students to synthesis information and make connections between course topics. It includes analysis of the primary literature, and emphasizes active testing.

In short, the use of this textbook will facilitate an instructional approach that incorporates active learning. The benefits of utilizing active learning techniques in the classroom have recently been validated in a study published in PNAS (Wiesman, 2014 and Freeman, et al, 2014). Active learning requires students to evaluate and apply the information they are learning in a variety of contexts. Examples of active learning techniques include: active testing using electronic student response systems (clickers) in the classroom, analytical discussion of case studies with peers, and the completion of worksheets, concept maps, and journal article critiques. This textbook is also designed to facilitate the mastery of skills gained by active, rather than passive learning. For example, key terms were deliberately not depicted in bold print. Rather, students are asked to actively identify and define unfamiliar terms. Many section headings are phrased as questions rather than declarative statements. In addition to standard review questions at the end of each chapter, challenge questions are included that query the student on cutting edge research, requiring students to actively explore the scientific literature to identify and peruse pertinent, up-to-date journal articles. Finally, it is an ardent expectation that the adroit student will add many of his own annotations to each and every page!

What the instructor gains when adopting this text for his/her course is more than just a textbook, but also included, are recommendations for vetted instructional strategies that can be potentially incorporated into a "blended" course design for a relatively large class size (200+ students).

References

Kolb, D.A. (1984). *Experiential learning: Experience as the source of learning and development.* Eaglewood Cliffs, NJ., Prentice Hall.

Weiman, C.P. (2014). Large-scale comparison of science teaching methods sends clear message. *PNAS, 111(23)*, 8319-8320. doi: http://dx.doi.org/10.1073/pnas.1407304111

Freeman, S., Eddy, S., McDonough, M., Smith, M., Okoroafor, N., Jordt, H., & Wenderoth, M. (2014). Active learning increases student performance in science, engineering and mathematics. *PNAS . Early Edition,* 1-6. doi: 10.1073/pnas.1319030111

Chapter 1

Reproductive Biology Today

Expect the Unexpected

Figure 1-1 Shown is Thomas Beatie, a transgender female-to-male individual. He has given birth to three children since 2008.

How, exactly, does one "produce again?"

Who are the key players?

G enetic and environmental influences interact to generate complex organisms with remarkably consistent design, yet with individual differences uniquely characteristic to a given species. Heredity is a fundamental and distinguishing quality of all life. It constitutes the ability of a parent organism to transmit the specific information that details the offspring's differentiating traits. The blueprint of heredity is DNA.

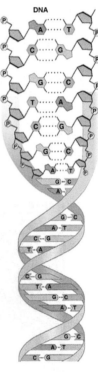

"It was so pretty, it had to be true."

Figure 1-2A: James Watson (circa 1950) and his colleagues, Francis Crick and Maurice Wilkins, were awarded the Nobel Prize in Physiology and Medicine in 1962 "for their discoveries concerning the molecular structure of nucleic acids and its significance for information transfer in living material."

Figure 1-2B: The Double Helix

In animal sexual reproduction, the vehicles for the heritable information that resides within the DNA are the specialized cells: the egg and the sperm. Eggs and sperm are also called gametes and are, by definition, haploid (having one copy of each type of chromosome in their nucleus; where n represents the number of chromosomes in the nucleus). Diploid ($2n$) cells have two copies of each chromosome. Somatic cells (cells that make up the body; "soma" is Greek for body) are diploid. In normal human somatic cells, there are 46 chromosomes, two copies of chromosomes 1 through 22 (the autosomes), plus the sex chromosomes, an X and Y chromosome in males ($\male$) or two X chromosomes in females ($\female$).

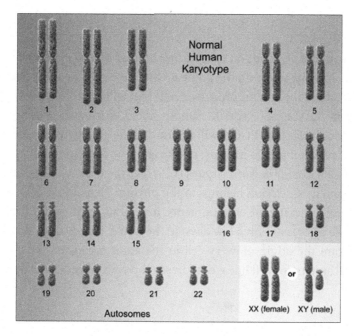

Figure 1-3 Human karyotype

By comparison, a fruit fly has 8 chromosomes, and a laboratory mouse has a diploid number (*2n*) of 40 which indicates it has a total of 40 chromosomes.

The life cycle of multicellular organisms—where does it begin?

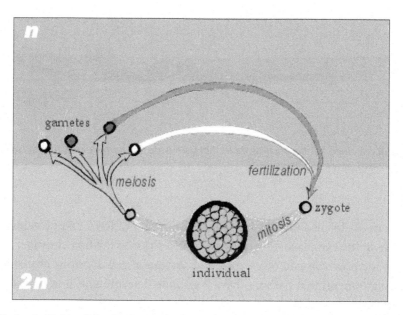

Figure 1-4 The Life Cycle of a Multi-cellular Organism. Specialized cells in the diploid (2n) individual develop into the sex organs of the male or female (i.e., gonads: testis or ovary). Particular gonadal cells will undergo meiosis to generate the gametes (either eggs or sperm). When an egg and a sperm from a mature organisms unite, fertilization and formation of a zygote occurs, which undergoes mitosis to form a new multi-cellular organism, and the cycle can begin again.

As the cyclic nature of life portends no specific beginning point or end point, we shall arbitrarily begin our description of development with the point at which the cell fate is determined in the primordial germ cells (PGCs). These are the specific precursor cells that will eventually proceed through the process of gametogenesis to produce eggs or sperm. Simply stated, during the development of multicellular organisms, certain diploid cells (the PGCs) will migrate to the emergent gonad (for example, the ovary or the testis), where they will undergo meiosis, resulting in the formation of haploid germ cells.

In the model organism *Caenorhabditis elegans* (*C. elegans*), germ cell fate is established very early in the process of development. *C. elegans* belongs to the phylum Nematoida. It is a roundworm (a nematode) that lives in the soil of temperate environments. It is about 1 millimeter (mm) in length, it has 959 somatic cells, and its life cycle lasts only a few days. In the mid-1970s, Sydney Brenner and his colleagues were the first to diagram the origin of every cell in the adult organism, thus establishing this simple creature as a canonical system for cell lineage studies and powerful genetic analysis.

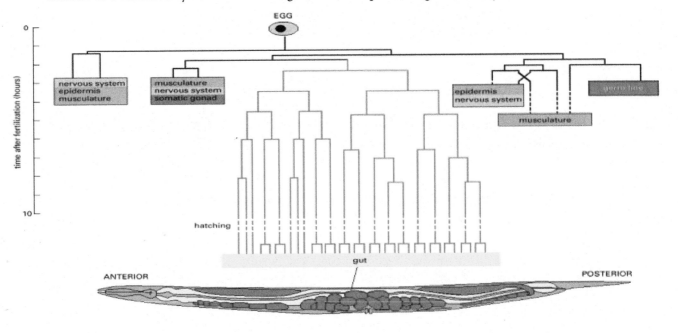

Figure 1-5 Note the relatively small number of cell divisions that give rise to the germline cells, thus the fate of the cells that will become the germ cells is fixed early in development.

Interestingly, in newly formed *C. elegans* zygotes, complexes of RNA and proteins are found widely distributed throughout the cytoplasm (Schisa *et al.*, 2001). Prior to the first cleavage, these "P granules" are repositioned to the posterior end of the zygote. Subsequent cell divisions give rise to a primordial germ cell (the P4 blastomere) that harbors these P granule determinants and whose descendants will become the adult gametes (eggs, sperm).

The precise function of the P granules with regard to the specification of germ cells in *C. elegans* is still being elucidated. However, there is evidence that they have a role in RNA organization and the regulation of translation in the germ cell cytoplasm. Additionally, it is believed that certain components of P granules serve to inhibit transcription, thereby preventing the expression of genes that would normally dictate a somatic cell fate (Voronina, et al., 2001).

In addition to studies performed in the nematode, the process of specifying the germ cell lineage has been studied in depth in a number of other model organisms, including *Drosophila melanogaster* (fruit fly), *Xenopus laevis* (frog), *Danio rerio* (zebrafish), and *Mus musculus* (mouse). Each has many similarities, as well as many unique features. The germ plasma in the eggs of fruit flies, zebrafish, and frogs harbor specific cytoplasmic determinants, somewhat analogous to the P granules in the nematode. These cytoplasmic determinants include mRNAs and protein that specify the primordial germs cells, which then migrate, by various means, to the developing gonad. In the mouse, no distinctive germ plasma (the cellular material containing the cytoplasmic determinants that independently specify PGCs) has been identified. Rather, during embryogenesis, certain posterior cells receive signals from neighboring cells that induce them to become primordial germ cells. Initially, a group of specific cells (the posterior proximal epiblast cells) in the developing mammalian embryo respond to a secreted signaling molecule, Wnt. Exposure to Wnt facilitates the action of another specific signaling molecule, BMP 4 (bone morphogenetic protein 4 (BMP4). BMP4 is a member of a large family of proteins involved in cell differentiation and growth. By binding to specific receptors on the plasma membrane, BMP4 initiates many important downstream effects. One important downstream effect is the transcription of particular genes that produce factors which restrict the PGCs to a germ cell fate. This can be accomplished by repressing genes that are normally activated when cells begin to differentiate into a somatic cell fate. Another important downstream effect is the activation of genes that are necessary to maintain the germline fate (Ohinata, et al. 2009). Thus, regardless of the mechanism (cytoplasmic determinants or cell signaling molecules), the specification of the fates of select primordial germs cells to become the future gametes is usually established relatively early during development. Once specified, the PGCs must then migrate to the region of the embryo that will develop into the gonad.

What is known about primordial germ cell migration?

Much of what is known about primordial germ cell migration is derived from studies using molecular markers to visualize cells at various locations at specific developmental time points in tissue that is then histologically fixed for analysis. Some examples include using labeled antibodies to specific proteins or to the mRNAs of particular genes that are differentially expressed during development. More recently, the movement of PGCs in cultured slices of living tissue can be visualized using the highly valuable green fluorescent protein (GFP) and confocal microscopy. For example, a genetically engineered construct can be made in which the expression of GFP can be placed under the control of the promoter from a gene that is known to be turned on in primordial germ cells. Transgenic mouse embryos can be created resulting in cells that specifically express GFP, thereby distinguishing the primordial germ cells with green fluorescence. The migration of the fluorescent PGCs in cultured tissue slices can be recorded on camera (Molyneaux, *et al.,* 2001).

The use of model organisms has been instrumental in the elucidation of the molecular mechanisms that underlie germ cell migration. Some common mechanisms of migration include diapedesis (an amoeboid type of movement) and the use of chemoattractants and chemorepellants. In general, cells move by extending their leading (or front) edge and then adhering it to the extra cellular matrix or to neighboring cells. This is followed by the retraction of their lagging (or back) edge. This concerted movement is moderated by external cues (such as chemoattractant signaling molecules) that bind to cell surface receptors (some examples include the BMP receptor and the kit receptor tyrosine kinase). Receptor binding activates signal transduction pathways, which facilitate the necessary structural changes needed for movement. These structural changes result from the regulation of adhesion molecules to generate traction and the regulation of actin and myosin filaments to produce a leading edge. Tarbashevich and Raz have proposed a model in which the activation of specific and localized surface receptors on the leading edge of the cell, as well as the distribution of chemoattractant signaling molecules (often as a gradient), establishes a directional migratory pathway for the PGCs (Tarbashevich & Raz, 2010). In this manner, primordial germ cells can be guided to the appropriate destinations (See Richardson & Lehman, 2010 for review).

Genetic studies in zebrafish (Weidinger et al., 1999) suggest PGCs migrate primarily by chemoattraction. Migration in the fruit fly, however, appears to be motivated by both chemoattractants and chemorepellants (Doren & Lehman, 1999, and Sano, *et al.*, 2005). In both zebrafish and fruit flies, PGCs organize into two distinctive groups during their migratory route. PGCs may also increase in number as they make their migratory trek. For example, by the time the PGCs enter the developing gonad in mice (around embryonic day 12), they have multiplied from a starting population of about 10 to 100 cells to 2500 to 5000 cells (Gilbert, 2010). This expansion in population is carried out by mitosis. (See figures 1-6 and 1-7 for a review of the cell cycle and mitosis.) These proliferating cells must maintain their undifferentiated status prior to becoming gametes. To do so, the PGCs must reside in an environment (or niche) that prohibits their differentiation into male or female gametes until the appropriate time.

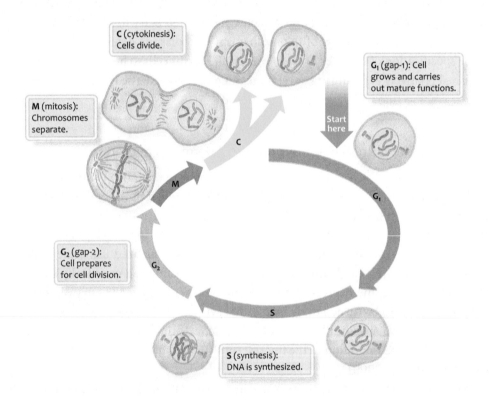

Figure 1-6 A review of the cell cycle.

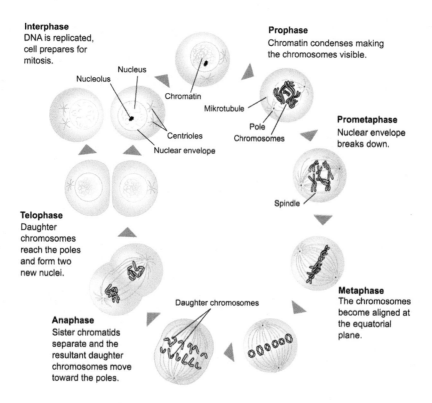

Figure 1-7 A review of mitosis.

Sex determination: testes or ovaries?

As the mammalian embryo develops, the primordial germs cells reach their final destination (which is the genital ridge of the gonadal rudiments) at about week 4 of development. At this point, the developing gonadal rudiments are bipotential (sexually indifferent). The germ cells (now known as *gonocytes*) remain undifferentiated until about the 8th week of development, at which time the process of primary sex determination establishes their fate. In mammals, primary sex determination is driven by the composition of the sex chromosomes; XY cells will form testes and XX cells will form ovaries. Located on the short arm of the Y chromosome, the *SRY* gene (sex-determining region of the Y chromosome) is believed to encode a transcription factor that serves as the primary testis determining factor in humans. The SRY protein activates the transcription of *SOX9*, an additional transcription factor that is vital for the continued activation of genes involved in testis development, as well as the suppression of genes involved in ovarian development. Also active is *FGF9* (fibroblast growth factor), an essential signaling molecule that promotes the up-regulated expression of *SOX9*. In females, ovarian development involves the expression of such key genes as *WNT4* and *RSPO1* (R-spondin 1). Both the WNT4 and the RSPO1 proteins bind to specific cell membrane receptors, which increase the production of another important factor, β-catenin. β-catenin can interact with a number of proteins and activate specific transcription factors that promote the ovarian path of development. Equally important, β-catenin is also a critical factor involved in preventing the testicular path of development. (For a review of sex determination in mammals, see Kocer et al., 2009.)

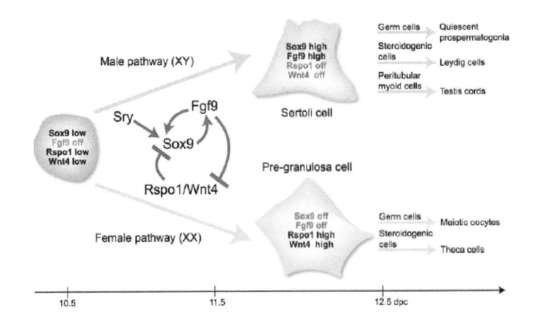

Figure 1-8 Genes involved in sex determination. Days post coitum (dpc) refers to the age of the embryo.

Thus, both the up-regulation and down regulation of key genes at specific times are necessary for sex determination during gonadal development. (Kocer, *et al.,* 2009)

Initially, two unique structures, known as the Wolffian and Müllerian ducts are present in the indifferent gonad early in human development. In the male fetus at 20 weeks, the Wolffian duct continues to develop under the influence of testosterone and will eventually give rise to the male internal genitalia (such as the epididymis, vas deferens, and seminal vesicles). The Müllerian duct, which eventually gives rise to the internal female genitalia (such as the uterus, oviducts, and cervix) will regress in the male, due to the production of AMF (anti-Müllerian factor). In the female, the Wolffian duct will regress (due to the absence of testosterone), and estrogen will promote the development of the Müllerian duct, which will give rise to the internal female genitalia. The mammalian male and female gonads will continue to mature throughout the course of development. A region within the developing male gonad establishes the testis cords, which eventually form the seminiferous tubules (the location of sperm formation). In the female, the germ cells that will become the ova are located at the periphery of the gonad and are surrounded by epithelial cells. These cells will differentiate into granulosa cells that, along with the theca cells, will form the follicles that contain a single oogonium (the precursor to the oocyte). See Figure 1-9 for review.

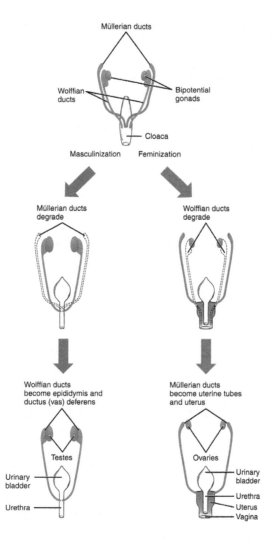

Figure 1-9 Sexual determination and development of the gonads in mammals.

What are some fundamental processes in gametogenesis?

Both mitosis and meiosis are essential processes in gametogenesis. The precise timing of these processes during embryogenesis is essential for normal germ cell production as germ cells commit to spermatogenesis and oogenesis at characteristic times during development, usually around 13.5 dpc (Kocer, et al., 2009)

Not surprisingly, the primary role of mitosis is to expand the precursor population that will give rise to the gametes. However, the primary objectives of meiosis during gametogenesis are somewhat more elaborate. They are:

1. The development of diploid germ cells into appropriate haploid gametes for sexual reproduction

2. The generation of variation by the independent assortment of chromosomes and by homologous recombination (also known as crossing over). See Table 1-1 for a comparison of mitotic and meiotic cell division.

Table 1.1   A comparison of mitotic and meiotic cell division.

	Mitotic cell division	**Meiotic cell division**
What kinds of new cells are produced by this process?	Identical daughter cells of most tissues of the body	Gametes: sperm or eggs
How many new cells are produced from one parent cell?	2 daughter cells	4 daughter cells
How much DNA does each new cell have?	Same amount of DNA as parent cell	Half of DNA of parent cell; gametes are haploid
In humans how many chromosomes does each new cell have?	46 chromosomes	23 chromosomes, one of each homologous pair
Where does the process take place in humans?	In cells of most tissues of the body	Only in cells of ovaries or testes
Why is this process essential?	It allows a fertilized egg to grow and develop into a mature adult; it also allows damaged or lost tissues to be repaired or replaced. Some species can use this process to reproduce a new individual.	Meiotic cell division produces gametes, and sexual reproduction relies on the production of gametes.

In sexual reproduction, normal development requires that the zygote contains two copies of each chromosome (one from each parent). When this is not the case, a cell is described as being aneuploid (that is, having an abnormal number of chromosomes). Aneuploidy can cause miscarriage and certain genetic disorders. It is also observed in some cancerous cells. Table 1-2 shows some common disorders resulting from errors in meiosis.

In order to advance proper development during gametogenesis and avoid aneuploidy, chromosomal number must not only be halved (from diploid, $2n$, to haploid, n), but individual chromosomes must also be appropriately allotted into gametes. To illustrate this point, compare the outcomes in Figures 1-10 and 1-11. The process of meiosis, when completed correctly, ensures this outcome. (See Figure 1-12 for a comprehensive review of meiosis.)

Table 1-2   Errors of meiosis.

Name of disorder	**Chromosome abnormality**	**Description**
Down syndrome	Trisomy*21	Mental retardation, heart malformations, dementia similar to Alzheimer's
Edward's syndrome	Trisomy 18	Mental retardation, abnormalities in head, feet, and kidneys
Patau's syndrome	Trisomy 13	Mental retardation, a variety of abnormalities, death usually by 3 months of age
Turner's syndrome	XO, lacking one sex chromosome	Lowered IQ, abnormal genitals, heart abnormalities

*Trisomy means having three homologous copies of that chromosome, rather than the normal two.

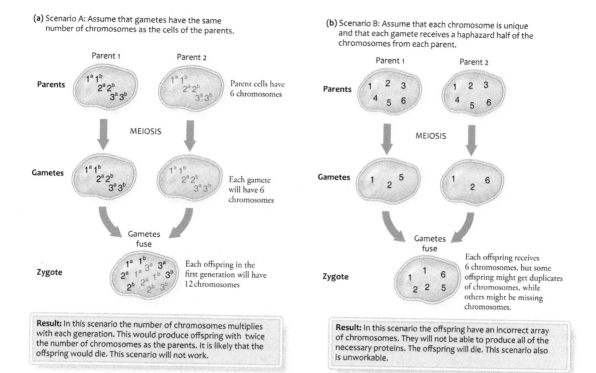

(a) Scenario A: Assume that gametes have the same number of chromosomes as the cells of the parents.

(b) Scenario B: Assume that each chromosome is unique and that each gamete receives a haphazard half of the chromosomes from each parent.

Parent cells have 6 chromosomes

Each gamete will have 6 chromosomes

Each offspring in the first generation will have 12 chromosomes

Each offspring receives 6 chromosomes, but some offspring might get duplicates of chromosomes, while others might be missing chromosomes.

Result: In this scenario the number of chromosomes multiplies with each generation. This would produce offspring with twice the number of chromosomes as the parents. It is likely that the offspring would die. This scenario will not work.

Result: In this scenario the offspring have an incorrect array of chromosomes. They will not be able to produce all of the necessary proteins. The offspring will die. This scenario also is unworkable.

Figure 1-10 Possible errors of meiosis.

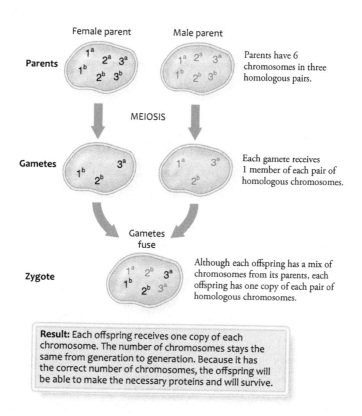

Parents have 6 chromosomes in three homologous pairs.

Each gamete receives 1 member of each pair of homologous chromosomes.

Although each offspring has a mix of chromosomes from its parents, each offspring has one copy of each pair of homologous chromosomes.

Result: Each offspring receives one copy of each chromosome. The number of chromosomes stays the same from generation to generation. Because it has the correct number of chromosomes, the offspring will be able to make the necessary proteins and will survive.

Figure 1-11

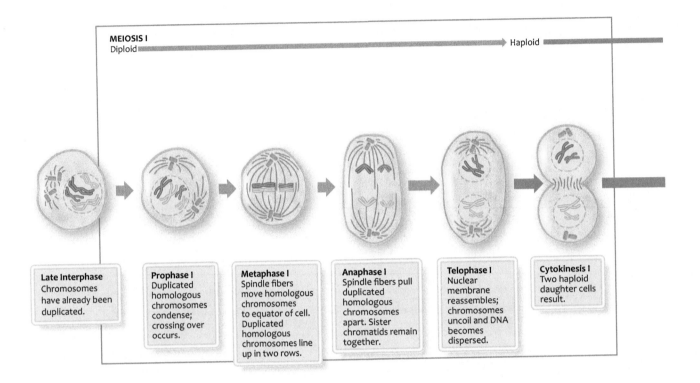

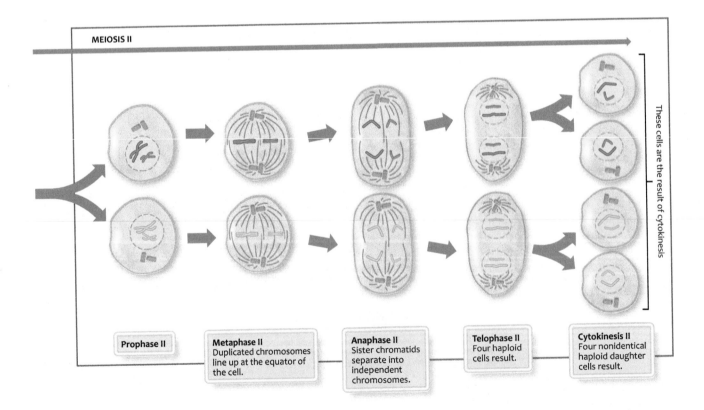

Figure 1-12 Result of normal meiosis.

The generation of genetic variation is another desirable outcome of meiosis. One way variation is obtained is via the random arrangement of two homologous chromosome pairs at the metaphase plate during meiosis I. This important process ensures the segregation of distinctive chromosomes into individual gametes. Figure 1-13 provides an example of the variability generated by the process of independent assortment.

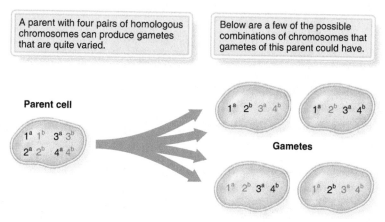

Figure 1-13 *An example of the variation that can be generated when gametes are formed. The random arrangement of two homologous chromosomes at the metaphase plate generates chromosomal variation in gametes. Each gamete shown has a different set of chromosomes.*

The potential number of novel chromosome combinations produced by meiosis in humans is 2^n, where n=number of haploid chromosomes (or 23) and 2=number of chromosomes in each pair. Thus 2^{23} =8,388,608 different combinations of maternal and paternal chromosomes are possible in cells produced in meiosis I (Cummings, 2010). Homologous recombination, or crossing over (which occurs during prophase of meiosis I), also results in genetic variation by creating new arrangements of chromosomal DNA.

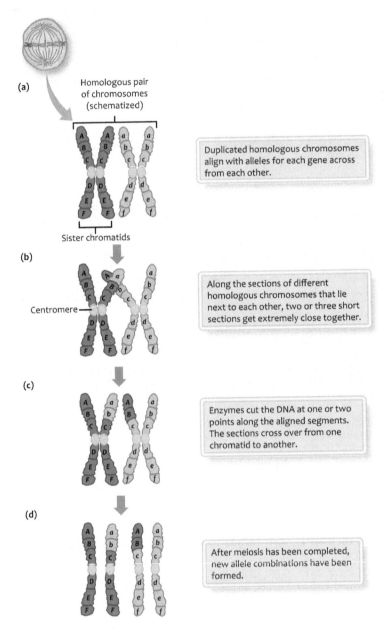

(a) Homologous pair of chromosomes (schematized)

Duplicated homologous chromosomes align with alleles for each gene across from each other.

Sister chromatids

(b)

Centromere—

Along the sections of different homologous chromosomes that lie next to each other, two or three short sections get extremely close together.

(c)

Enzymes cut the DNA at one or two points along the aligned segments. The sections cross over from one chromatid to another.

(d)

After meiosis has been completed, new allele combinations have been formed.

Figure 1-14 Homologous recombination during meiosis I generates new arrangements of DNA in chromosomes.

The formation of sperm and eggs involves more than just the expansion of precursor cell populations (by mitosis) and the configuration of genetically diverse haploid (*n*) cells (by meiosis). The formation of each type of gamete entails a number of specialized events that generate their unique features. In comparison to the oocyte, sperm are small, have relatively few organelles (mostly mitochondria and centrioles), are motile (have a flagella), and have a specialized Golgi structure (the acrosomal vesicle) used to bind and penetrate the egg coat.

By contrast, eggs are larger and non-motile with an abundance of raw materials that aid in early development of the zygote (e.g., proteins, RNAs, nucleic acids, ribosomes, mitochondria, etc.). Oocytes generally have an outer protective coat (such as a jelly coat or a shell) and specialized Golgi structures (cortical granules) that protect the egg from polyspermy (or multiple sperm entry).

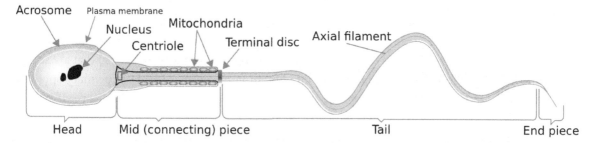

Figure 1-15 Diagram of a sperm.

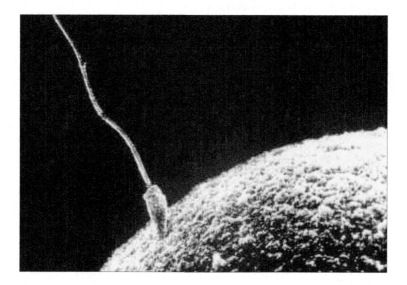

Figure 1-16 Interaction of a sperm cell with an egg cell.

How is a sperm cell generated from a germ cell?

A germ cell is a precursor cell that is destined to become either an egg or a sperm. Spermatogenesis is the developmental process resulting in the specific transition from a germ cell to a sperm cell. The process of spermatogenesis takes place in the seminiferous tubules, which are located in the testes. It involves the specific cells that will eventually become the actual sperm cells, as well as additional cells that facilitate the process of spermatogenesis by providing nourishment and secreting androgens.

During human fetal development in males, the cells of the presumptive testes descend from their original position near the developing kidneys to their final position in the scrotum. Descent of the testis through the abdomen begins at about 7 months of fetal development, and the testes enter the scrotum about 1 month before birth. This process enables spermatogenesis to proceed at temperature 1.5°C to 2.5°C lower than normal body temperature, as the scrotal sac resides outside the warm body cavity. At puberty, lumenal tissue is formed in the seminiferous tubules, and there is an increase in the number of interstitial cells (also called Leydig cells). These cells are located in between the seminiferous tubules, and secrete androgens (such as testosterone). The epithelium of the seminiferous tubules differentiates into sustentacular cells (also known as Sertoli cells), which will provide support and nourishment for the spermatogonium. The spermatogonia are a mitotically active stem cell population derived from the gonadocytes.

A specific sub-population of spermatogonium commits to spermatogenesis and, thus, comprises the specialized cells that are the precursors to the primary spermatocytes. These spermatogonia respond to factors, such as SCF (stem cell factor) and GDNF (glial cell line-derived growth factor) that are secreted by neighboring Sertoli cells. SCF promotes the differentiation of spermatogonia to primary spermatocytes, whereas high levels GDNF promote the production of more spermatogonium (or self-renewal) (de Rooij, DG, 2009). The primary spermatocytes are the cells that will enter into meiosis and proceed through spermatogenesis. As you might imagine, in addition to SCF and GDNF, there are a number of other factors (e.g., receptors, transcription factors, polymerases, etc.) that are additionally up-regulated in order to facilitate the process of spermatogenesis.

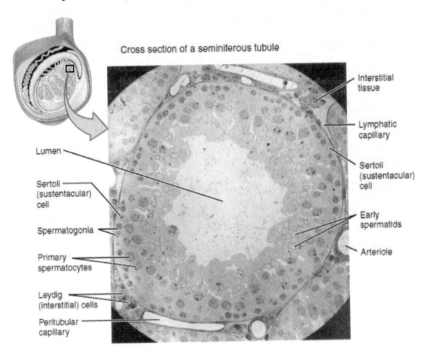

Figure 1-17 Cross-section of a seminiferous tubule indicates key cell types.

The process of spermatogenesis begins near the basal lamina of the seminiferous tubule and progresses toward the border of the lumen, where the mature sperm are found. The first step is the production and differentiation of a population of spermatogonia that divide by mitosis, producing two cells. One cell will remain a spermatogonium and can continue to self-renew (or undergo mitosis to make more stem cells); the other will commit to the pathway of becoming a sperm cell (spermatozoa) and will give rise to a population of spermatogonia that are the precursors to primary spermatocytes. Primary spermatocytes will undergo meiosis I to produce haploid secondary spermatocytes. These cells proceed through meiosis II, thereby generating immature haploid spermatids. Throughout the successive cell divisions, incomplete cytokinesis causes the formation of a syncytium, in which the cells are interconnected by cytoplasmic bridges. These connections permit the passage of molecules and ions, which facilitate the synchronous maturation of the cells. The cytoplasmic bridges are eliminated as the spermatids advance to mature sperm, at which time they are released into the lumen of the seminiferous tubules. Development from a stem cell to a sperm cell in the human male takes about 74 days, and human males can produce over 1 trillion sperm during the course of their lives (Gilbert, 2010). (See Figure 1-18 for a summary of spermatogenesis.)

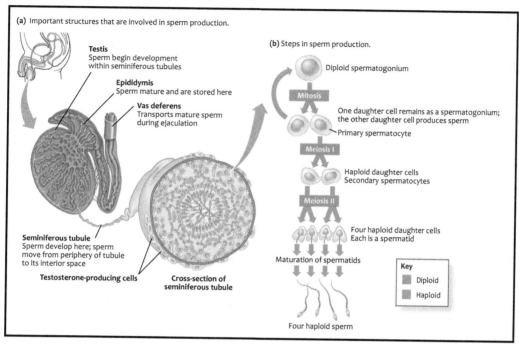

Figure 1-18 A summary of spermatogenesis.

In contrast to female gametogenesis, spermatogenesis in males is not initiated until puberty. During embryogenesis, spermatogonia undergo mitosis but do not continue to mature. At puberty, GnRH (gonadotropin-releasing hormone) secreted from the hypothalamus (a structure in the brain) stimulates the anterior pituitary gland to release FSH (follicle-stimulating hormone) and LH (luteinizing hormone). The production of both SCF and GDNF in Sertoli cells is regulated by FSH (Tadokoro, *et al.,* 2002). FSH also stimulates the Sertoli cell to produce inhibin, which, like GDNF, is a member of the TGFβ family of growth and differentiation factors. Inhibin prevents sperm cell formation by a negative feedback mechanism in which it inhibits the secretion of additional FSH by the anterior pituitary gland. LH stimulates the production of testosterone from the interstitial cells of Leydig, which promotes spermatogenesis. Testosterone is also a component of a negative feedback loop that inhibits the production of LH from the anterior pituitary and GnRH from the hypothalamus.

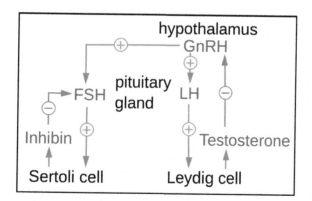

Figure 1-19 Hormone secretion involved in male reproductive development.

How is an egg cell generated from a precursor germ cell?

Oogenesis is the developmental process resulting in the transition from a germ cell to an ovum. Like the process of spermatogenesis, it utilizes a number of additional cells for support and nourishment, in addition to the specialized precursor germ cells that will become the actual ova. In mammals, oogenesis commences in the early embryonic female gonad and continues in the ovaries, which began their development in the abdomen and then descended to their final location in the pelvic region. Oogonia are the female germ cells that will give rise to mature ova (or egg cells). Between the second and seventh month of gestation, oogonia divide by mitosis to produce about 7 million germ cells (Gilbert, 2010). Many of these cells die before birth. Of those that remain, most will begin the process of meiosis, pausing at the Prophase I stage. At this point, the cells are called primary oocytes and are encased in a primordial follicle that consists of a single layer of epithelial granulosa cells. At the time of birth, there are about 2 million of them. Because primary oocytes continue to die, only about 400 remain that may advance through oogenesis in a female's lifetime (Gilbert, 2010).

At puberty, follicular development continues to progress. The granulosa cells enlarge, and the primordial follicle differentiates into a primary follicle. A secondary follicle is then formed as a specialized cell type known as the thecal cells distribute themselves around the granulosa cells. The follicle then reaches its maximum size and is considered fully mature. After being arrested at prophase I from before birth to the onset of puberty, the primary oocyte resumes meiosis I and proceeds through the first meiotic division in a mature follicle just prior to ovulation. Because the metaphase plate migrates to the cell periphery, this division is unequal, producing one daughter cell (the first polar body) that contains very little cytoplasm and one daughter cell, called the secondary oocyte, that contains the majority of the cellular contents, thus conserving these important factors for later use in the zygote. The remaining polar body may or may not divide prior to degenerating. The secondary oocyte begins meiosis II but is arrested at metaphase II. Ovulation occurs, releasing the secondary oocyte from the mature follicle into the oviduct. When a sperm penetrates the plasma membrane during the process of fertilization, the secondary oocyte will complete meiosis II, generating another polar body and the haploid ovum. As fertilization continues, the nucleus from the sperm joins with the nucleus from the ovum, generating a zygote (which is the term for the initial cell that is formed from the union of the sperm and the egg). See Figure 1-20 for an overview of oogenesis.

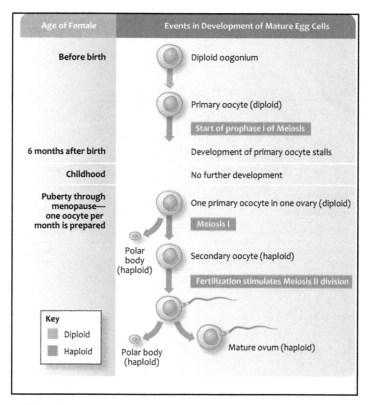

Age of Female	Events in Development of Mature Egg Cells
Before birth	Diploid oogonium
	Primary oocyte (diploid)
	Start of prophase I of Meiosis
6 months after birth	Development of primary oocyte stalls
Childhood	No further development
Puberty through menopause— one oocyte per month is prepared	One primary oocyte in one ovary (diploid)
	Meiosis I
	Polar body (haploid) Secondary oocyte (haploid)
	Fertilization stimulates Meiosis II division
	Polar body (haploid) Mature ovum (haploid)

Key
- Diploid
- Haploid

Figure 1-20 An overview of Oogenesis.

The production of one or more mature eggs from the primary oocytes, as well as the release of an ovum into the oviduct, normally occurs monthly after the onset of puberty. This process, known as the ovarian cycle, is concomitant with the menstrual cycle and is characterized by specific uterine changes. Both cycles are hormonally regulated. Menses, the sloughing off and release of the endometrium, distinguishes the beginning of the menstrual cycle. The endometrium is the blood and nutrient rich lining of the uterine wall produced from the growth and proliferation of the endometrial cells. If there is no fertilization, menses ensues. As menses concludes, GnRH from the hypothalamus stimulates the anterior pituitary to release LH and FSH, which promote follicular growth and maturation. The expanding follicles secrete estrogen. Estrogen causes the endometrial cells to proliferate and form the thick endometrium. Estrogen levels peak just prior to the midpoint of the menstrual cycle, which causes LH and FSH levels to rapidly rise. At mid-cycle (around day 14) ovulation (the release of a secondary oocyte from a mature follicle) is triggered by a surge in LH production. During the second half of the menstrual cycle, LH, FSH, and estrogen levels return to baseline, but progesterone levels increase. At this stage, progesterone is secreted by the corpus luteum, a temporary structure that has developed from the ovarian follicle. It will degenerate prior to the start of the next ovarian cycle. Progesterone also causes the endometrial cells to enlarge, thickening the endometrium in preparation of a potential pregnancy. Progesterone levels continue to increase, peaking around day 21 and decline to baseline levels just prior to the onset of the next menstrual cycle. Figure 1-21 summarizes the hormonal control of the menstrual and ovarian cycles.

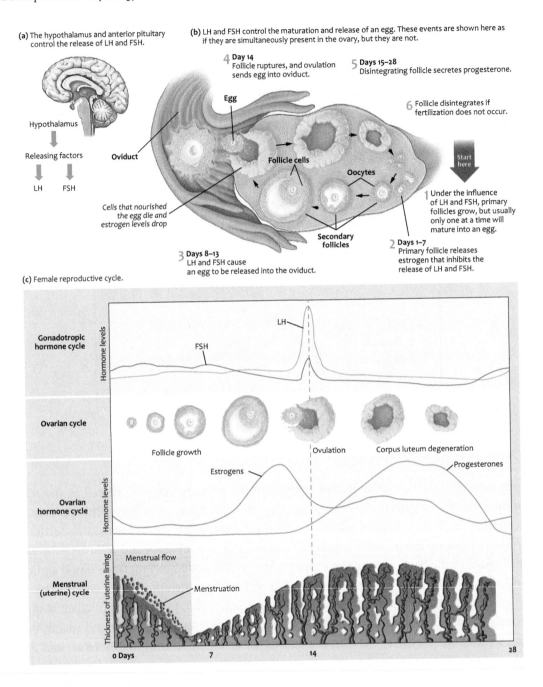

(a) The hypothalamus and anterior pituitary control the release of LH and FSH.

Hypothalamus

Releasing factors

LH   FSH

(b) LH and FSH control the maturation and release of an egg. These events are shown here as if they are simultaneously present in the ovary, but they are not.

4 Day 14
Follicle ruptures, and ovulation sends egg into oviduct.

5 Days 15–28
Disintegrating follicle secretes progesterone.

6 Follicle disintegrates if fertilization does not occur.

Egg

Oviduct

Follicle cells

Oocytes

Secondary follicles

Cells that nourished the egg die and estrogen levels drop

Start here

1 Under the influence of LH and FSH, primary follicles grow, but usually only one at a time will mature into an egg.

2 Days 1–7
Primary follicle releases estrogen that inhibits the release of LH and FSH.

3 Days 8–13
LH and FSH cause an egg to be released into the oviduct.

(c) Female reproductive cycle.

Gonadotropic hormone cycle

Hormone levels

LH

FSH

Ovarian cycle

Follicle growth   Ovulation   Corpus luteum degeneration

Ovarian hormone cycle

Hormone levels

Estrogens   Progesterones

Menstrual (uterine) cycle

Thickness of uterine lining

Menstrual flow

Menstruation

0 Days   7   14   28

Figure 1-21   *A summary of the hormonal control of the menstrual and ovarian cycles.*

Chapter 1 Review

I. Helpful and interesting animations:

1. P granules in C. elegans: https://www.youtube.com/watch?v=aVUWLSlMkxQ

2. Embryonic development of C. elegans: https://www.youtube.com/watch?v=M2ApXHhYbaw

3. Cytoplasmic factors: http://www.hhmi.org/biointeractive/cytoplasmic-factors

4. Germ cell migration: http://www.sciencedirect.com/science/article/pii/S0012160601904361

5. The cell cycle and mitosis: http://outreach.mcb.harvard.edu/animations/cellcycle.swf

6. The cell cycle:
   http://www.youtube.com/watch?v=Wy3N5NCZBHQ&list=PLXwnj gs_UWpLcVHARCbbglQJPwFl-kD_v&index=26

7. Mitosis:
   http://www.youtube.com/watch?v=q4UFTC8Y8Uw&list=PLXwnjgs_ UWpLcVHARCbbglQJPwFl-kD_v&index=28

8. Meiosis overview:
   http://www.youtube.com/watch?v=Gvjz9k19J1M&list=PLXwnj gs_UWpLcVHARCbbglQJPwFl-kD_v&index=29

9. Meiosis I:
   http://www.youtube.com/watch?v=m_EgKyhp7oo&list=PLXwnjgs_ UWpLcVHARCbbglQJPwFl-kD_v&index=33

10. Meiosis II:
    http://www.youtube.com/watch?v=cO8ESg_BRT4&index=34&list=PLXwnjgs_ UWpLcVHARCbbglQJPwFl-kD_v

11. Random orientation of chromosomes during meiosis:
    http://www.youtube.com/watch?v=iCnlSgQPOlw&list=PLXwnj gs_UWpLcVHARCbbglQJPwFl-kD_v&index=30

12. Unique features of meiosis:
    http://www.youtube.com/watch?v=PICF-_yiAQ8&list=PLXwnjgs_ UWpLcVHARCbbglQJPwFl-kD_v&index=32

13. A comparison of mitosis and meiosis:
    http://www.youtube.com/watch?v=OGX8Bn7Kjjc&list=PLXwnj gs_UWpLcVHARCbbglQJPwFl-kD_v&index=36

14. Sex determination and meiosis: http://www.hhmi.org/biointeractive/meiosis

II. Active Testing: Do you know the facts?

A. List the words in this chapter you would have printed in bold type.
Can you define these words?

B. What are the main, "take home" messages of this chapter?
Is your answer the same as your instructor's answer?

C. Some Questions:

1. Within what "framework" do cells make developmental decisions?

2. Define "reproduction".

3. List and describe the function of some important signaling molecules involved in sex determination.

4. List some common features of eggs and sperm.

5. Illustrate the structure of a human sperm.

6. What is the purpose of mitosis and of meiosis during gametogenesis?

7. Describe two methods to generate variation in organisms.

8. Compare and contrast mitosis to meiosis by drawing a diagram of each and pointing out the similarities and differences as well as the overall purpose and result of each.

9. Illustrate the stages of mitosis.

10. Starting with 4 total chromosomes (for example, a pair of chromosome #1 and a pair of chromosome #2, with the blue chromosomes from the father and the red chromosomes from the mother), illustrate the 4 possible combinations of chromosomes that can be found in the gametes due to the two equally probable arrangements at metaphase I.

11. Draw and illustration of, and explain the steps of oogenesis.

12. Illustrate the stages of meiosis.

13. Name the following hormones and describe their function in males and females: GnRH, FSH, and LH.

14. Diagram the hormonal control of the various stages the female ovarian and menstrual cycle.

15. Draw and illustration of, and explain the steps of spermatogenesis.

16. List similarities and differences between spermatogenesis and oogenesis.

17. Describe the negative feedback pathways of the key hormone secreted during male reproductive development.

III. Inquiring minds want to know...

Challenge Questions:

1. Germ cell migration can be visualized by using genetically engineered constructs in transgenic mice. How, exactly, is this done?

2. How do birth control pills prevent pregnancy?

Chapter 1 References

Franck, R. (1821) *Northern memoirs, calculated for the Meridian of Scotland: To which is added, the the contemplative and practical Angler.* Edinburgh, A. Constable and Co. doi: http://dx.doi.org/10.5962/bhl.title.22627

Schisa, J. A., Pitt, J.N., & Priess, J.R. (2001). Analysis of RNA associated with P granules in germ cells of C. elegans adults. *Development, 128.* Retrieved from http://dev.biologists.org/content/128/8/1287.long

Voronina, E. (2013). The diverse function of germline P-granules in Caenorhabditis elegans. *Molecular Reproduction and Development, 80,* 1098-2795. doi: *http://dx.doi.org/10.1002/mrd.22136*

Ohinata, Y., Ohta, H., Yamanaka, K., Wakayama, T., & Saitou, M. (2009). A signaling principle for the specification of the germ cell lineage in mice. *Cell, 137(3),* 571-84. doi: 10.1016/j.cell.2009.03.014

Molyneaux, K., Stallock, J., Schaible, K., & Wylie, C. (2001). Time-lapse analysis of living mouse germ cell migration. *Developmental Biology, 240 (2),* 488-498. doi: 10.1006/dbio.2001.0436

Lehmann, R. [iBiology]. (2011, January 9). *Part 3: Germ cell migration [video file].* Retrieved from: http://www.youtube.com/watch?v=jHynDv-y94E

Tarbashevich, K., & Raz, E. (2010). The nuts and bolts of germ-cell migration. *Current Opinion Cell Biology, 22(6),* 715-21. doi: 10.1016/j.ceb.2010.03.005

Richardson, B., & Lehmann, R. (2010). Mechanisms guiding primordial germ cell migration: Strategies from different organisims. *Nature Reviews Molecular Cell Biology, 11,* 37-49. doi: 10.1038/nrm2815

Weidinger, G, Wolke, U., Köprunner, M., Klinger, M., & Raz, E. (1999). Identification of tissues and patterning events required for distinct steps in early migration of zebrafish primordial germ cells. *Development, 126(23).* Retrieved from http://www.ncbi.nlm.nih.gov/pubmed/10556055?dopt=Abstract

Doren, MV., & Lehmann, R. (1997). Cell migration: Don't tread on me. *Current Biology, 7 (3)* doi: ttp://dx.doi.org/10.1016/S0960-9822(97)70075-7

Sano, H., Renault, AD., & Lehmann, R. (2005). Control of lateral migration and germ cell elimination by the Drosophila melanogaster lipid phosphate phosphatases Wunen and Wunen 2. *Journal of Cell Biology, 171 (4),* 675-683. Retrieved from http://www.ncbi.nlm.nih.gov/pubmed/16301333 Gilbert, S. (2010). *Developmental Biology.* (9th ed.). Sinauer Associates.

Kocer, A., Reichmann, J., Best, D., & Adams, I. (2009). Germ cell sex determination in mammals. *Molecular Human Reproduction, 15 (4).* doi: 10.1093/molehr/gap008

Cummings, M. (2010). *Human heredity: Principles and issues.* (9th ed.). Brooks/Cole Cengage Learning

De Rooji, DG. (2009). The spermatogonial stem cell niche. *Microscopy Research and Technique, 72 (8).* doi: 10.1002/jemt.20699

Tadokoro, Y., Yomogida, K., Ohta, H., Tohda, A., & Nishimune, Y. (2002). Homeostatic regulation of germinal stem cell proliferation by the GDNF/FSH pathway. *Mechanisms of Development, 113(1).* Retrieved from http://www.ncbi.nlm.nih.gov/pubmed/11900972

Chapter 2

Fertilization and Development

Figure 2-1   A sea urchin.

Decisions … death or life?

If a mature sperm and a mature egg do not meet and complete the process of fertilization, they will both die. This vital reproductive process, which gives rise to a new life, has been well studied in many organisms, including the simple echinoderm, the sea urchin. Sea urchin fertilization is external; each gender discharges its gametes into the unconfined ocean environment. The female sea urchin egg releases a substance found in its external coat (or jelly coat) called resact, which diffuses as a gradient. Even after being greatly diluted in the seawater, resact exerts a very strong chemoattractant effect, drawing sperm to swim toward the highest resact concentration, which is near the egg. Resact also increases sperm motility. The binding of resact to a specific receptor on the sperm cell membrane causes the activation of guanyl cyclase, which increases the intracellular cGMP concentration, opening Ca^{2+} channels (Kirkman-Brown, 2003). These changes enhance sperm motility by activating the ATP production in mitochondria, as well as the ATPase activity that is responsible for movement of the sperm's tail (flagellum). The egg jelly is also a repository for specific carbohydrate molecules (such as fucose sulfate). These molecules bind to receptors on the sperm cell in a process known as contact recognition, which is, for the most part, highly species specific. This contact initiates the acrosome reaction, which consist of two unique events: 1) the cap-like structure of the sperm head (the acrosome vesicle) fuses with the sperm cell membrane, facilitating the release of proteolytic enzymes, and 2) the acrosomal process is extended by the polymerization of actin monomers, forming actin microfilaments. The exocytosed proteolytic enzymes digest a section of the jelly coat, providing a path so that the acrosome vesicle can both penetrate the vitelline membrane (a structure rich in glycoproteins that envelopes the egg cell membrane), and secure the sperm to the egg. Bindin, another essential protein for the species-specific association of the sperm and egg, is localized to the outer surface of the acrosomal process. Bindin, along with other specialized proteins, also assists in the fusion of the sperm and egg cell membranes.

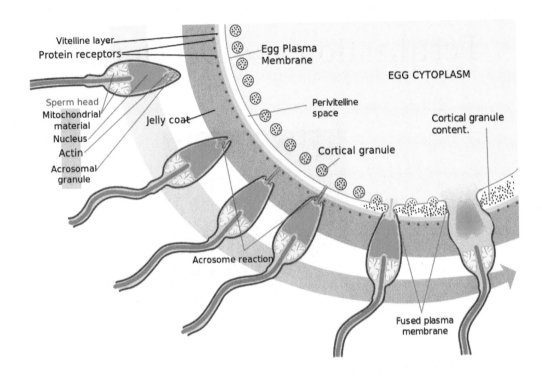

Figure 2-2 Fertilization in the sea urchin.

How does the urchin egg prevent multiple sperm entry?

The two methods of blocking polyspermy in the sea urchin membrane are quite simply termed the fast block and the slow block. The fast block is transient and entails a rapid change (depolarization) in the potential difference across the egg plasma membrane caused by an increase in internal Na+ concentration. When sea urchin sperm encounter an egg with a positive membrane potential, sperm-egg fusion is blocked. This shift to a positive membrane potential is sustained for only about 1 minute. A second mechanism, the slow block to polyspermy, is activated about 20 seconds after sperm entry. Here, polyspermy is prevented by secretion of materials that establish a mechanical barrier, known as the fertilization envelope. The process of fertilization initiates a rapid increase in the intracellular concentration of Ca^{2+} in the egg cell cytoplasm. This triggers the fusion of vesicles with the plasma membrane. These vesicles, known as cortical granules, contain and release several proteins that are responsible for the cortical granule reaction, or the slow block to polyspermy. Cortical granule serine protease (CGSP) helps to separate the vitelline membrane from the egg cell plasma membrane by cleaving the proteins that connect them. It also cleaves the bindin receptors, disassociating them from the membrane and, thereby, removing any attached sperm. The gap between the vitelline membrane and the cell membrane is enlarged by the formation of an osmotic gradient, which is generated by the water-attracting mucopolysaccharide molecules released from the cortical granules. Water enters the space, effectively displacing the vitelline envelope. The vitelline envelope is then hardened by the action of peroxidases and cross-linking proteins, such as transglutaminase. In this manner, the vitelline envelope is converted to the fertilization envelop. Hyalin, another protein released from the cortical granules, coats the outer egg surface and plays an essential role in support during the cleavage stage of embryogenesis (Gilbert, 2010, and see Santella, *et al.*, 2012, for review).

Collectively, the processes that occur in the egg as a result of sperm-egg interaction are known as egg activation. They include calcium increase, the cortical reaction, and the initiation of various metabolic reactions in the egg. Because fertilization occurs after the second meiotic division, the oocyte is haploid when the sperm enters. The genome from the sperm and the egg combine in a process called syngamy, and protein synthesis increases. DNA synthesis then commences and when ready, the newly formed zygote will begin its first cell division, which usually occurs around 90 minutes after fertilization.

Is fertilization in mammals different than in the sea urchin?

The fertilization process in mammals shares many of the same features as sea urchin fertilization. In mammals, though, fertilization is internal (occurring inside the female oviducts), and there is no fast block to polyspermy. Although sperm motility provided by flagellar movement is crucial when individual sperm reach the vicinity of the egg, the muscular contractions of the female uterus are necessary to propel the sperm on its journey through the oviduct. Capacitation is another unique feature of mammalian fertilization. It occurs in the female reproductive tract and entails a number of physiological changes that enable a sperm to become capable of fertilizing an egg. These include modifications to the sperm membrane, such as the repositioning of proteins that will bind the glycoprotein-rich extracellular matrix layer of the mammalian egg (or the zona pellucida), the loss of specific proteins and carbohydrates that are thought to block binding sites, changes in membrane potential, and the phosphorylation of proteins thought to be involved in receptor formation (Gilbert, 2010, and see Guraya, 2000, for review).

In mice, the zona pellucida is composed of three main glycoproteins (ZP1, ZP2, and ZP3), as well as a number of accessory proteins. Proteins on the sperm plasma membrane specifically bind to Zona Protein 3 (ZP3), which initiates the acrosomal reaction, resulting in the release of enzymes that break down the zona pellucida, creating a space for sperm to move through, facilitating egg penetration. Like the sea urchin, mammals also utilize a cortical granule–based slow block to polyspermy. In this case, though, the cortical granules release enzymes that modify the sperm binding proteins of the zona pellucida, thereby preventing sperm from binding (Gilbert, 2010). Thus, mammalian eggs do not form a fertilization envelope. As activation of the egg continues, the interaction of the sperm with the egg, and the increase in calcium that ensues, causes the meiotic cycle of the oocyte to resume from its arrested metaphase state of meiosis II. This results in the extrusion of the second polar body and the production of a haploid oocyte. Maternal mRNAs are translated and utilized, and egg and sperm pronuclei are fused, merging the genetic material and creating a diploid cell (known as the zygote).

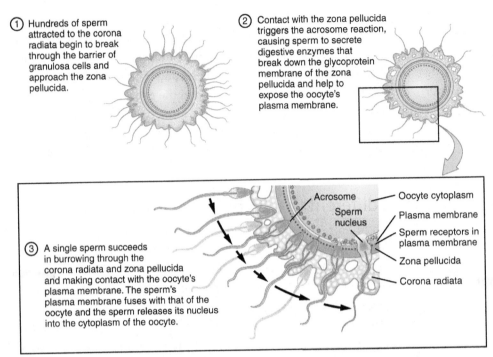

① Hundreds of sperm attracted to the corona radiata begin to break through the barrier of granulosa cells and approach the zona pellucida.

② Contact with the zona pellucida triggers the acrosome reaction, causing sperm to secrete digestive enzymes that break down the glycoprotein membrane of the zona pellucida and help to expose the oocyte's plasma membrane.

③ A single sperm succeeds in burrowing through the corona radiata and zona pellucida and making contact with the oocyte's plasma membrane. The sperm's plasma membrane fuses with that of the oocyte and the sperm releases its nucleus into the cytoplasm of the oocyte.

Acrosome
Sperm nucleus
Oocyte cytoplasm
Plasma membrane
Sperm receptors in plasma membrane
Zona pellucida
Corona radiata

Figure 2-3 Fertilization in mammals.

What are the main stages of early development that lead to the production of a multicellular organism?

Much of what is known about early animal development is derived from studies of a number of model organisms. The most well studied organisms include the sea urchin, the fruit fly, the zebrafish, the frog, the chicken (*Gallus domesticus*), and the mouse. Regarding the process of development, we once again reiterate the opening phrase of this textbook: "Genetic and environmental influences interact to generate complex organisms with remarkably consistent design, yet with individual differences uniquely characteristic to a given species." Thus, the developmental plans of many different organisms share a number of common features, in addition to a number of unique characteristics. Some of these common attributes include axis formation, cell specification, cleavage, blastula formation, gastrulation (including specific types of cell movement), and organogenesis. Axis formation and cell specification occur simultaneously as the embryo progresses through various developmental processes, such as cleavage, blastula formation, and gastrulation.

Axes formation and cell specification

Proper development necessitates the timely specification of three main axes during embryogenesis. These axes serve as the foundation of the body plan. They are: the anterior–posterior axis (or anteroposterior), which extends from head to tail; the dorsal–ventral (or dorsoventral) axis, which denotes the back side (dorsal) to belly side (ventral); and the medial–lateral (or right–left) axis, which describes the regions adjacent to the midline of the body. These axes are set up as cells become restricted to particular locations and specified to particular fates (e.g., cells located at the anterior of the embryo would give rise to anterior structures, such as the brain). A cell's fate is generally specified by two primary means: the unequal distribution of specific molecules, such as transcription factors, that can regulate the expression of other genes (e.g., activate genes that give rise to anterior characteristics, repress genes that give rise to posterior characteristics) and cell-to-cell signaling (e.g., signaling molecules released from one cell bind to receptor molecules of another cell, initiating signal transduction events that result in the production and regulation of other, functionally significant cellular molecules). Factors from the maternal cytoplasm initially direct cell specification. Maternal factors generally refer to mRNA and proteins deposited by the mother during egg formation. In the frog, for example, the embryo contains roughly 4,000 cells before there is any transcription of zygotic genes. In the sea urchin, maternal factors, such as Otx and β-catenin, are localized to one side (the vegetal pole). These factors are involved in a pathway that regulates the transcription of chromosomal genes (such as *Pmar1* and *HesC*) from embryonic cell nuclei. *HesC* also regulates genes that encode proteins involved in cell communication (such as *Delta*). Cells that have a receptor encoded by the Notch gene can interact with the Delta ligand, which guide cells to a unique fate (such as mesenchymal) (Gilbert, 2010). The Delta/Notch signaling pathway is a well-known and widespread mechanism for cell communication. In addition to the notable examples mentioned above, numerous other genes are involved in cell specification, which continues not only throughout the formation of the major axes, but also throughout much of the development of an organism.

Control of organization during development—What have studies in fruit flies and mice taught us?

Early studies of Drosophila mutants provide seminal information as to the means by which maternal factors, morphogen gradients, and differential gene expression initiate the design of the body plan. The term pattern formation is often used to denote the elaboration of a particular spatial organization, such that the tissues, organs, and organ systems are ultimately positioned correctly. Control of patterning during development can be likened to how a maestro conducts an orchestra—instructing each specific component to start at a certain time and in a certain place (e.g., temporal and spatial gene expression) and directing each as to when to intensify or when to diminish in order to create the meticulous symphony of the body.

Powerful examples of pattern formation are provided by the drosophila *bicoid* gene and the highly conserved <u>Hox</u> genes, homologues of which are found in a number of phyla. *Bicoid* (or "two-tailed") is a gene that acts as a <u>morphogen,</u> a substance that spreads from a localized source to form a concentration gradient across a developing tissue. It also belongs to a class of genes known as homeobox genes. A homeobox is a DNA segment that is about 180 base pairs long. It encodes a protein domain (the homeodomain, composed of about 60 amino acids), which can bind DNA. Homeobox genes generally encode proteins that function as transcription factors. By binding (via their homeodomain) to enhancer regions of target genes, these proteins can switch on the expression of other genes. The highly regulated spatial and temporal expression of homeobox genes is essential for the specification of particular regions (or compartments, such as the anterior compartment of the fruit fly wing) during development. In addition to being a homeobox gene and morphogen, *bicoid* is also classified as a maternal effect gene: when it is mutant in the mother, the offspring will have a <u>mutant phenotype</u>, regardless of their own genotype. Thus, an embryo whose mother has two <u>mutant copies of *bicoid*</u> has <u>posterior structures</u> (such as tails) at <u>both of its ends</u>.

Thus, the *bicoid* gene product is essential for specifying the anterior end of the fly. Normally, *bicoid* mRNA is concentrated at the anterior end of the mature egg. Once the egg is fertilized, it is translated into protein, which diffuses toward the posterior, resulting in a gradient. Bicoid protein binds to enhancers of other genes involved in pattern formation, turning on the expression of genes that will direct cells to form appropriate anterior structures at the correct developmental time and location.

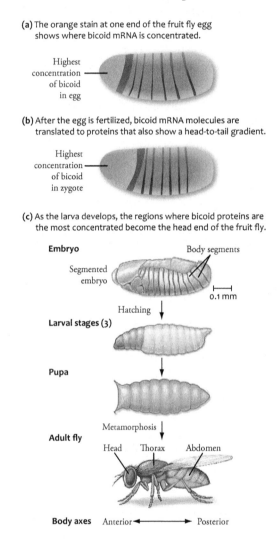

(a) The orange stain at one end of the fruit fly egg shows where bicoid mRNA is concentrated.

Highest concentration of bicoid in egg

(b) After the egg is fertilized, bicoid mRNA molecules are translated to proteins that also show a head-to-tail gradient.

Highest concentration of bicoid in zygote

(c) As the larva develops, the regions where bicoid proteins are the most concentrated become the head end of the fruit fly.

Embryo
Body segments
Segmented embryo
0.1 mm
Hatching
Larval stages (3)

Pupa

Metamorphosis
Adult fly
Head   Thorax   Abdomen

Body axes   Anterior ◄————► Posterior

Figure 2-4 The role of the bicoid gene in the specification of anterior structures.

As development continues and maternal mRNAs diminish, the embryonic program of gene expression ensues, utilizing both transcription factors and signaling molecules to activate or repress additional gene expression, thereby orchestrating further differentiation and development by "refining" the original specifications. General specifications such as "anterior" or "posterior" are established initially. Specific segments (or compartments) within the anterior or posterior regions are specified as development proceeds. Continued refinement results in the formation of specialized structures in each segment (such as antennae in segments of the fly's anterior compartment). Many drosophila pattern formation genes have homologues in mammals. Hox proteins, in particular, are instrumental in ensuring that the appropriate structures form in the appropriate segment. Hox proteins also contain a homeodomain and can function as both activators and repressors of transcription. Interestingly, in many organisms, members of the Hox gene family are aligned along the chromosome in the same order that they are expressed along the anterior-posterior body axis.

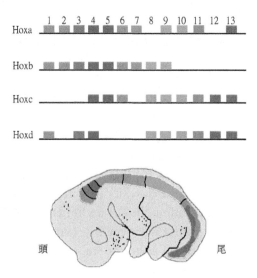

Figure 2-5 Hox gene expression during mouse development.

Making a multi-cellular organism: cleavage and blastula formation

Axis formation and cell specification is accompanied by massive cell proliferation. The first stage of early embryonic development after fertilization is the cleavage stage. It is characterized by a series of mitotic cell divisions that partition the embryo into smaller cells called blastomeres. In many invertebrates, cell divisions during cleavage are rapid, as cells essentially skip the G1 and G2 stages of the cell cycle. In the fruit fly, for example, around 50,000 cells result from cleavage in the first 12 hours of embryonic development (Cullen, 2009). Various organisms have unique cleavage patterns. The location of the cleavage furrow (or the indentation of the cell surface formed prior to the completion of cell division) in many types of organisms is primarily determined by the distribution of yolk protein, which serves as a principal source of nutrients for the embryo of a number of species, such as insects, fish, and birds. Yolk protein is often (but not always) concentrated in one area of the early embryo, known as the vegetal pole. High concentrations of yolk at the vegetal pole tend to impede cell division. Cleavage in an early embryo often occurs more rapidly and to a much greater extent at the yolk deficient, animal pole. In insects, fish, and birds, cleavage such as this is characterized as meroblastic. In these organisms, the cleavage furrow does not penetrate the region of the cytoplasm containing the highest yolk concentration. Meroblastic cleavage results in the embryo having many small cells at the animal pole relative to the rest of the embryo. Sea urchins and mammals, on the other hand, have comparably less yolk that is evenly distributed in the embryo. Cell division is not impeded at any particular location. Cleavage in these organisms is characterized as holoblastic, indicating that the cleavage furrow passes all the way through the embryo, resulting in cells that are relatively equal in size after division. Interestingly, even though the frog has a significant amount of yolk concentrated at the vegetal pole, its cleavage process is also complete and, thus, is characterized as holoblastic.

The well-understood echinoderm, the sea urchin, provides the foundation for a more extensive examination of many key features of embryonic development. Initially, the sea urchin embryo undergoes a very stereotypic pattern of development. The first two cell divisions are classified as meridional (or longitudinal) extending from the animal pole to the vegetal pole. This cleavage produces four cells of similar size. The next cleavage is horizontal (or equatorial), separating the animal and vegetal poles. The next division is distinctive in that the cleavage pattern of the animal and vegetal region deviate. In the animal pole, the cleavage is uniform, resulting in eight equal cells (known as mesomeres). The vegetal pole undergoes uneven division, resulting in four large cells (the macromeres) and four small cells (the micromeres). Cell division proceeds in a unique fashion, eventually forming a ball of cells that encircle a central hollow space (the blastocoel). At this stage of embryonic development, the embryo is now known as a blastula. Depending on the species, the sea urchin embryos reach the blastula stage of development about 9 hours after fertilization. As development progresses, cilia form on the outer edge of the cells. The ciliary movement causes the blastula to rotate, and enzymes are secreted that digest the fertilization envelope, resulting in the release, or "hatching" of the blastula from the fertilization envelope. By about 10 hours post fertilization, the sea urchin embryo consists of approximately 1,000 cells positioned around the blastocoel, with the vegetal side (known as the vegetal plate) appearing flat and thick. Continuation through additional stages of embryonic development results in the pluteus stage, a larval form that still must progress though many steps of additional growth in order to acquire the distinctive characteristics of the adult sea urchin.

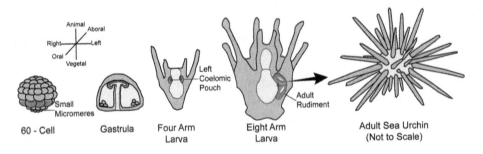

Figure 2-6 Sea Urchin Development.

The cleavage process during blastula formation in the frog (e.g., *Xenopus laevis*) embryo incorporates some unique variations when compared to that of the sea urchin. As mentioned above, the frog embryo has a significant amount of yolk concentrated at the vegetal pole. Sperm entry occurs specifically at the animal pole and is a critical cue in establishing the dorsoventral axis, as it triggers an upward rotation of the outer cortex of the nascent zygote. This rotation exposes a portion of non-pigmented cytoplasm, called the grey crescent, which harbors cytoplasmic determinants that are essential for the specification of dorsal regions and, thus, initiate the generation of the dorsoventral axis. As cleavage continues in the frog, cell division at the animal pole occurs more rapidly than at the vegetal pole. This results in the animal pole housing numerous, yet smaller, cells than the vegetal pole, which affects the formation and location of the blastocoel cavity. Because of this, in the frog embryo, the blastocoel cavity is not centrally located (like it is in the sea urchin) but rather, resides in the upper portion of the developing embryo. Note that the location of the hollow blastocoel cavity is highly significant, as it facilitates cell movement during the next stage of development: gastrulation.

Gastrulation

As the embryo progresses through the gastrulation stage, localized cell division continues, and specific blastomeres reposition themselves via an extensive synchronized movement, further establishing the embryonic axes and, ultimately, forming the three fundamental layers of the organism: the ectoderm (or outer layer, which is composed of cells that will form the skin and nervous system), the endoderm (or inner layer, which forms the epithelial lining of organ systems, such as the gut and respiratory systems) and the mesoderm (or middle layer, which gives rise to the skeleton, muscles, and organs such as the heart and kidney).

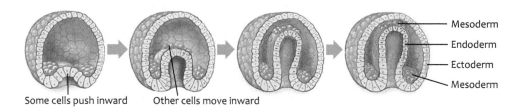

Some cells push inward   Other cells move inward

Mesoderm
Endoderm
Ectoderm
Mesoderm

Figure 2-7   The formation of the three primary cell layers during gastrulation.

These layers result from highly coordinated, yet relatively basic types of cell movements classified as: invagination, ingression, involution, epiboly, and delamination. These unique movements involve changes in cell motility, cell shape, and cell adhesion. Invagination is characterized by the inward bending of a sheet of cells. Ingression refers to the movement of individual cells from an epithelial sheet to become freely migrating, often moving to the inner portion of the embryo. The process of involution occurs when an epithelial sheet rolls inward from an underlying layer, whereas epiboly refers to the spreading out of a sheet of cells, often over another sheet of cells. The expansion of cell sheet layers that occurs during epiboly may be accomplished by division of the existing cells in the sheet; the intercalation of cells, where rows of cells move between one another; and/or the individual cells in the sheet changing shape (e.g., elongating).

Comparison of the gastrulation process in various model organisms can further illuminate many key features of this universal activity. Once again, we begin with the well-studied sea urchin. Some of the earliest movement of cells in the sea urchin embryo is executed by the mesenchymal stem cells. These are multipotent cells that can differentiate into a variety of cell types in various organisms, including osteoblasts (bone cells) and chondrocytes (cartilage cells). In the sea urchin, mesodermal mesenchymal cells migrate from the vegetal pole toward the blastocoel and will eventually secrete calcium carbonate to form the internal skeleton. As these cells continue their migration, movement of presumptive endodermal cells results in an invagination of the vegetal plate, which gives rise to the archenteron (or the future digestive tube). To facilitate this process, non-skeletogenic mesenchyme cells extend filopodia that attach to the internal surface of the blastocoel wall, pulling the emergent archenteron toward the animal pole. At the opposite end (the vegetal pole) an opening known as the blastopore, is formed. Continued development of the archenteron results in the formation of the digestive tube with a mouth at the animal pole end and an anus (derived from the blastopore) at the opposite end. Because the sea urchin's early embryonic development progresses in this fashion, where the blastopore becomes the anus, it is classified as a deuterostome. This is in contrast to the developmental program in protostomes (such as a squid), where the blastopore is believed to form the mouth.

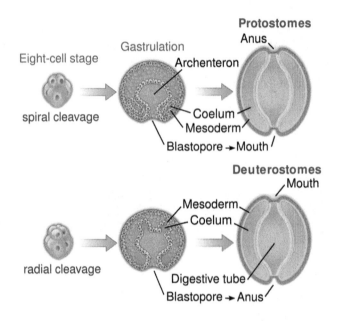

Figure 2-8 Comparison of digestive tube formation in protostomes and deuterostomes.

Although gastrulation in frogs and chicks share many of the same characteristics as in the sea urchin, there are some distinguishing aspects that are worth noting. In the frog, gastrulation initiates with the formation of the blastopore, which begins on the dorsal surface of the embryo about 180 degrees from the point of sperm entry. The blastopore originates from a distinctive feature known as the dorsal blastopore lip, which develops from the invagination of cells on the dorsal surface of the embryo and resembles a slit. Cells of the dorsal lip are involved in the overall body plan organization of the frog embryo. Through a genetic mechanism involving the expression and interaction of a number of genes, these "organizer" cells direct the formation of the embryonic axes and cell fates. Cells that migrate through the blastopore develop a mesodermal fate. Cells outside this area become the ectoderm, which widens to encase the whole embryo, and the endoderm derives from the large cells that reside at the vegetal pole. As the blastocoel cavity diminishes, the archenteron develops from endodermal cells.

As embryogenesis in the frog continues, a mass of endodermal cells, known as the yolk plug, becomes visible. It is formed by cells that have moved into the circular blastopore. These cells will become internalized as development proceeds. Analogous to the sea urchin, the anus end of the archeteron in the frog embryo will develop from the blastopore, and the mouth will develop on the opposite end.

Examination of gastrulation in the chick uncovers additional distinctive features, many of which are shared with mammals. Prior to the onset of gastrulation, cleavage takes place in the region known as the blastodisc, which is located at the animal pole of the egg and resides on top of the yolk. Ongoing cleavage gives rise to the blastoderm, which, in a newly laid egg, contains about 20,000 blastoderm cells (Gilbert, 2010). A specific region of the blastoderm, known as the area pellucida, marks the location where gastrulation begins. Cell migration during gastrulation results in the formation of two layers: the epiblast, or the surface layer cells that contain precursors to all three germ layers (and, thus, will form the intact embryo), and the hypoblast, consisting of cells that reside below the epiblast. The hypoblast cells will function as extra-embryonic tissue, forming external membranes and providing chemical signals directing the migration of epiblast cells.

Arising from a localized thickening of epiblast is the primitive streak. This structure is an early sign of gastrulation in amniotes (which include reptiles, birds, and mammals whose embryos form an amnion, a sac filled with amniotic fluid surrounding a developing embryo). The primitive streak forms along the midline of the developing embryo and elongates as the formative cells undergo intercalation and convergent extension (Gilbert, 2010). It extends from posterior to anterior and creates a left/right body axes. It has a distinctive depression (the primitive groove) through which cells migrate on their way to the deeper embryonic layers. Thus, the primitive groove is comparable to the frog blastopore, as both structures serve as openings for cell migration. The pronounced region at the anterior end of the primitive streak is known as Hensen's node, which is analogous to the amphibian dorsal lip of the blastopore. Hensen's node serves as the organizer region of the chick embryo. Cells in this region produce factors that are involved in axes formation and cell fate determination. Proteins, such as chordin, noggin, and nodal, serve to repress the signaling action of another important factor, bone morphogenic protein (BMP). These important proteins contribute to the dorsalization the ectoderm and mesoderm (Gilbert, 2010). In sum, then, the primitive streak is a highly recognizable structure in gastrulation, with vital roles in the formation of germ layers and body plan axes during this key stage of development.

Key features of mammalian embryonic development

Recall that fertilization in mammals occurs in the oviduct when sperm entry triggers the completion of meiosis in the oocyte. As the embryo is directed by cilia through the oviduct toward the uterus, the cleavage process in mammals continues relatively slowly, with some cell divisions occurring several hours after the preceding division. During this early embryonic development in mammals, maternal factors from the egg cytoplasm are less influential, as zygotic genes are activated relatively early (around the two- to four-cell stage). At the eight cell stage, mammalian embryos undergo the process of compaction, whereby cell adhesion proteins (such as E-cadherin) produced by the blastomeres facilitate the formation of a closely packed sphere of cells. The subsequent stage, called the morula, is composed of 16 cells that are partitioned into two groups of cells, an internal group known as the inner cell mass (ICM) that give rise to the embryo proper, and an external group, which give rise the trophectoderm. Cells of the trophectoderm (or trophoblast cells) will bind to the uterus during implantation and also give rise to the extraembryonic membrane known as the chorion. The chorion is the embryonic portion of the placenta in mammals and, as such, is vital for the exchange of gases (oxygen and CO_2) and the uptake of nutrients from the mother (as mammalian embryos do not contain large amounts of yolk). The trophoblast cells are responsible for another essential event: the formation of the blastocoel cavity. Na+ transporter proteins on the plasma membrane of trophoblast cells pump Na+ into the inner area of the developing embryo. Because of osmosis, water diffuses into this area, thereby creating and expanding the blastocoel and positioning the ICM to one side of the embryo. The result of this process is the mammalian form of the blastula, known as the blastocyst, in which the blastocoel is encircled by trophoblast cells, with the ICM situated toward the rim.

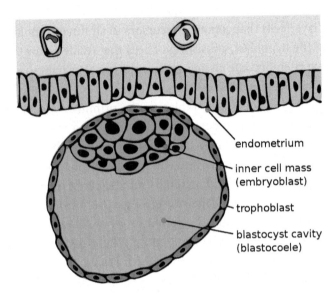

Figure 2-9 The mammalian blastocyst stage embryonic development.

As cell division continues, the blastocyst must emerge (or "hatch") from the zona pellucida (which still envelops it) and attach to the epithelial lining of the uterus (known as the endometrium) via the process of implantation. In humans, implantation occurs about 7 days after fertilization. It is facilitated by the enzymatic breakdown of the endometrium by proteases secreted by trophoblast cells. The cells of the ICM configure into two layers: the hypoblast (or the lower layer) and the epiblast (the upper layer). Cells of the hypoblast will develop into extra-embryonic tissues (which include the amnion, chlorion, yolk sac and allantois, and form the placenta). Cells of the epiblast will give rise to the ectoderm, endoderm, and mesoderm during the process of gastrulation. As with avian development, primitive streak formation is a hallmark of gastrulation in the mammal. Formation of the node (which is analogous to Henson's node in the chick) at the posterior end of the embryo and the primitive groove are both indicative of cell migration. These processes, along with cell specification and axes formation, characterize the gastrulation stage. Figure 2-10 summarizes some of the major events that occur during early embryogenesis in humans.

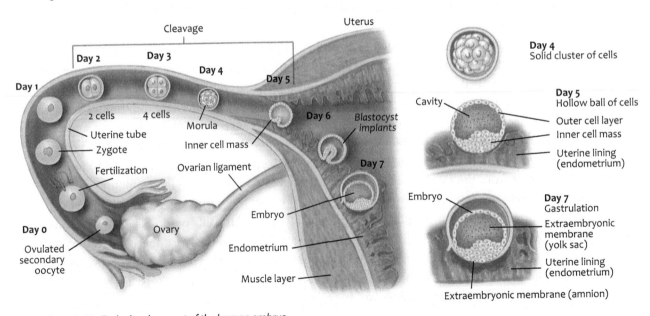

Figure 2-10 Early development of the human embryo.

As growth and development progresses, the primary cell layers (endoderm, mesoderm, ectoderm) that have arisen during gastrulation will continue to develop to form the organs, the body systems (such as the circulatory system, the respiratory system, etc.), as well as the unique features of the adult organism.

Germ Layer	Gives rise to:
Ectoderm	Epidermis, glands on skin, some cranial bones, pituitary and adrenal medulla, the nervous system, the mouth between cheek and gums, the anus 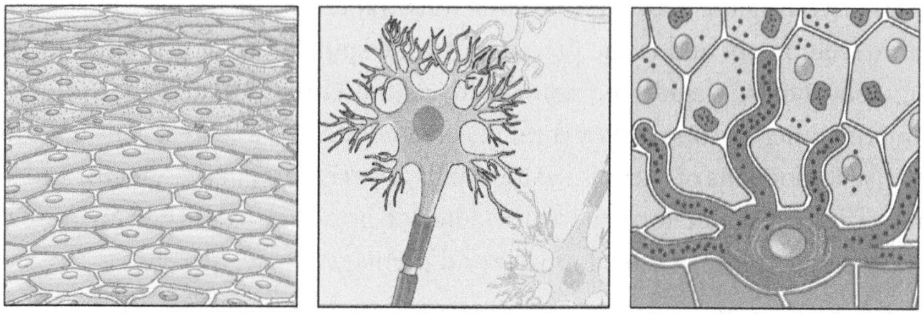 Skin cells Neurons Pigment cell
Mesoderm	Connective tissues proper, bone, cartilage, blood, endothelium of blood vessels, muscle, synovial membranes, serous membranes lining body cavities, kidneys, lining of gonads 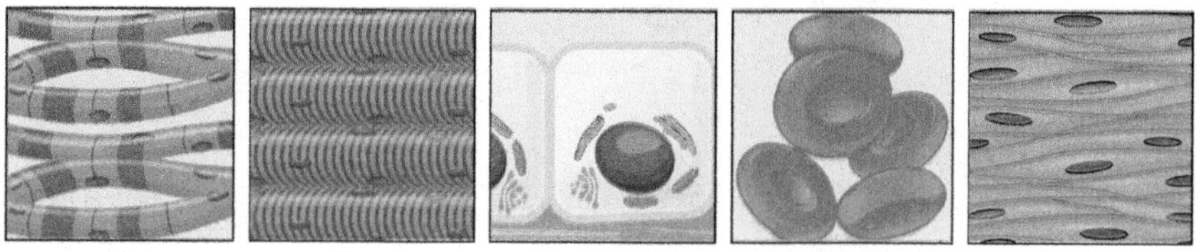 Cardiac muscle Skeletal muscle Tubule cell of kidney Red blood cells Smooth muscle
Endoderm	Lining of airways and digestive system except the mouth and distal part of digestive system (rectum and anal canal); glands (digestive glands, endocrine glands, adrenal cortex) 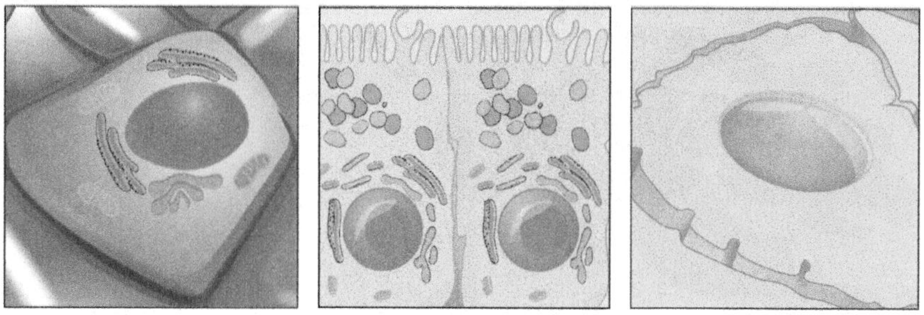 Lung cell Thyroid cell Pancreatic cell

Figure 2-11. The three primary germ cell layers give rise to specific adult tissues.

Neurulation

One early and essential process of organogenesis is neurulation, the formation of the nervous system. The appearance of the neural plate, which occurs around 18 days of development in the human, signifies the initiation of neurulation. The neural plate is derived from cells of the ectoderm that have been induced by signals (such as BMPs) from neighboring cells to thicken and flatten. Cells in the center of the neural plate move inward (invaginate) to form the neural groove. On each side of the neural groove are the neural folds. Cells of the neural folds migrate toward each other, making contact at the midline, thereby converting the neural groove into a neural tube. The neural tube closes around 24 to 26 days of human development and is the precursor to the spinal cord and brain. Other distinguishable features during neurulation include the notochord, neural crest cells, and the somites. Parts of the notochord become the inner portion of vertebral disks in adults. Neural crest cells will migrate to other locations, giving rise to portions of various tissues, such as peripheral nerves, teeth, and skull. Somites are derived from the mesoderm and form along the anterior-posterior axis. They give rise to components of a number of tissues, including skeletal muscle and cartilage.

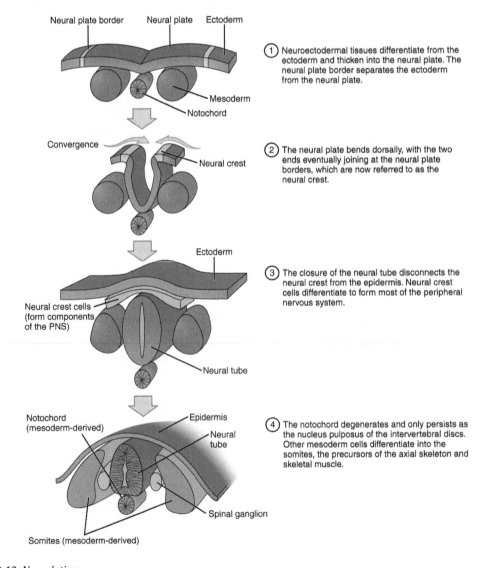

1. Neuroectodermal tissues differentiate from the ectoderm and thicken into the neural plate. The neural plate border separates the ectoderm from the neural plate.

2. The neural plate bends dorsally, with the two ends eventually joining at the neural plate borders, which are now referred to as the neural crest.

3. The closure of the neural tube disconnects the neural crest from the epidermis. Neural crest cells differentiate to form most of the peripheral nervous system.

4. The notochord degenerates and only persists as the nucleus pulposus of the intervertebral discs. Other mesoderm cells differentiate into the somites, the precursors of the axial skeleton and skeletal muscle.

Figure 2-12 Neurulation.

Neurulation is directed by precisely orchestrated gene expression, which, as we learned previously by the example of the pattern formation and *Hox* genes in the fruit fly and the mouse, is a common feature of developmental processes. For example, one highly significant group of genes that are differentially expressed are those of the cadherin family. Cadherins (calcium dependent adhesion molecules) are transmembrane proteins that play an important role in cell adhesion, thus ensuring that cells within tissues are bound together. They are dependent on Ca^{2+} for their function, hence their name.

Limb bud development—an example of cell specification

Another well-studied developmental process is the specification and growth of the limb bud. Each component of a limb (such as a specific bone or muscle) develops at a precise location due to positional information. The precursor to a limb is the limb bud: an outgrowth of mesodermal tissue covered by ectoderm.

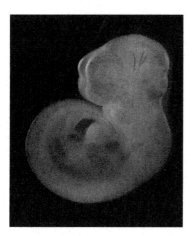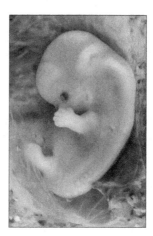

Figure 2-13 Limb bud development. The left panel shows a mouse embryo at 12.5 days. The right panel shows a 9-week-old human embryo.

Much of what is understood about limb bud development originates from early studies in the chick model system. There are two main organizing regions in a limb bud, the *apical ectodermal ridge* (AER) and the *zone of polarizing activity* (ZPA).The AER consists of a dense layer of ectoderm located at the outer edge of the limb bud. Cells in the AER produce factors that contribute to proximal–distal organization and promote limb bud out growth. Some key factors secreted by cells of the AER include proteins in the fibroblast growth factor (FGF) family, an important group of signaling molecules that can stimulate cellular differentiation by binding to specific transmembrane receptors (known as FGFRs: fibroblast growth factor receptors) on cells and initiating specialized signal transduction pathways. The ZPA consists of a distinct region of mesodermal tissue located posteriorly on the limb bud and is involved in anterior–posterior organization of the limb. In general, cells in close proximity to the ZPA give rise to posterior structures (such as an outer digit). Cells that reside further from the ZPA give rise to more anterior structures (such as digits analogous to a human thumb). This is due in part to a principal molecule secreted by cells of the ZPA: the sonic hedgehog (Shh) protein. Shh is a secreted protein that binds to a transmembrane receptor (known as Patched: Ptc). It controls a major signal transduction pathway that is essential for proper limb development. Shh is also morphogen that is present in a gradient. A region of high Shh concentration will develop into an outer digit (i.e., digit five, analogous to the human pinkie) whereas regions of lower Shh concentration give rise to structures that will form more inner digits.

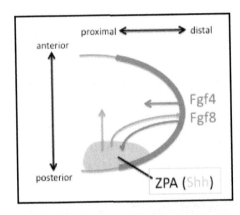

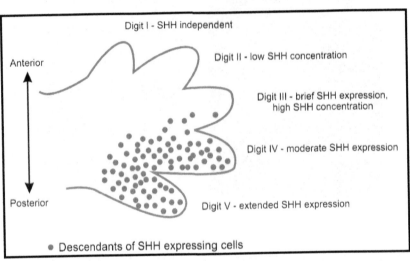

Figure 2-14A and 2-14B Important components of limb bud development include: FGF, Shh, the ZPA and the AER.

An elegant transplantation experiment performed by Honing and Summerbell (1985) supports these conclusions. The researchers transplanted the ZPA (a normally posterior region) from a donor chick limb bud to the anterior region of a recipient, resulting in the formation of extra digits. As expected, the newly formed digits were aligned such that the innermost digit (two) formed in the region where there was the least Shh concentration (that is, close to the same, relatively more anterior location where the recipient's own second digit normally forms). Digits normally located more posteriorly (three and four) formed on the outer edge of the recipient's limb, suggesting the cells of the transplanted ZPA maintained the expected concentration gradient: higher concentration in the posterior ZPA, lower concentration in the anterior ZPA. Thus, the data from this experiment suggests that a molecule (such as Shh) concentrated in posterior regions of the ZPA specifies "posterior." As this molecule diffuses and becomes less concentrated, the posterior signal is diminished, permitting anterior structures to form.

Recall that the expression of *Hox* genes is fundamental for specifying the anterior-posterior body axis in a number of animals. Specific *Hox* gene expression is also essential for specifying a region as "limb" and determining what type of limb (forelimb, hind limb) develops at a precise location. Different *Hox* genes are activated in a temporal and spatial fashion as development progresses, resulting in a refinement of the original expression pattern. This ultimately gives rise to the development of the appropriate and defining structures at the correct locations, which characterize the normal limb.

Interestingly, it has been suggested that the *Hox* genes interact with both FGF and Shh, as the protein product of certain *Hox* genes appear to be necessary for the proper expression of Shh and the FGFs expressed from cells of the AER (Sheth et al., 2013).

Thus, in our examination of a number of developmental organisms, we have reviewed the main stages of early development, as well as some pertinent factors that give rise to these stages, leading to the production of a multi-cellular organism. Continued specification and movement of cells, directed by differential gene expression and cell signaling, give rise to the gradual development of organs and organ systems and, ultimately, a unique individual. Many of the key developmental features we have studied can be applied to human development.

Chapter 2 Review

I. Helpful and interesting animations:

1. Bicoid explained: http://www.ibiology.org/ibioeducation/exploring-biology/development/patterning/bicoid-protein-gradient.html
2. Genes control body segmentation: https://www.youtube.com/watch?v=OHR5K2o7uQU
3. Fertilization in sea urchin: http://bcs.whfreeman.com/thelifewire/content/chp43/4301s.swf
4. Sea urchin development: https://www.youtube.com/watch?v=AD4t5ijilYM
5. Embryonic development in the frog explained: https://www.youtube.com/watch?v=JceGik3Q5A8
6. Live video of frog embryonic development: https://www.youtube.com/watch?v=dXpAbezdOho
7. Chick embryonic development: https://www.youtube.com/watch?v=-Ah-gT0hTto
8. Human Embryonic Development:
     http://www.hhmi.org/biointeractive/human-embryonic-development
9. Differentiation and the fate of cells:
     http://www.hhmi.org/biointeractive/differentiation-and-fate-cells

II. Active Testing: Do you know the facts?

A. List the words in this chapter you would have printed in bold type. Can you define these words?

B. What are the main, "take home" messages of this chapter? Is your answer the same as your instructor's answer?

C. Some Questions:

1. List 5 common features of fertilization and give an example of each.

2. List 3 mechanisms that underlie development.

3. Define cleavage. What is the result of cleavage?

4. Define gastrulation and list the embryonic components that result from it.

5. List the three layers of an embryo and the structures that each gives rise to.

6. Compare and contrast some of the key features of the early development of the sea urchin, frog, chick and human.

7. Briefly describe the process of neurulation.

8. What is meant by the term "pattern formation"?

9. What is meant by "maternal effect gene"? Give an example and explain how it functions.

10. The *Hox* genes are considered master regulatory genes. Concisely summarize their activity.

11. Describe the function of the key genes involved in limb bud development.

III. Inquiring minds want to know...

Challenge Questions:

1. What would you expect to happen if the AER were removed from a developing limb bud? How could the resulting phenotype be rescued?

2. What is a teratogen? What factors influence the effects of teratogens?

References

Kirkman-Brown, JC., Sutton, KA., & Florman, HM. (2003). How to attract a sperm. *Nature Cell Biology, 5 (2).* doi 10.1038/ncb0203-93

Gilbert, S. (2010). *Developmental Biology.* (9th ed.). Sinauer Associates.

Santella, L., Vasiley, F., & Chun, JT. (2012). Fertilization in echinoderms. *Biochemical and Biophysical Research Communications, 425 (3).* doi: 10.1016/j.bbrc.2012.07.159

Guraya, S. (2000). Cellular and molecular biology of capacitation and acrosome reaction in spermatozo *International Review of Cytology, 199,* 1-64. Retrieved from http://www.ncbi.nlm.nih.gov/pubmed/10874576

Cullen, K. (2009). *Encyclopedia of Life Science.* Facts on File.

Honing, L.S., & Summerbell, D. (1985). Maps of strength of positional signaling activity in the developing chick wing bud. *Journal of Embryology and Experimental Morphology, 87,* 163-174. Retrieved from http://www.ncbi.nlm.nih.gov/pubmed/4031751

Sheth, R., Gregoire, D., Dumouchel, A., Scotti, M., Pham, JM, Nemec, S., Bastida, MF., Ros, MA, & Smita, M. (2013). Decoupling the function of Hox and Shh in developing limb reveals multiple inputs of Hox genes on limb growth. *Deveopment, 140,* (10.) doi: 10.1242/dev.089409

Chapter 3

Cell Differentiation

Stem Cells and Cloning

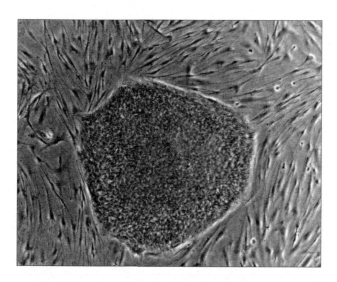

Figure 3-1 A colony of healthy human embryonic stem (ES) cells growing on top of a feeder cell layer composed of fibroblasts.

Can cells be reprogrammed to their de-differentiated state?

All somatic cells (that have a nucleus; mature erythrocytes lack a nucleus) in a given organism have the same number of chromosomes and, thus, contain the same DNA content. As we have seen, differences between cells and their unique functions in a multi-cellular organism generally result from the variation of gene expression, rather than from alterations in the genome. These differences arise during development, as regulatory mechanisms elicit the expression (and repression) of specific genes, at specific times, in specific cells, and at specific locations in the developing organism. Nuclear transplantation experiments using the frog model system were some of the first studies to demonstrate the concept of genomic equivalence (King & Briggs, 1952). During the process of nuclear transplantation, the nucleus of an unfertilized egg cell (or of a newly formed zygote) is replaced with the nucleus from a cell acquired from a very early embryo (such as a four-cell stage embryo). Local factors inside the enucleated egg stimulate the donor nucleus to initiate normal development and, in most cases, will result in the formation of a normal tadpole. However, if the donor nucleus is obtained from a cell (such as adult frog's intestinal cell), whose fate has been firmly established (and, thus, is considered *terminally differentiated*), the resulting embryo will not give rise to a normal organism. Because the nucleus acquired from the blastomeres of a very early embryo can support the development of an entire organism, these cells are described as being totipotent. A zygote is also totipotent, as it, too, has the ability to give rise to every type of cell in the adult body. The term pluripotent refers to the ability to give rise to any of the three germs layers (endoderm, mesoderm, ectoderm) of an organism. The inner cell mass of a blastocyst is considered to be pluripotent, as its cells can be removed and cultured, yielding embryonic stem cells (ESC). These cells can potentially generate any cell in the adult organism and also retain the ability for essentially limitless self-renewal.

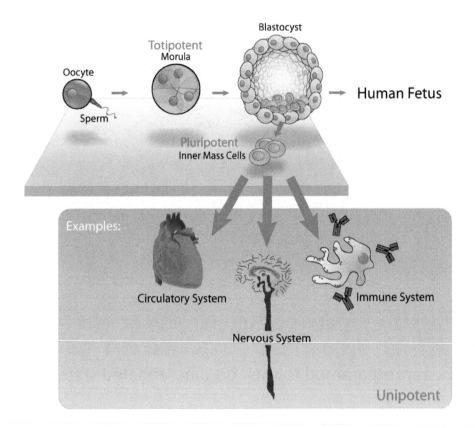

Figure 3.2 Embryonic stem cells can differentiate into a variety of cell types.

In 1997, the first mammal, Dolly the lamb, was cloned by somatic cell nuclear transfer (SCNT) (Wilmut et al., 1997). Mammary cells from the udder of a sheep were cultured under conditions of nutrient deprivation in order to arrest their cell cycle and induce de-differentiation. These adult cells were fused with enucleated egg cells from a donor sheep and were exposed to mitosis stimulating factors, leading to the formation of early embryos. The early embryos were transplanted into a surrogate mother. After many attempts, this process resulted in the successful birth of a lamb, Dolly, who was the clone (or the genetic match) of the of the sheep whose udder cells were used in the experiment. Although her lifespan was shorter than normal, Dolly matured to adulthood and was able to produce offspring. She did, however, experience arthritis and had shortened telomeres, both believed to be age-related conditions. It has been postulated that some of Dolly's cells aged prematurely, perhaps due to the incomplete reprograming of the donor nucleus to its dedifferentiated state. In recent years, many mammals, including dogs, cats, mice, cows, and horses have been cloned by nuclear transplantation. Although clones, such as human identical twins, share the same genome, they sometimes have differences in their appearance and behavior due to environmental influences and random events during development. In addition to premature death, animals cloned by transplantation of a nucleus from a somatic cell also tend to experience various health complications, including obesity, birth defects, and poor lung development. Abnormalities such as these are thought to be associated with the inadequate reprogramming of the genetic material contained in the donor nucleus.

Studies involving the concept of genomic equivalence progressed from nuclear transplantation to the elucidation of embryonic stem cells and their potential uses. A monumental challenge regarding the therapeutic use of ESCs was (and still is) mastering the ability to maintain the exact transcriptional and epigenetic state of these invaluable pluripotent cells in culture. The tremendous theoretical potential of ESCs to differentiate into a variety of distinct cell types (such as skin, cardiac, neuronal, muscular, and more) inspired many researchers to try to elucidate the characteristics that account for and preserve their dedifferentiated state, in order to enable their use for disease therapies. In 1998, the first human embryonic stem cells lines were derived from the inner cell mass of donated human embryos produced by *in vitro* fertilization (Thomson et al., 1998). In the journal *Science*, Thomson et al. reported their ability to culture human ESC lines for several months and detect cell surface markers and telomerase activity consistent with undifferentiated cells. They also reported the capability of these ESCs to generate cells from all three embryonic germ layers. Another seminal discovery was made in 2006, when Takahashi and Yamanaka (Takahashi & Yamanaka, 2006) reported that terminally differentiated mouse fibroblast cells could be induced to become pluripotent stem cells. Using a retroviral vector, four specific reprogramming factors (OCT 4, SOX2, KLF 4, and C-Myc) were introduced and expressed in the fibroblast cells.

These mature fibroblast cells were then grown in standard ESC culture conditions and after 2 to 3 weeks, yielded *induced pluripotent stem cells* (iPSCs) with characteristics that were consistent with ESCs derived from the ICM. Thus, the addition of the four reprogramming factors and the appropriate culture conditions enabled the mature fibroblast cells to be reprogrammed to a de-differentiated state. About a year later, researchers showed that the same four factors could be used to reprogram human fibroblasts to an embryonic stem cell-like phenotype (Takahashi, K. *et al* 2007). Due to concerns that some of the introduced genes could be oncogenic (cancer causing), a different research group used OCT4, SOX2, NANOG, and LIN28 to create human iPSCs from fibroblasts (Yu, J. *et al* 2007). A notable difference between iPSCs and ESCs were alterations in the epigenetic landscape of the genomes. The term epigenetics refers to changes in gene expression that do not involve changes in the DNA sequence proper, but rather to additional modifications, such as adding methyl groups to cytosine residues. This modification, in particular, is believed to generally repress gene expression. Another epigenetic modification consists of adding acetyl groups to histones. This is postulated to help uncoil chromatin from histones, thereby exposing DNA for active gene transcription. Thus, the term *epigenetic landscape* can be thought of as the total epigenetic modifications of a DNA sequence. Because the regulation of gene expression is essential to the most fundamental processes of normal development (such as cell differentiation), recapitulating the correct epigenetic landscape of the genome in undifferentiated, pluripotent stem cells is essential if these cells are to be used for disease-based therapies.

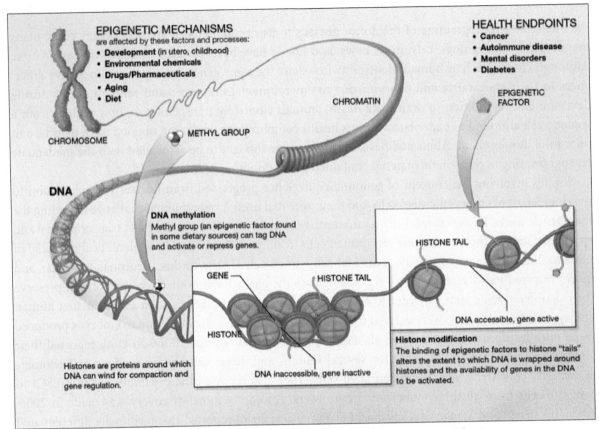

Figure 3-3 Examples of two primary epigenetic mechanisms: DNA methylation and histone modification.

In addition to the difficulty of accurately replicating the correct epigenetic landscape in iPSCs, it is also necessary to ensure that using these cells for treatment of diseases does not create further complications (such as immune rejection, creating new mutations in the recipient DNA at insertion sites, cancer, etc.). Furthermore, successfully reprograming somatic cells to iPSCs has not proven to be a very efficient process. For example, only a 0.01% to 0.1% efficiency rate was reported in the initial study of reprograming mouse somatic cells into iPSCs. A more recent protocol for producing iPSCs from renal epithelial cells reported only a 4% efficiency rate (Zhou et al., 2012).The figure below summarizes some of the strategies currently being investigated for the production of iPSCs.

Year	Group	Strategy	Contribution
2006	Yamanaka et al.	First to demonstrate	iPS cells were first generated using retroviruses and the four key pluripotency genes; failed to produce viable chimera.
2007	Yamanaka et al.	Different Selection Method	iPS cells were generated again using retroviruses, but this time produced viable chimera (they used different selection methods).
2007	Thomson et al.	Vector	iPS cells were generated again using lentiviruses, and again produced viable chimera.
2008	Melton et al.	Small Compound Mimicking	Using HDAC inhibitor valproic acid compensates for C-Myc.
2008	Ding et al.	Small Compound Mimicking	Inhibit HMT with BIX-01294 mimics the effects of Sox2, significantly increases reprogramming efficiency.
2008	Hochedlinger et al.	Vector	The group used an adenovirus to avoid the danger of creating tumors; however, this led to lower efficiency.
2008	Yamakana et al.	Vector	The group demonstrated reprogramming with no virus (they instead used a plasmid)
2009	Ding et al.	Proteins	Used recombinant proteins ; proteins added to cells via arginine anchors was sufficient to induce pluripotency.
2009	Freed et al.	Vector	Adenoviral gene delivery reprogrammed human fibroblasts to iPS cells.
2009	Blelloch et al.	RNA	Embryonic stem-cell specific microRNAs promted iPS reprogramming.
2011	Morrisey at al.	RNA	Demonstrated another method using microRNA that improved the efficiency of reprogramming to a rate similar to that demonstrated by Ding.

Table 3-1 Summary of recent research on iPSCs.

Whether the pluripotent cells are derived from the nucleus of a somatic cell (SCNT), the inner cell mass of an embryo (ESCs), or from successfully reprogrammed mature cells (iPSCs), there remain many potential therapeutic uses for stem cells. One example is for use in the treatment of Parkinson's Disease, a common neurodegenerative disorder that is characterized by the progressive death of neurons that produce the neurotransmitter, dopamine. Methods of differentiating *in vitro* cultures of ESCs and iPSCs into non-defective dopaminergic neurons, followed by the transplantation of these cells into the appropriate brain region, are currently being investigated in animal models (Nishimura & Takahashi , 2013). Thus, the potential for pluripotent stem cells to be used for the treatment of numerous diseases (see Figure 3-4, below) is likely to keep these invaluable cells at the forefront of research for many years to come.

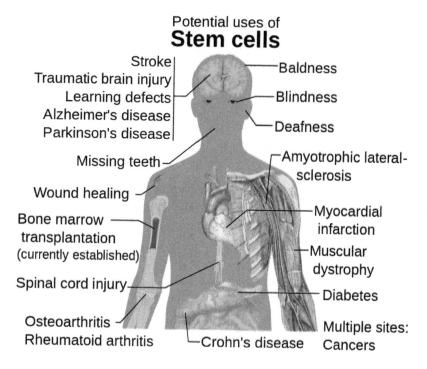

Figure 3-4 *Potential uses for stem cells.*

Chapter 3 Review

I. Helpful and Interesting Animations:

1. Creating embryonic stem cell lines:
   http://www.hhmi.org/biointeractive/creating-embryonic-stem-cell-lines
2. Somatic cell nuclear transfer:
   http://www.hhmi.org/biointeractive/somatic-cell-nuclear-transfer-animation
3. Dolly the sheep:
   https://www.youtube.com/watch?v=-Qry1gYYDCA

II. Active Testing: Do you know the facts?

A. List the words in this chapter you would have printed in bold type.
Can you define these words?

B. What are the main, "take home" messages of this chapter?
 Is your answer the same as your instructor's answer?

C. Some Questions:

1. Describe the initial nuclear transplantation experiment performed in the frog. How was this experiment different from what was done with Dolly the sheep?

2. Describe the process of somatic cell nuclear transfer (SCNT) and how embryonic stem cells (ESCs) and induced pluripotent stem cells (iPSCs) are made. Compare and contrast the benefits and caveats of SCNT, ESCs, and iPSCs.

III. Inquiring minds want to know...

Challenge Questions

1. Can iPSC technology be used for disease modeling? How?

2. How could pluripotent stem cells be used to treat diabetes?

3. Is it acceptable to destroy a human blastocyst in order to obtain and culture the cells of the ICM to generate useful embryonic stem cells? Why or why not?

REFERENCES

Briggs, R., & King, T. (1952). Transplantation of living nuclei from blastula cells into enucleated frogs' eggs. *PNAS*, 38 (5), 455-463 Retrieved from http://www.ncbi.nlm.nih.gov/pmc/articles/PMC1063586/

Wilmut, I., Schnieke, AE., McWhir, J., Kind, AJ., & Campbell, KH. (1997). Viable offspring delivered from fetal and adult mammalian cells. *Nature*, 385 (6619), 810-813. Retrieved from http://www.ncbi.nlm.nih.gov/pubmed/9039911

Thomsom, JA., Itskovitz-Eldor, J., Shapiro, SS., Waknitz, MA., Swiergiel, JJ., Marshall VS., & Jones, JM. Embryonic stem cell lines derived from human blastocysts. *Science*, 282 (5391). doi 10.1126/science.282.5391.1145

Kazutoshi, T., & Yamanaka, S. (2006). Induction of pluripotent stem cells from mouse embryonic and adult fibroblast cultures by defined factors. *Cell*, 126 (4). doi http://dx.doi.org/10.1016/j.cell.2006.07.024

Takahashi, K., Tanabe, K., Ohnuki, M., Narita, M., Ichisaka, T., Tomoda, K., & Yamanaka, S. (2007). Induction of pluripotent stem cell from adult human fibroblasts by defined factors. *Cell*, 131. doi http://dx.doi.org/10.1016/j.cell.2007.11.019

Yu, J., Vodyanik, MA., Smugo-Otto, K., Antosiewicz-Bourget, J., Frane, J., Shulan, T., Nie, J., Jonsdottir, G. Ruotti, V., Stewart, R., Slukvin, I., & Thomson, J. (2007). Induced pluripotent stem cell lines derived from human somatic cells. *Science*, 318 (5858). doi 10.1126/science.1151526

Zhou, T., Benda, C., Dunzinger, S., Huang, Y., Ho, J.C., Yang, J., Wang, Y., Zhang, Y., Zhuang, Q., Yanhua, B., Xichen, T., Hung-Fat, G., Grillari, J., Grillari-Voglauer, R., Pei, D., & Estaban, M. (2012). Generation of human induced pluripotent stem cells from urine samples. *Nature Protocols,* 7 (12). doi 10.1038/nprot.2012.115.

Nishimura, K., & Takahashi, J. (2013). Therapeutic application of stem cell technology towards the treatment of Parkinson's Disease. *Biological Pharmaceutical Bulletin,* 36 (2), 171-175. Retrieved from http://www.ncbi.nlm.nih.gov/pubmed/23370347

Chapter 4

Homeostasis and the Body Plan

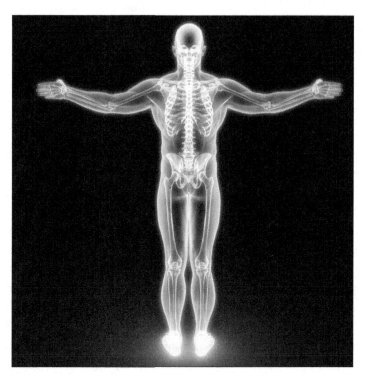

Figure 4-1 The human body.

What two concepts are fundamental to physiology?

A ll living organisms require energy to sustain them. They need to carry out such essential body functions as growth, reproduction, movement, cognition, and more. Efficient regulation of an animal's physiological systems is crucial to proper functioning. Animals must actively engage in adjusting their body's mechanisms to respond to a multitude of conditions, such as changes in temperature, pH, metabolism, respiration rates, blood pressure regulation, osmoregulation, etc. that are associated with each of the eleven organ systems listed in Table 4-1.

Table 4-1   *Major Human Organ Systems and Their Functions.*

Organ System	Major Components	Function
Integumentary	Skin, hair, nails	Protection from water loss, mechanical injury, and infection
Muscular	Skeletal muscles	Movements of body parts and of whole body
Skeletal	Bones, ligaments, tendons	Support of body and protection of internal organs
Digestive	Mouth, pharynx, esophagus, stomach, intestines, liver, pancreas, gallbladder, anus	Digestion and absorption of food, and elimination of food wastes
Circulatory	Heart, blood vessels, blood	Movement of substances to and from individual cells
Respiratory	Trachea, breathing tubes, lungs	Gas exchange: obtaining oxygen and releasing carbon dioxide
Lymphatic and immune	Lymphatic vessels, lymph nodes, lymph, immune cells, bone marrow, thymus, spleen, white blood cells	Defense against infection and cleanup of dead cells
Excretory	Kidneys, ureters, bladder, urethra	Elimination of metabolic wastes and regulation of chemistry of blood
Endocrine	Pituitary, thyroid, pancreas, ovaries, testes, and other glands that secrete hormones	Coordination of body functions by hormones
Nervous	Brain, spinal cord, nerves, sense organs	Sensing internal and external stimuli and coordination of entire body's functions
Reproductive	Ovaries, testes, and related organs	Reproduction

An organism partakes in active regulatory processes in order to successfully maintain homeostasis. In physiology, homeostasis refers to a stable internal condition of the body resulting from the body's ability to elicit responses to counteract changes, thereby restoring stasis, or balance. An organism's adjustment to change is carried out by the physiological processes of its body. These processes maintain the physical and chemical parameters that will ensure proper functioning of the body and allow for the maximum efficiency of its component cells, tissues, organs, and organ systems. For example, enzymes function best when in an environment where an optimal pH is maintained. The pH of the blood is normally maintained within the narrow range of 7.35 to 7.45, whereas the gastric fluid in the stomach has a pH that generally ranges from 1 to 2. Likewise, ionic concentrations in the extracellular fluid (ECF) are also highly regulated. This is important for a number of functions, including enabling cells to maintain osmotic balance.

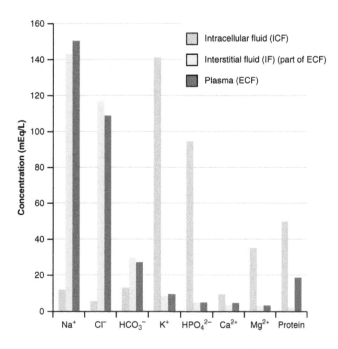

Figure 4-2 Concentrations of substances inside and outside of cells.

Other vital functions that are regulated in order to preserve homeostasis include such processes as maintaining appropriate concentrations of oxygen and carbon dioxide (CO_2). Recall that oxygen serves as final acceptor for electrons removed in oxidative reactions, and CO_2 is a by-product of many metabolic reactions. Additionally, regulating the volume and pressure of extracellular fluid, controlling nutrient usage and the removal of wastes, and balancing the body's electrolytes are also essential to maintain homeostasis. Organisms strive to achieve homeostasis by coordinating the activities of the 11 organ systems, utilizing the nervous system and the endocrine system as the body's major control centers.

What are some examples of how an organism maintains homeostasis?

Homeostasis is a mechanism based on negative feedback regulation. For example, when an organism detects a change from a normal set point, it can initiate signals (such as electrical impulses known as action potentials) along neurons. These are most often conducted to the central nervous system (CNS), where this new information is integrated. The CNS then elicits the response that will appropriately compensate for the initial change. The body has a number of sensors, which can be actual cells or specialized endings of neurons, which can convert a stimulus (or change) to action potentials (APs). To illustrate, consider the sensory cells (rods and cones) in the retina. They convert the physical energy from photons of light into action potentials that travel to the visual cortex of the brain via the optic nerve in order to perceive an image. Baroreceptors provide another example. They are sensors that are located in the walls of the atria of the heart, the aortic arch, and the carotid sinuses. These specialized sensors detect the amount of stretch in vessel walls and thus are sensitive to changes in blood pressure. They can transmit action potentials to the brain stem, where the centers that regulate the heart rate are located. The brain stem sends signals via the autonomic nervous system to the elicit the necessary changes, such as increasing the rate and force of the heartbeat in order to raise the blood pressure if it is too low.

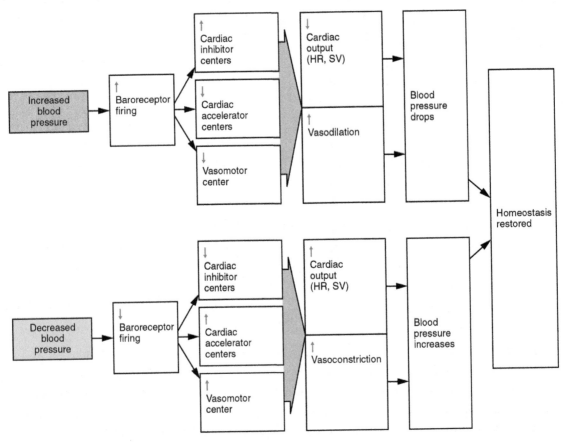

Figure 4-3 Baroreceptors help maintain blood pressure homeostasis.

Chemoreceptors are sensors that detect changes in chemical content, such as the amount of O_2 in the blood. They are found in the aorta and carotid arteries and can also send signals to the cardiac centers in the brainstem where the information they provide is integrated with the information from the baroreceptors. If O_2 levels are lower than normal, signals will be sent to increase the rate and force of the heartbeat, effectively increasing the flow of oxygenated blood to the systemic circulation. Chemoreceptors can also detect levels of plasma H+, and thus are important for pH regulation. To help tightly regulate the pH of the ECF, the body often employs the bicarbonate buffering system which can be described by the equation:

$$CO_2 + H_2O \Leftrightarrow H_2CO_3 \text{(carbonic acid)} \Leftrightarrow HCO_3^- \text{ (bicarbonate)} + H+$$

Certain conditions can cause the body to become too acidic. Respiratory acidosis, for example, may result when one's ability to breathe is debilitated. This can be caused by diseases such as chronic obstructive pulmonary disease (COPD), where poor air flow results from the breakdown of lung tissue (often due to smoking). COPD can also be caused by diseases that affect the muscles used for breathing, such as amyotrophic lateral sclerosis or myasthenia gravis. Respiratory acidosis results when decreased respiration causes an increase in the blood CO_2 levels. This can occur because carbon dioxide is produced constantly as the body uses energy. CO_2 will accumulate rapidly if the lungs do not adequately dispel it. CO_2 accumulation tends to shift the equation above to the right, producing relatively more H+ and decreasing blood pH. Another condition that can cause the body to become too acidic is metabolic acidosis. This can occur if the kidneys are not adequately removing enough acid from the body, or if other compensatory mechanisms (such as the bicarbonate buffering system, or respiratory compensation, whereby the rate and depth of breathing is increased in order to exhale more CO_2) are insufficient. Metabolic acidosis can be caused by a condition known as ketoacidosis, which is due to the body's inability to adequately control the production of ketone bodies (e.g., acetoacetic acid, acetone, beta-hydroxybutyric acid), which are byproducts of fatty acid breakdown. A decrease in blood pH results from the accumulation of these acidic molecules. Conditions that can cause the accumulation ketones include Type 1 diabetes and alcoholism. In Type 1 diabetes, the body does not produce insulin in adequate amounts. Insulin is necessary for the cellular uptake of glucose. The body responds to a lack of glucose absorption by switching to fatty acid metabolism for energy, thereby producing acidic ketone bodies. Alcoholic ketoacidosis may occur in alcoholics who have developed liver or pancreatic conditions after consuming large amounts of alcohol. In this situation, alcohol can inhibit the process of gluconeogenesis, which reduces glucose production. This, in turn, directs the body to metabolize fatty acids for energy, again resulting in the production of ketones. As one might expect, a common symptom of ketoacidosis is the smell of acetone on one's breath. However, in normal, healthy individuals, rising ketone levels are detected and the pancreas produces insulin to counteract the effects of excess ketones, thereby preventing ketoacidosis and maintaining pH homeostasis.

Other conditions may cause the pH of the blood to be abnormally high. Hyperventilation, for example, can result from vigorous physical exercise (such as sprinting). In this situation, a person may take rapid, deep breaths in order to restore the oxygen that has been depleted. This increased respiration causes the body's CO_2 levels to fall, because the amount of CO_2 lost during rapid expiration is often greater than the amount being produced in the body. When the CO_2 concentration of the blood falls below the normal set point, the bicarbonate buffering chemical equation shown above is shifted to the left. This reduces the amount of free H+ and raises the blood's pH value (making it too basic or alkaline). When necessary, athletes who are hyperventilating may exhale into a paper bag and then inhale this same air, which enables them to replenish the CO_2 in their bloodstream and, thus, restore homeostasis.

In sum, then, an important mechanism the body uses to maintain pH homeostasis involves the bicarbonate buffering system, represented by the equation:

$$CO_2 + H_2O \Leftrightarrow H_2CO_3 \text{ (carbonic acid)} \Leftrightarrow HCO_3^- \text{ (bicarbonate)} + H+$$

When the pH of the blood plasma drops below normal, the corresponding increase in plasma H+ shifts the equation to the left (due to the law of mass action). This shift yields an increase in plasma CO_2, which is detected by the central chemoreceptors located in the respiratory control centers of the medulla (a region of the brainstem). Action potentials are then sent via somatic motor neurons to the muscles that control ventilation, resulting in an increase in the rate and depth of breathing and the expiration of CO_2. This reduces the plasma level of CO_2. Due to the law of mass action, a decrease in plasma CO_2 shifts the equation to the left, resulting in a decrease in plasma H+ and a corresponding increase in plasma pH, thereby restoring homeostasis. Similarly, an initial increase of plasma H+ above normal levels can be directly detected by peripheral chemoreceptors located in the carotid arteries and aortic bodies. From here, sensory neurons transmit signals (action potentials) to the respiratory control centers in the medulla, which then carry out the process described above to restore pH homeostsis.

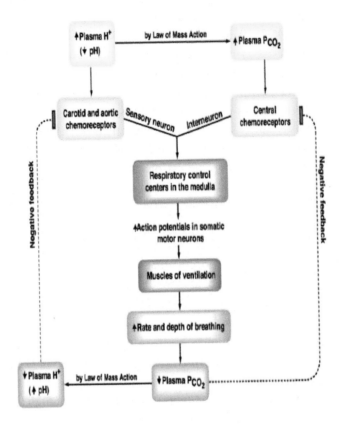

Figure 4-4 *Mechanisms for maintaining pH homeostasis*

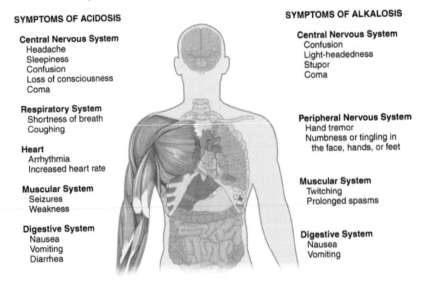

SYMPTOMS OF ACIDOSIS

Central Nervous System
Headache
Sleepiness
Confusion
Loss of consciousness
Coma

Respiratory System
Shortness of breath
Coughing

Heart
Arrhythmia
Increased heart rate

Muscular System
Seizures
Weakness

Digestive System
Nausea
Vomiting
Diarrhea

SYMPTOMS OF ALKALOSIS

Central Nervous System
Confusion
Light-headedness
Stupor
Coma

Peripheral Nervous System
Hand tremor
Numbness or tingling in
the face, hands, or feet

Muscular System
Twitching
Prolonged spasms

Digestive System
Nausea
Vomiting

Figure 4-5 *Potential consequences of inadequate pH homeostasis.*

Maintaining appropriate concentrations of solutes in the blood is another important example of a homeostatic process that is essential to proper body function. When excessive amounts of water are lost, osmoreceptors that reside the hypothalamus of the brain have the ability to detect the accompanying increase in solute concentration in the ECF. The hypothalamus works to restore homeostasis by two primary methods. First, it simply stimulates thirst. Second, it directs the posterior pituitary to secrete antidiuretic hormone (ADH) which acts on the kidney to increase water retention and reduce urine production. Both of these homeostatic mechanisms act to restore the solute concentrations to normal levels.

Thermoregulation—a fundamental homeostatic process

Although animals can survive in environments that vary widely in temperature, it is essential that they maintain an appropriate internal body temperature to avoid life-threatening complications. If internal temperatures fall much below the freezing point, ice crystals can form in the normally fluid lipid layers that comprise the plasma membrane and the membranes surrounding organelles. Freezing of these essential cell membranes and the important proteins associated with them can have catastrophic consequences. Alternatively, elevated kinetic energy that accompanies increased temperatures can cause proteins and nucleic acids to denature, greatly diminishing their ability to function properly. Thermoregulation not only allows an animal to maintain an appropriate internal temperature and accommodate changes in environmental temperature, it also enables an animal to function efficiently and at optimal levels.

Regulation of body temperature can be accomplished by both behavioral and physiological methods. Animals that are ectothermic primarily obtain heat energy from the environment by controlling the rate of heat exchange with their surroundings. Generally, ectotherms can only reside in environments that are favorable to their body temperature requirements. In contrast, endotherms can generate heat metabolically via internal reactions (in addition to gaining or losing heat from the environment). Ectotherms typically have a lower metabolic rate than endotherms, and their metabolic rate usually increases with environmental temperature. This affords ectotherms some advantages over endotherms. Usually, ectotherms, which include invertebrates, fish, and amphibians, can be relatively small in size and live in small habitats. A small surface to volume ratio enables them to retain more body heat than larger endothermic animals. In general, ectotherms can sustain themselves with little food and, thus, may live in areas where food is often scarce. Ectotherms that reside in terrestrial environments often employ various behavioral means to thermoregulate. Some examples include moving to a warmer/cooler location (i.e., basking in the sun/jumping in a pond), decreasing daily activity when temperatures are high, participating in annual migration, and optimizing the design of their habitat. The mound that termites inhabit, for example, is designed with chambers that serve as a type of built-in air conditioning system. Termite activity produces heat in the main chamber, where they usually reside. This heat passes by way of vents into another chamber and can be dissipated to the outside. Cooler air entering from additional outside vents can enter the main chamber, replacing the hotter air.

Like ectotherms, endotherms can also thermoregulate by modifying their behavior. Torpor is a period of inactivity aligned with variations in temperature. Two common types of torpor are hibernation and estivation. Hibernation refers to extended torpor during the winter months (as exhibited by some bears and woodchucks), whereas estivation describes seasonal torpor during the summer (such as when toads and frogs burrow into the soil on days when environmental temperatures are high and water is scarce).

Endotherms primarily obtain heat energy from internal reactions. They normally maintain body temperature over a narrow range by balancing internal heat production against heat loss from their body surface. Altering heat conductance can be accomplished by modifying insulation, minimizing heat uptake, engaging in evaporative cooling, and redirecting blood flow. For example, fur or feathers can be adjusted to extend fuller and higher (fluffed up) to increase insulation. Heat lost from the body will be trapped in the air between the skin and the thickened layer of insulation, thus retaining warmth. The light coloration of the skin surface of an animal, such as a gazelle, can serve to reflect solar radiation and, thus, reduce heat uptake. Panting and perspiration are both common examples of evaporative cooling, whereby heat is discharged from the body as water is vaporized. The controlled vasodilation or vasoconstriction of local blood vessels is another important mechanism for regulating heat conductance.

In response to lower environmental temperatures, an organism can conserve body heat by constricting blood vessels near the body surface and enlarging more proximal blood vessels that are nearer to the body core. This redirects blood flow away from the body surface where the heat carried by the blood would be dissipated to the environment. Similarly, blood vessels that reside adjacent to the surface of the body can be dilated, while those residing more internally can be constricted, thereby shunting warm blood to the body surface, where heat can be released to the surrounding air.

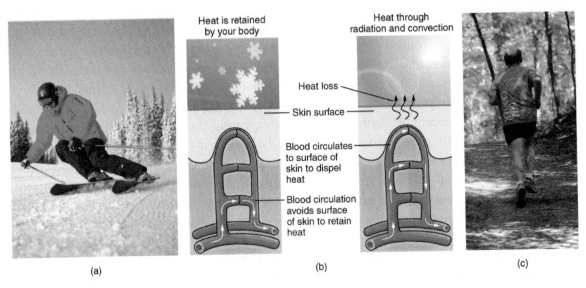

Figure 4-6 An example of thermoreguation.

Many animals utilize the highly efficient mechanism of counter current exchange to facilitate heat retention in the body. In this process, a temperature gradient is established between the warm arterial blood flowing outward in the body's extremities and the cooler venous blood returning inward from the extremity to the body core. At any given point, heat is transferred between an artery and an adjacent vein, resulting in the conservation of heat.

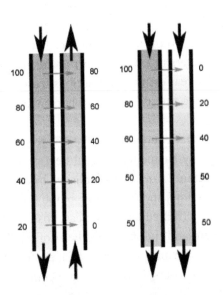

Figure 4-7 Contrasting countercurrent with concurrent heat exchange.

How does the body actually detect changes in temperature? Temperature sensors, known as thermo-receptors, are located in the skin and the hypothalamus of the brain. When a change in temperature is detected either at the surface or core of the body, signals (action potentials) are sent to the hypothalamus, where the information is integrated. The hypothalamus then initiates responses to return the body's temperature to its set point. Such responses include: behavioral changes (e.g.,putting on a sweatshirt), initiating small changes in muscle activity to generate friction and, thus, warmth (shivering); perspiration; panting; and vasodilation or vasoconstriction of blood vessels.

Structure and function are inseparable

In the study of living organisms, the relationship between form (anatomy) and function (physiology) cannot be underrated. Simply stated, the design of physiological systems is optimized for function. The 11 body systems listed in Table 4-1 are composed of well-designed units: organs, tissues, cells, etc., that function extremely well together. The cells of the four basic tissue types, epithelial, muscle, nervous, and connective, have unique morphologies that facilitate their specific functions.

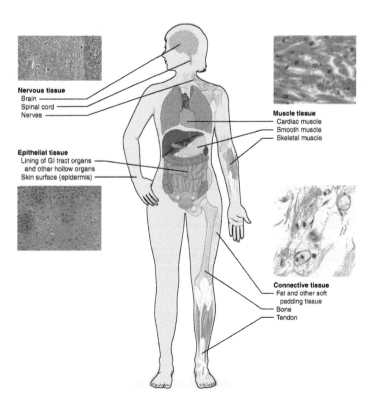

Figure 4-8 The four main tissue types.

Different types of epithelial tissue can be found in glands, the walls of blood vessels, the aveoli of the lungs, and in the lining of the gut and respiratory tract. Epithelial cells are well suited to aid in essential processes such as absorption, secretion, and diffusion.

Cells	Location	Function
Simple squamous epithelium	Air sacs of lungs and the lining of the heart, blood vessels, and lymphatic vessels	Allows materials to pass through by diffusion and filtration, and secretes lubricating substance
Simple cuboidal epithelium	In ducts and secretory portions of small glands and in kidney tubules	Secretes and absorbs
Simple columnar epithelium	Ciliated tissues are in bronchi, uterine tubes, and uterus; smooth (nonciliated tissues) are in the digestive tract, bladder	Absorbs; it also secretes mucous and enzymes
Pseudostratified columnar epithelium	Ciliated tissue lines the trachea and much of the upper respiratory tract	Secretes mucus; ciliated tissue moves mucus
Stratified squamous epithelium	Lines the esophagus, mouth, and vagina	Protects against abrasion
Stratified cuboidal epithelium	Sweat glands, salivary glands, and the mammary glands	Protective tissue
Stratified columnar epithelium	The male urethra and the ducts of some glands	Secretes and protects
Transitional epithelium	Lines the bladder, uretha, and the ureters	Allows the urinary organs to expand and stretch

Table 4-2 Types of epithelium.

The three varieties of *muscle tissue* are skeletal, smooth, and cardiac; they function to provide movement of body parts, movement in internal organs, and the pumping of blood, respectively.

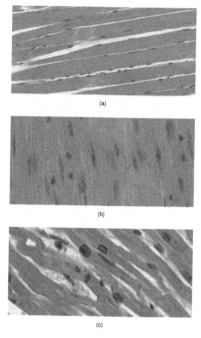

Figure 4-9 Three types of muscle tissue: (a) skeletal, (b) smooth and (c) cardiac.

Many different types of neurons (bipolar, unipolar, multipolar, etc.), as well as accessory cells (microglia, astrocytes, etc.) comprise the nervous system, which is necessary to transmit information in the form of action potentials. The figure below illustrates some primary components of nervous tissue.

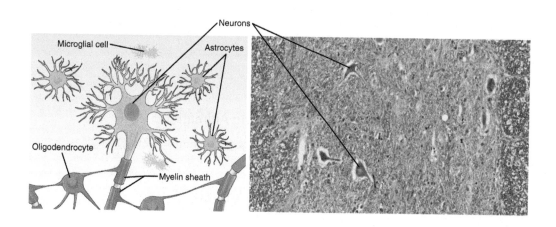

Figure 4-10 Nervous tissue.

There are six types of connective tissue: loose, fibrous, cartilage, bone, adipose, and blood. Loose connective tissue is commonly found under epithelial layers and below the skin. Its tasks include support, elasticity, and diffusion. Fibrous connective tissue comprises the tendons and ligaments and provides strength and flexibility. Cartilage is found at many locations in the body, such as at the ends of long bones, between vertebrae, around the airways, and in the nose and ear. It is used for support and flexibility. Movement and support are primary roles for the bones. Adipose tissue (or body fat) serves as insulation, padding, and energy reserves. Blood, the only fluid connective tissue, is necessary for the transport of nutrients, oxygen, and wastes. Figure 4-11 provides an example of connective tissue.

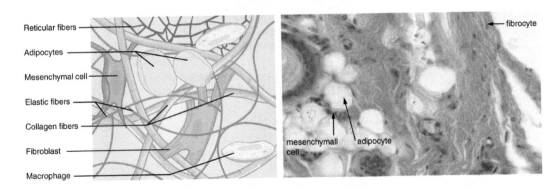

Figure 4-11 An example of connective tissue.

Finally, it is important to note that organs can be made from many different types of tissue. The stomach, for example, is composed of four distinct tissue layers: an inner layer of epithelial cells, known as the mucosa; the submucosa, made of elastic connective tissue that has neurons and blood vessels associated with it; muscularis, which is made of smooth muscle that generates peristalsis; and the outermost layer, known as the serosa, which is made of connective tissue. It functions to help hold the stomach in place and reduce friction with other local organs.

We now return to the question that we began with at the start of this chapter: what two concepts are fundamental to physiology? Both homeostasis and the relationship between form and function are two basic principles of physiology. Appropriate design gives rise to proper function, and maintenance of homeostasis results in the maximal efficiency of body functioning.

Review

I. Helpful and Interesting Animations

1. An example of homeostasis: https://www.youtube.com/watch?v=XZxuQo3ylII

II. Active Testing: Do you know the facts?

A. List the words in this chapter you would have printed in bold type.
   Can you define these words?

B. What are the main, "take home" messages of this chapter?
Is your answer the same as your instructor's answer?

C. Some Questions:

1. Define homeostasis.

2. With regard to homeostasis, what does "internal responses" mean? Give an example of an "internal response" in the context of homeostasis?

3. Give some examples of homeostasis and identify the main components of homeostasis.

4. What are some advantages of being an ectotherm? An endotherm?

5. Explain how counter-current blood flow aids heat retention in the limb of an animal.

6. Name the four basic tissue types, their primary function, and give an example of where you would find them in the body.

III. Inquiring minds want to know...

Challenge Question

1. Chemoreceptors in the carotid arteries monitor changes in oxygen, carbon dioxide and pH. Impulses form these chemoreceptors are conducted to control centers in the brain stem (specifically, to the cardioregulartory and vasomotor centers of the medulla oblongata). Describe the specific mechanisms the body would employ in response to a decrease in blood oxygen, and increase in carbon dioxide and a decrease in pH.

Chapter 5

Information Flow

The Neuron

There are billions of neurons in our brains, but what are neurons?
Just cells.
The brain has no knowledge until connections are made between neurons.
All that we know, all that we are, comes from the way our neurons are connected.
—Tim Berners-Lees

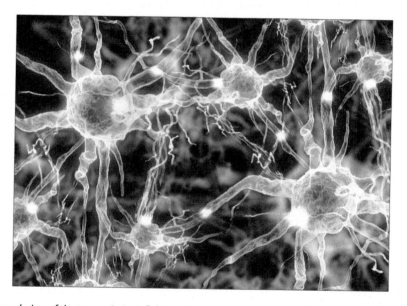

Figure 5-1 An artist's rendering of the transmission of electrical impulses (or action potentials) in nervous tissue

What do neurons do, and how do they do it?

Neurons are remarkably specialized cells whose main function is to receive, transmit, and integrate information. Their morphologies are unique and befitting to their particular function.

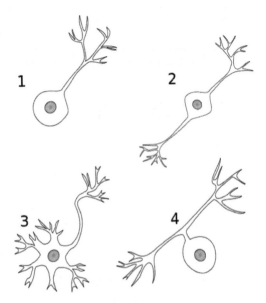

Figure 5-2   Types of neurons:1: Unipolar 2: Bipolar 3: Multipolar 4: Pseudounipolar

Neurons are the major cell types of the nervous system, which is organized into two major components: the central nervous system (CNS) and the peripheral nervous system (PNS). The CNS consists of the brain and spinal cord, whereas the peripheral nervous system is composed of the neurons that are assembled into nerves residing outside of these regions.

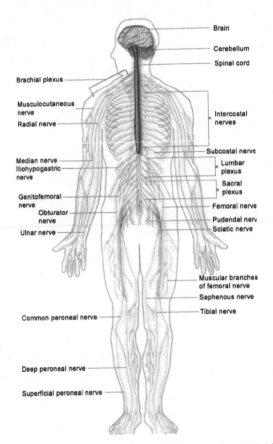

Figure 5-3A   The two subdivisions of the nervous system include the CNS (red) and the PNS (blue).

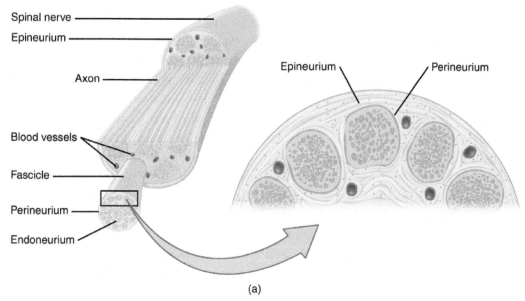

(a)

Figure 5-3B   Shown is a cross section of a spinal nerve.

In contrast to a neuron (which is a type of nervous system cell) a nerve is a cordlike structure that contains many axons (axons are often referred to as fibers). A nerve provides a common pathway for the electrochemical nerve impulses that are transmitted along each of the axons. Nerves are found only in the PNS. In the CNS, the analogous structures are known as tracts.

The neurons of the CNS, often referred to as interneurons, function to receive, integrate, and generate a response to the incoming impulses carried by the afferent neurons from the PNS. These neurons receive stimulus from sensory receptors, which is then transmitted along their axons, as electrical impulses (action potentials), to a specific region in the brain. The interneurons of the CNS assimilate this information and generate an appropriate response, which is conducted via the efferent neurons of the PNS to elicit the appropriate effect (such as a muscle contraction). Sensory receptors may be a specialized portion of the plasma membrane of an afferent neuron or a separate cell closely associated with the neuronal ending.

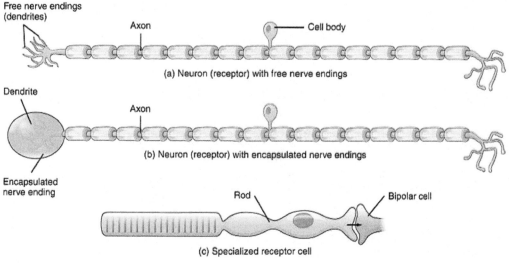

Figure 5-4   Some examples of sensory receptor types.

In addition to neurons, specialized support cells are located in the both the CNS and the PNS. Four of these non-neuronal cell types are found in the CNS: oligodendrocytes, microglia, astrocytes, and ependymal cells. Oligodendrocytes produce myelin, a material with a high lipid content that wraps around the axons of neurons, providing insulation to enhance the conduction of electrical impulses. Microglia are immune cells that respond to infection and inflammation. They frequently function as macrophages, with the ability to phagocytize pathogens and cellular debris. Astrocytes are the most common type of support cell in the CNS. They provide structural support, as well as help maintain ion concentrations in the interstitial fluid surrounding neurons. Ependymal cells provide support by various means. Some cells are ciliated and line the brain ventricles. The cilia move in a synchronized fashion, directing nutrients toward neurons. Ependymal cells are also found in a region of the brain known as the choroid plexus (a group of blood vessels located near the lateral ventricle) and can produce cerebral spinal fluid (CSF). The satellite cells of the PNS encompass neuronal cell bodies and are thought to have similar functions as the astrocytes in the CNS. The Schwann cells form the myelin sheath around the axons of neurons in the PNS.

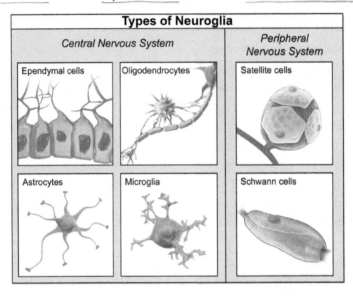

Figure 5-5A Types of support cells in the nervous system.

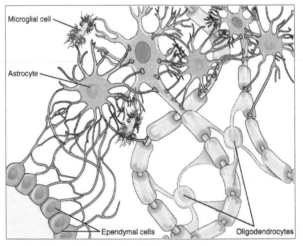

Figure 5-5B Illustration of the interactions between cells in the CNS.

The myelin that surrounds axons is usually whitish in color and thus is responsible for the appearance of "white matter" in both the brain and spinal cord. Grey matter is composed of the cell bodies of neurons.

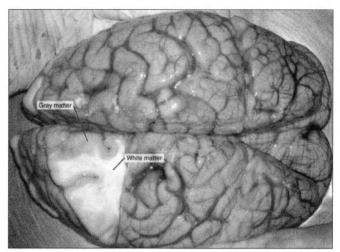

Figure 5-6 Grey matter and white matter in the human brain.

The signals (or action potentials) that neurons conduct to other neurons or to other cells (such as muscle cells) are transmitted by means of a synapse, which is the junction between the transmitting neuron (the presynaptic cell) and the recipient (the postsynaptic cell). Synapses between neurons can be classified as axodendritic, axosomatic, or axoaxonic. Neurons can also be characterized as neurosecretory and can release substances directly into the bloodstream or ECF. The neuron terminals of one neuron may form many synapses.

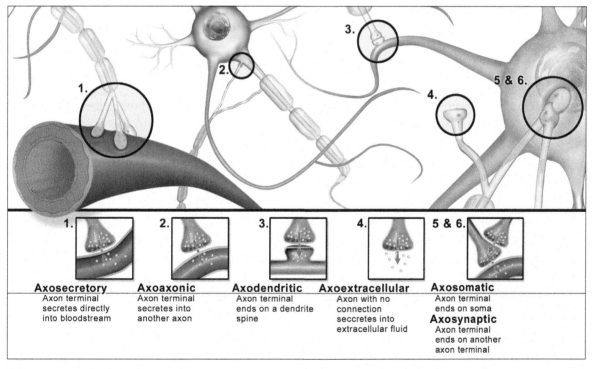

Figure 5.7 Types of synapses.

Synapses can also be classified as electrical or chemical. In electrical synapses, gap junctions directly connect the presynaptic and postsynaptic cells, permitting current to flow between juxtaposed cell membranes. In this manner, electrical synapses facilitate coordinated signaling and, as such, are often found at neuronal connections in cardiac and smooth muscle. Chemical synapses utilize neurotransmitters that are released from the terminal of the presynaptic cell, diffuse across the synaptic cleft (or space between the presynaptic and postsynaptic cell) and bind with specialized receptor proteins on the plasma membrane of the postsynaptic cell. If the necessary conditions are met, a new electrical impulse will be generated in the postsynaptic cell.

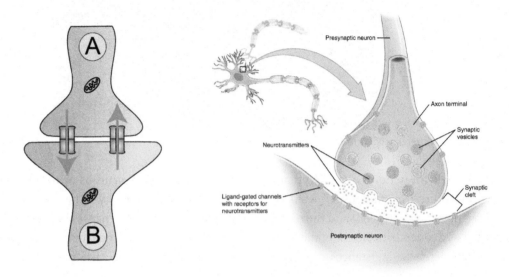

Figure 5-8 Comparison of electrical and chemical synapses.

How are electrical impulses (or action potentials) generated?

In order to understand how signals are transmitted between the electrically excitable cells of the nervous system, we must first understand the basis of cell membrane potentials. An electrical potential difference (measured as a voltage) can be generated across a plasma membrane by the separation of positive and negative charges. A membrane potential arises when there is a difference in electrical charge on the two sides of the membrane.

Both positively and negatively charged ions can be transported from one side of a membrane to the other. Ionic movement is influenced by two primary mechanisms, concentration gradients and electric fields, which together comprise what is known as an electro-chemical gradient. An electro-chemical gradient gives rise to the net driving force on an ion and is derived from both the concentration gradient and electrical gradient.

When a chemical gradient is present, the movement of an ion is from a region of higher concentration to lower concentration (down the ion's concentration gradient). An electrical field is established when there is an electrical force between charges (such as an attractive force between opposite charges: +/– or a repulsive force between like charges: +/+ or –/–). If, for example, the driving force of an ion's concentration gradient across a membrane is greater than the driving force of an opposing, repulsive electrical field on that ion, the stronger chemical gradient will dictate the direction of movement of the ion down its concentration gradient. Similarly, if the electrical driving force is greater than the driving force of the chemical gradient, the electrical force will exert the most influence on the direction of movement of the ion.

The electrical potential difference across a cell membrane can be measure with a voltmeter and is usually recorded as mV (millivolts).

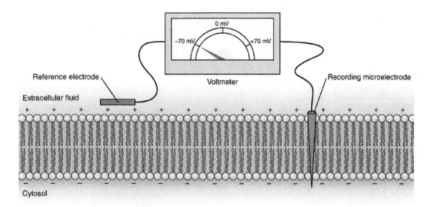

Figure 5-9 A voltmeter is used to measure the electrical potential across a cell membrane.

When a neuron is at rest (and is not actively transmitting an electrical impulse), the unequal distribution of ions produces a membrane potential that is generally recorded as about a -70 mV. (Resting potential measurements can vary from this number, depending on the actual cell type). This means that, at rest, the interior of an axon is "more negative" than the interstitial fluid surrounding its exterior. This is primary due to the influence of two important factors: the permeability of the membrane to potassium ions (K+) and the sodium potassium pump (Na+/K+ pump). In addition to these two major factors, the cytoplasm of a cell, in contrast to the interstitial fluid, generally contains more negatively charged molecules, such as nucleic acids, and negatively charged proteins, which cannot readily pass through the cell membrane.

Key components of the plasma membrane of a neuron include ungated K+ ion channels, ungated Na+ ion channels, the Na+/K+ pump, and voltage gated Na+, K+, and Cl- ion channels. There are many more ungated K+ ion channels in a typical neuron's plasma membrane, and in a neuron at rest, it is primarily the ungated (leak) channels that are open, which is the reason why the K+ ion concentration is a predominant contributory factor to the resting membrane potential. Ion channels are integral membrane proteins that transverse the lipid bilayer of a cell's plasma membrane and permit the passage of ions through their interior. Ion channels comprise a superfamily of proteins that are related by structural and functional motifs. Main characteristics of ion channels include their type of gating mechanism (such as ungated, voltage gated, ligand gated, or mechanically gated) and the type of ion they conduct.

Many types of ion channels can be found in the membranes of neurons: ungated channels (leak), voltage gated channels (in axon membranes), ligand gated channels (primarily at synapses), and mechanically gated (in sensory receptors). Despite the small differences in their radii, ions rarely go through the "wrong" channel. For example, sodium or calcium ions rarely pass through a potassium channel. The pore through which ions pass opens and closes in response to conformational changes in the protein structure of the channel molecule. Voltage gated channels have specialized regions of the polypeptide chain that serve as sensors, thus reacting to changes in local electrical current. Gates on these channels have unique dynamics; they can activate or inactive relatively quickly or relatively slowly, thereby opening the channel pore, closing it, or temporarily occluding it.

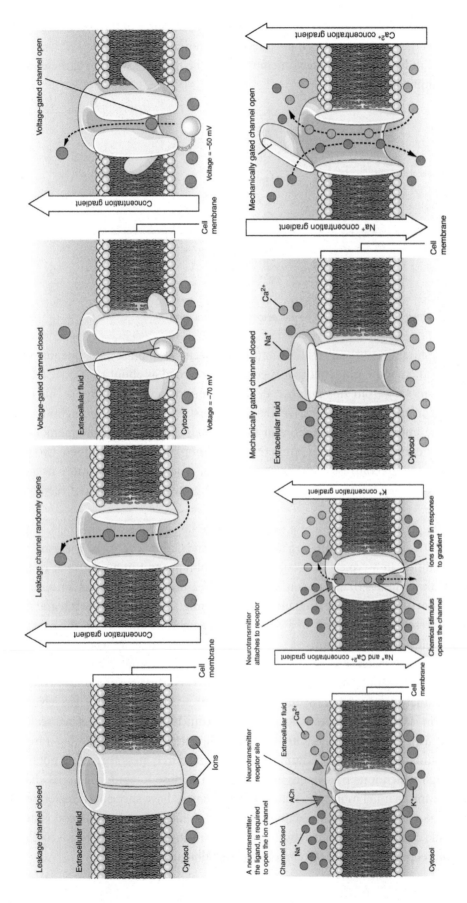

Figure 5-10 ABCD The four classes of ion channels that can be found in cell membranes.

Along with the ungated potassium (K+) channels, another vital component of the neuronal cell membrane is the Na+/ K+ pump, as it is a major contributor to the uneven distribution of charged particles on either side of a neuronal membrane. In one pumping cycle, the Na+/K+ pump uses the energy derived from ATP hydrolysis to actively transport three Na+ ions from the cell interior to the extracellular fluid, and two K+ ions from the cell exterior to the cell cytoplasm. This helps to maintain a higher Na+ concentration outside of the cell, and a higher K+ concentration inside the cell. (See Figure 5-11 below and review Figure 4-2 for a comparison of intracellular and extracellular ion concentrations.)

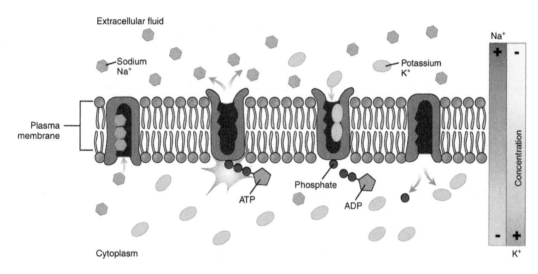

Figure 5-11   The Activity Of The Sodium/Potassium Pump (Na+/K+ Pump).

When a neuron is not actively transmitting impulses, the normal distribution of ions and molecules inside and outside of an area of a neuronal axon generate a resting membrane potential of about -70 mV.

Due to the uneven charge distribution, potassium (K+) tends to passively diffuse down its concentration gradient, through its open channels, out of the cell. Likewise, sodium (Na+) tends to passively diffuse down its concentration gradient, into the cell. Because the membrane is more permeable to K+ than to Na+, (that is, it has many more open ungated potassium channels open than ungated sodium channels), more K+ tends to leave the cell than Na+ enters. However, the cell interior also has negatively charged organic molecules, which create an electrical force that attracts K+ to stay in the cell, and balances the tendency of K+ to leak out of cell. Consider the situation where the membrane potential is measured at zero, which indicates that there is no voltage difference across a cell membrane. Since the concentration of K+ is higher inside the cell, there will be a tendency of the K+ to leak out of the cell, where it is less concentrated. This moves positive charges to the cell exterior, leaving an unbalanced negative charge inside the cell. This creates an electrical field, or membrane potential, in which the increased positive charge on the outside of the cell opposes the further efflux of K+. In fact, the efflux of K+ will stop when the electrical driving force on the potassium ion balances the driving force of its concentration gradient. The membrane potential at which the driving force of the voltage gradient of a given ion balances the driving force of the concentration gradient of that the ion, such that there is no net flow of ions through its channels is termed the equilibrium potential for that specific ion. The classic equation for predicting the equilibrium potential (in mV) for a singly charged ion across a typical, unstimulated neuronal cell membrane is called the Nerst equation. The Nerst equation takes into account certain constants, such as the ideal gas constant, the Faraday constant, and the temperature, as well as the concentration of a given ion both inside and outside the cell. For a singly charged positive ion, such as K+, the Nernst equation is:

$$E_{ion} = 62mV \log_{10} \frac{[X]_{outside}}{[X]_{inside}}$$

$E_{K+} = -90mV$

Consequently, the Nerst equation predicts that when the inside of the cell is 90 mV more negative than the outside, K+ is at equilibrium, and there no net flow of K+ through its ungated ion channels.

When the Nertz equation is used to predict the equilibrium potential of Na+, a value of +60 mV is calculated. This means that if the membrane were permeable only to sodium, the potential across the membrane that would just balance the driving force of the concentration gradient on sodium would be +60 mV inside with respect to the outside. Recall that there are, in fact, some open Na+ channels in a resting neuron. The open sodium channels permit Na+ ions to flow into the cell, making the inside of the cell a little less negative than -90 mV. The concentration gradient of a particular ion and the cell's permeability to it determine the contribution of that ion to the overall membrane potential of the cell. The Goldman equation provides the prediction of the membrane potential (V_m) when the membrane is permeable to more than one ion.

$$Vm = 62 \log 10 \quad \frac{P_K[K+]_o + P_{Na}[Na+]_o + P_{Cl}[Cl-]_i}{P_K[K+]_i + P_{Na}[Na+]_i + P_{Cl}[Cl-]_o}$$

Legend: Vm= membrane potential, P=permeability of a particular ion, [ ]= concentration, i=inside the cell, o=outside the cell

Using the Goldman Equation, the membrane potential of a neuron at rest is calculated at a value of about -70 mV.

How is information transmitted from one neuron to another?

Graded receptor potentials and action potentials

In the nervous system, sensory receptors (i.e., sensory cells or neuronal endings) respond to stimuli (such as light, heat, chemicals, mechanical stress, etc.) by changing their conductance to ions. This results in a change in membrane potential that is known as a graded potential (or a receptor potential or a post-synaptic potential). Graded potentials are generated in a sensory cell or neuronal cell ending when a sensory stimulus excites it, or in a postsynaptic cell when a chemical neurotransmitter binds to ligand gated ion channels. Each results in the opening of ion channels, which in turn, produce graded potentials.

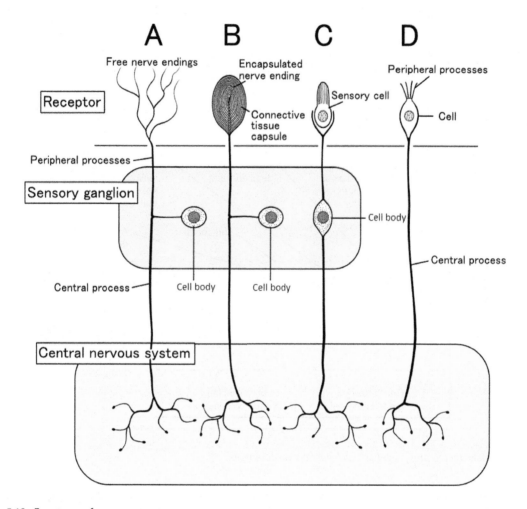

Figure 5.12 Four types of sensory receptors.

Graded potentials can generate local responses that can be classified as depolarizations or hyperpolarizations. For example, if a stimulus causes Na+ channels to open, resulting in the influx of positive Na+ ions, the interior of the cell will become more positive (or less negative), resulting in a depolarization, thereby raising the membrane potential. If a stimulus causes potassium channels to open, resulting in an efflux of K+, the interior of the cell will become more negative, resulting in a hyperpolarization and a decrease in membrane potential. Graded potentials are generated at localized areas of the cell membrane and spread passively outward from the area of initiation. The strength of a graded potential will decrement with distance. The size of a graded potential is related to the stimulus intensity (or amount of neurotransmitter released at a synapse, and a graded potential may last for as long as a stimulus persists. Furthermore, graded potentials can combine. For example, if two stimuli that cause depolarizations, each raising the membrane potential, occur in close spatial proximity, or if a second stimulus occurs before the response to the first has ended, the change in potential can summate. Similarly, if one stimulus causes a depolarization and another causes an equivalent hyperpolarization, their net affect will nullified.

If the graded potentials collectively cause a significant increase in membrane potential such that it reaches a threshold level, an action potential can be produced. The action potential is usually generated at the region of the neuron that is rich in voltage gated ion channels, known as the axon hillock. An action potential refers to the immediate and transient change in membrane potential that occurs when a neuron conducts an electrical impulse. A stimulus is received from sensory receptors (or presynaptic neurons) and information is transferred over distance by the propagation of action potentials (or "all or none" electrical impulses) along neuronal axons.

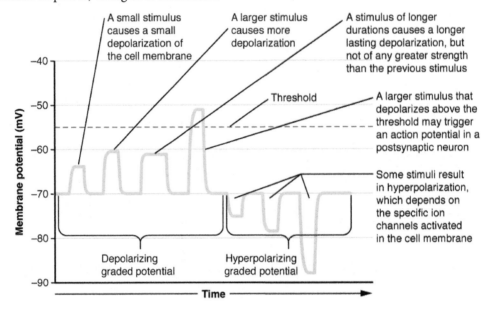

Figure 5-13 Graded (or receptor potentials) can cause action potentials.

In order for an action potential to occur, a region of the axonal membrane must depolarize, raising the membrane potential to a particular "threshold" level. This depolarization, which is usually the result of the summation of graded potentials, occurs relatively slowly until the membrane potential reaches the threshold level, at which point an action potential can be generated. A sub-threshold stimulus that results in a depolarization, is referred to as excitatory postsynaptic potential (EPSP). This graded potential moves the postsynaptic membrane potential closer to the threshold level. An inhibitory postsynaptic potential IPSP), results if a hyperpolarization is produced in the postsynaptic membrane.

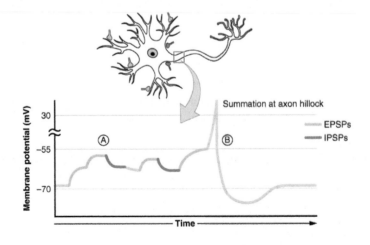

Figure 5-14 Summation at an axon hillock. a.) Sub-threshold potential, b.) an action potential.

When the threshold level (which is roughly around 20 mV greater than the membrane potential at rest) is reached, an action potential is triggered. This sudden increase in membrane potential (or "firing") is due to the abrupt opening of numerous voltage gated Na+ ion channels and the rapid influx of these positive ions into the cell. This causes a significant increase in the membrane potential and, thus, a depolarization. Na+ channels will then transit from an open conformation to an inactive state, such that the channel pore is occluded, prohibiting the further passage of Na+ ions. As this is occurring, voltage gated K+ channels open, permitting the passage of these positive ions down their concentration gradient and out of the cell. The movement of positive (K+) ions out of the cell effectively causes the interior of the cell to be "more negative." This counteracts the increased membrane potential due to depolarization and brings about cellular repolarization, causing the membrane potential to decrease. As the membrane potential falls, activation gates on the K+ channels begin to close. As the membrane potential reaches the resting value, the activation gate of the Na+ channels close, and the inactivation gate opens, resetting it to its original closed configuration in preparation for the next action potential. For a brief time, the cell enters into a hyperpolarized state, where the membrane potential drops below the resting potential voltage. As the ion channels stabilize, the cell membrane potential returns to its resting potential voltage (~-70 mV). This entire process that characterizes an action potential generally occurs in a few milliseconds.

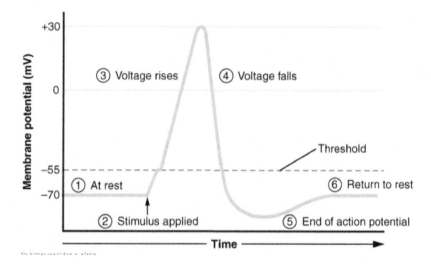

Figure 5-15 An action potential.

Although action potentials are generated locally on patches of excitable membrane, the resulting currents can activate action potentials on neighboring stretches of membrane. The initiation of action potentials on neighboring stretches of membrane results in the propagation of action potentials along an axon.

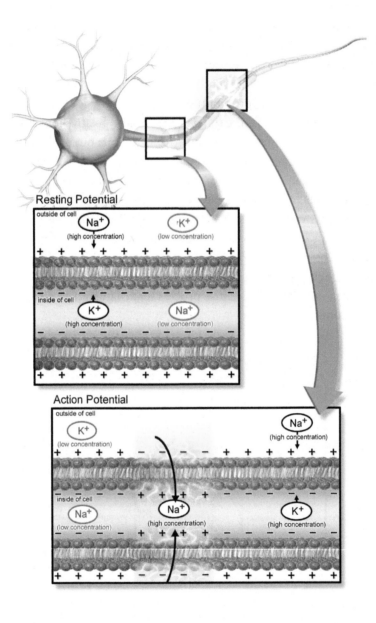

Figure 5-16 The propagation of an action potential along an axon.

A unique quality of action potentials is that they are an "all or none response." Once the threshold level is attained, the neuron will proceed to fire. All action potentials generated on a particular axon are the same strength. Even as action potentials are regenerated down an axon, their magnitude does not decline. On a given neuron, the next action potential is usually exactly the same strength and duration as its predecessor. If all action potentials are the same strength, how are the differing strengths between weak and intense stimuli encoded in the nervous system? The intensity of a stimulus is indicated by the frequency of action potentials.

Action potentials have an absolute refractory period in which no other action potential will be generated in that area of membrane, regardless of the stimulus strength. This complete insensitivity occurs when the voltage gated Na+ channel are either already open or have proceeded to the inactive state. In order for another action potential to be generated, enough Na+ channels must be in a closed state and, thus, be prepared to be reopened. Action potentials also have a relative refractory period. At this time, a stronger-than-threshold stimulus can initiate another action potential. During the relative refractory period, some, but not all, of the voltage gated Na+ channels have returned to the resting state (closed). Some of the K+ channels (that have repolarized the membrane) are still open. At this point, a new stimulus can depolarize the membrane to above threshold levels. However, in this unique situation, the magnitude of the action potential evoked during the relative refractory period is smaller than normal. This is because there are still some K+ channels open (that are acting to repolarize the cell) and some Na+ channels are still inactivated, rather than closed (and thus, are not in the proper conformation to be opened). These events also cause the threshold required for generation of an action potential to be higher than normal. Also, if a second stimulus occurs during the brief hyperpolarization phase, when the membrane potential is even lower than the resting value, an even greater change in membrane potential (depolarization) is required to reach threshold and generate an action potential. Because the quantity, subtypes and corresponding characteristics (such as conductance rates, velocity, and duration of gate opening and closing, etc.) of ion channels can vary widely on different types of neurons, the extent of the relative refractory period is highly variable.

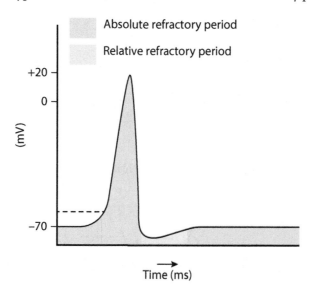

Figure 5-17 Absolute and relative refractory periods.

Another significant ramification of the refractory period is the one-way conduction of an electrical impulse down an axon. Because the region of the axon undergoing the initial portion of the action potential is already depolarized (and, thus, in the absolute refractory period), most voltage gated sodium channels will not be in the proper closed formation that can be opened by diffusion of any local current in this area.

Conduction velocity

The speed at which electrical impulses (or action potentials) can move along axons serves as a compelling example of the interrelatedness of structure and function. Two primary factors that affect the conduction velocity of a neuron are axonal diameter and myelination. Axons with a relatively large diameter will conduct action potentials more rapidly than those with a smaller diameter.

Frequently, large-diameter axons can be found in animals (such as a squid) that rely on a swift escape response. A fast response is facilitated by the rapid conduction rate of large diameter axons that initiate muscle movements. In an axon with a large diameter, the resistance of the axoplasm to the movement of electrical charge is lower. The relationship between resistance and conduction velocity is described by the lambda length constant. It refers to the characteristic length that the voltage across a membrane decays for a particular axon. Thus λ (lambda) indicates how far a current will spread along the inside of an axon and, thereby, influence the voltage along that distance. The larger λ is, the farther the current will flow. For example, at the length given by lambda, the size of an applied voltage will decline to roughly one-third of the original size. If a voltage of 90 mV is applied on a specific point on an axon, at the distance of 1 λ, the voltage will be about 30mV. At a distance of 2λ, the voltage will be about 10 mV. When λ is larger, the AP can regenerate another AP at a greater distance and as a consequence, does not have to be regenerated as often. A larger λ results in a greater conduction velocity, because the threshold voltage can be reached further down an axon each time the AP is generated.

Figure 5-18 The lambda length constant.

The lambda length constant is described mathematically by the following equation:

$$\lambda = \sqrt{\frac{r_m}{r_l}}$$

where r_m = the resistance of the membrane and r_l = the longitudinal resistance, which is the internal resistance found in the axoplasm.

Increasing the membrane resistance (r_m) will increase lambda, which will increase the conduction velocity. When the r_m is greater, more of current generated will remain inside the cytosol to diffuse along the neuron. Myelination is a remarkable adaptation that insulates regions of the axon, effectively increasing the r_m. In a myelinated axon, the local current generated by an action potential diffuses beyond the adjacent myelin sheath to the next, unmyelinated region of the axon. These gaps in the myelin sheath are known as nodes of Ranvier and contain a high-density of voltage gated Na+ and K+ channels. When the local current reaches a node of Ranvier, it initiates the opening of voltage gated Na+ channels, causing a depolarization and action potential generation. This type of conduction is often referred to as salutatory conduction from the Latin word *saltare*, which means to jump. The action potentials propagate along a myelinated essentially by "jumping" from one node of Ranvier to the next, effectively increasing conduction velocity.

Neurotransmission at the chemical synapse

An AP propagates longitudinally down an axon until it reaches the axon terminals. As previously mentioned, there are two main types of junctions between neurons: electrical synapses, which utilize gap junctions for the direct ion transfer of ions between neurons, and chemical synapses, which employ unique chemical compounds known as neurotransmitters to relay signal to the postsynaptic neuron. Neurotransmission at the chemical synapse can be classified as direct or indirect. Direct neurotransmission is rapid. A neurotransmitter binds directly to a ligand gated ion channel on the postsynaptic membrane. This initiates the opening (or closing) of specific activation (or inactivation) gates, which in turn affects the conductance of the channel and the flow of ions into the postsynaptic cell. Recall that the flow of positive ions into a cell can cause a depolarization, whereas the flow of negative ions into a cell, or of positive ions out of a cell, can result in hyperpolarization. Indirect neurotransmission is a significantly slower process whereby a neurotransmitter first binds to integral membrane receptor (such as a G-protein coupled receptor) on the postsynaptic membrane. This binding initiates the activation of a second messenger signal transduction pathway, which causes changes to ion conductance in the postsynaptic cell, resulting in signal transmission.

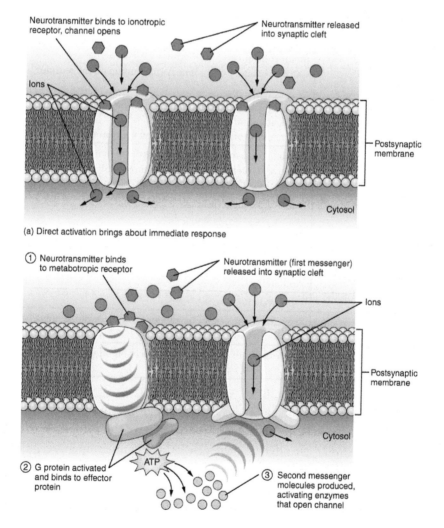

Figure 5-19 Direct and indirect neurotransmission.

At the chemical synapse, information received by the postsynaptic neuron is integrated. The resulting response reflects the sum of the combined effects of all the information (or signals) received. Neurotransmitters can have a stimulatory, inhibitory, or modulatory effect. Some important neurotransmitters and their key attributes are listed in Table 5-1, below.

Table 5-1

Neurotransmitter	Key Attributes
Acetylcholine	Neurotransmitter between nerves and muscle Neurotransmitter in the brain (memory, attention, learning) Degeneration of acetylcholine releasing neurons occurs in Alzheimer's disease
Gamma Aminobutyric Acid (GABA)	Generally an inhibitor of neurotransmission; opens Cl- channels on the post synaptic membrane
Glycine	Generally an inhibitor of neurotransmission
Glutamate	Involved with learning and memory; often excitatory
Norepinephrine /Epinephrine (Adrenaline)	Duel roles as hormones and neurotransmitters; involved in attention and mental focus Plays a role in the pleasure/reward pathway (addiction and thrills), memory, and motor control Can be excitatory or inhibitory (depending on the receptor binding)
Dopamine	Behavior and cognition, voluntary movement, motivation, and reward, sleep, mood, attention and learning. Degeneration of dopamine releasing neurons occurs in Parkinson's disease
Serotonin	Regulates intestinal movements, involved in mood, appetite, sleep Selective serotonin re-uptake inhibitors (SSRIs) increase the level of serotonin at the synapse; used to treat Depression
Endorphins (endogeneous morphines)	Released during pleasurable experience Reduce the perception of pain Work in the PNS
Enkephalins	Subset of endorphins, Modulate pain response Work in the CNS
Substance P	Pain perception
Carbon monoxide	Regulates the release of hormones from the hypothalamus
Nitric oxide	Relaxes smooth muscle in the walls of blood vessels, causes vessel dilation

Direct neurotransmission at the chemical synapse is a well-understood process that involves a number of essential steps. Synaptic vesicles store neurotransmitters in the cytoplasm of an axon terminal. When an AP arrives at neuronal terminal, voltage gated Ca^{2+} channels open, resulting in an influx of Ca^{2+} into the axon terminal of the presynaptic neuron. This initiates vesicular fusion with the membrane and the release of neurotransmitters into the synaptic cleft. The neurotransmitters can then bind to ligand gated ion channels on the postsynaptic membrane to initiate a response in the postsynaptic cell.

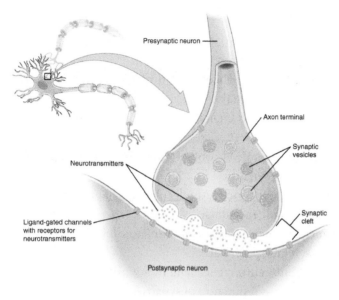

Figure 5-20 The chemical synapse.

For example, the binding of the neurotransmitter to ligand gated ion channels on the postsynaptic membrane can cause a conformational change resulting in the opening of the channels. An influx of positive ions into the cell would produce a depolarization and an excitatory post synaptic potential (EPSP) would be generated. This graded potential would move the post-synaptic membrane potential closer to threshold potential level. On the other hand, an inhibitory post synaptic potential (IPSP), results if a hyperpolarization is produced in the postsynaptic membrane. This could occur if a specific neurotransmitter binds to and opens channels that permit an influx of negatively charged ions (such as chloride, Cl-). As mentioned previously, numerous chemical synapses can be formed on a typical neuron. Some presynaptic neuronal terminals may generate EPSPs, some may generate IPSPs. The response of the postsynaptic neuron is determined by the sum of the EPSPs and IPSPs received at a given time. There are two primary types of summation: temporal and spatial. Temporal summation is produced by successive firing of a single presynaptic neuron over a short period of time. Spatial summation results from the firing of different presynaptic neurons. If the membrane potential of the postsynaptic neuron reaches its threshold level, an action potential will be generated.

When there are no longer any action potentials generated on the presynaptic neuron, the system is reset. Voltage gated Ca^{2+} channels close, and Ca^{2+} is pumped to the outside of the axon terminal. Vesicles return to the interior of the neuronal terminal. Any remaining neurotransmitters in the synaptic cleft can be degraded, diffuse away, or taken back into the postsynaptic neuron to be recycled.

Chapter 5 Review

I. Helpful and Interesting Animations

1. Understanding membrane potential:
   http://www2.yvcc.edu/Biology/109Modules/Modules/RMP/RMP.htm
2. The origin of the resting membrane potential:
   http://www.st-andrews.ac.uk/~wjh/neurotut/mempot.html

3. The K+ equilibrium potential:
   http://www.youtube.com/watch?v=4kx9_0YwShE&index=14&list=PLBC3B4C5B158840BF

4. The membrane potential of a neuron:
   http://www.sumanasinc.com/webcontent/animations/content/electricalsignaling.html

5. Graded (or post-synaptic) potentials:
   http://sites.sinauer.com/neuroscience5e/animations05.02.html

6. The action potential:
   http://www.sumanasinc.com/webcontent/animations/content/action_potential.html

7. Information transfer at the synapse:
   http://www.hhmi.org/biointeractive/molecular-mechanism-synaptic-function

8. Ionotropic and metabotropic receptors:
   http://sites.sinauer.com/neuroscience5e/animations05.03.html

9. Summation of post-synaptic potentials:
   http://sites.sinauer.com/neuroscience5e/animations05.02.html

10. Autism and the structure and function of synapses:
    http://www.hhmi.org/biointeractive/autism-structure-function-synapses

II. Active Testing: Do you know the facts?

A. List the words in this chapter you would have printed in bold type.
Can you define these words?

B. What are the main, "take home" messages of this chapter?
 Is your answer the same as your instructor's answer?

C. Some Questions:

1. Describe the difference between a nerve and a neuron.

2. Draw and label picture of a pre and a post-synaptic neuron.

3. Compare and contrast an electrical synapse and a chemical synapse.

4. Describe a resting membrane potential and the basis for it.

5. Describe the distribution of ions (Na+ and K+) when a cell is at its resting membrane potential.

6. What determines the contribution of a particular ion to the membrane potential?

7. Name four types of ion channels that can be found in neurons and give an example of each.

8. Name and explain the 3 main properties of action potentials.

9. Draw a diagram of an action potential with mV on the y axis and time on the x axis. Indicate which channels are opening and closing and when. Include labels such as: stimulus, threshold depolarization, repolarization, hyperpolarization, absolute refractory period and relative refractory period.

10. How is the intensity of a stimulus encoded?

11. Which has the greater conduction velocity and why?
A. a small diameter axon or large diameter axon.
B. a myelinated or unmyelinated axon.

12. What's the difference between direct and indirect neurotransmission?

13. Name 10 neurotransmitters and give an example of their function.

14. Explain the process of neurotransmission at a direct, chemical synapse.

15. Name and illustrate the two types of graded potentials.

16. Define and explain the basis of and characteristics of graded potentials.

III. Inquiring minds want to know…

Challenge Questions

1. The impulsive behavior of individuals with attention deficit hyperactivity disorder (ADHD) is often treated with drugs that *stimulate* certain brain neurons. What could be the biological basis of this counterintuitive effect?

2. When dopamine levels in the brain are elevated, symptoms of the mental illness, Schizophrenia may occur. Schizophrenics are often treated with dopamine lowering drugs. What problem could this treatment potentially cause?

Chapter 6

Information Flow

The Nervous System

The brain is the last and grandest biological frontier, the most complex thing we have yet discovered in our universe. It contains hundreds of billions of cells interlinked through trillions of connections.
The brain boggles the mind.
—James D. Watson

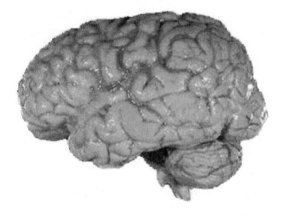

Figure 6-1 The human brain.

What does the brain do and how does it do it?

Anatomy, connections, integration, and the nervous system

Over the course of evolution, there became a greater demand for animals to develop more refined and proficient nervous systems that would better enable them to accomplish such necessary tasks as attaining food, shelter, and partners, as well as escaping dangerous predators. The strong selection pressure for animals to successfully compete led to the development of more complex and more competent nervous systems. Essential adaptations of animal nervous systems provide additional support to the tenet that form and function are synergetic. For example, organisms in the phyla cnidaria (such as the sessile sea anemone and other radially symmetric animals) have a rather primitive, decentralized meshwork of neurons called nerve nets. The more organized nervous system found in some echinoderms (such as a sea star) entails radial nerves emanating from a centralized nerve ring. The advent of bilateral symmetry and cephalization led to the development of an anterior head where sensory organs and nervous tissues are concentrated, with paired nerves linking specialized brain regions to specific body regions. This arrangement allowed for more sophisticated neural processing, enabling animals to achieve more coordinated, rapid movement to optimize their daily task of staying alive.

The human brain is, indeed, highly sophisticated. It develops from the neural tube and, by about 5 weeks of embryonic development, is composed of five distinct subdivisions: the telencephalon, diencephalon, mesencephalon, metencephalon, and myelencephalon. These regions give rise to principal structures in the adult brain, which include the cerebrum, thalamus, hypothalamus, midbrain, cerebellum, pons, and medulla oblongata.

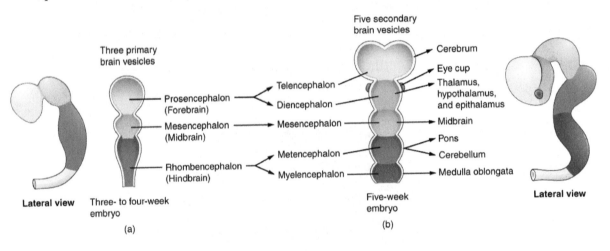

Figure 6-2 The development of adult brain structures.

The specialized regions of the mammalian brain interact to execute the vital functions of acquiring, processing, storing, retrieving, and relaying information. Considering the anatomy of the brain from different viewpoints is helpful to better understand the relatedness of its structure. Throughout the course of this chapter, the brain will be illustrated from different perspectives.

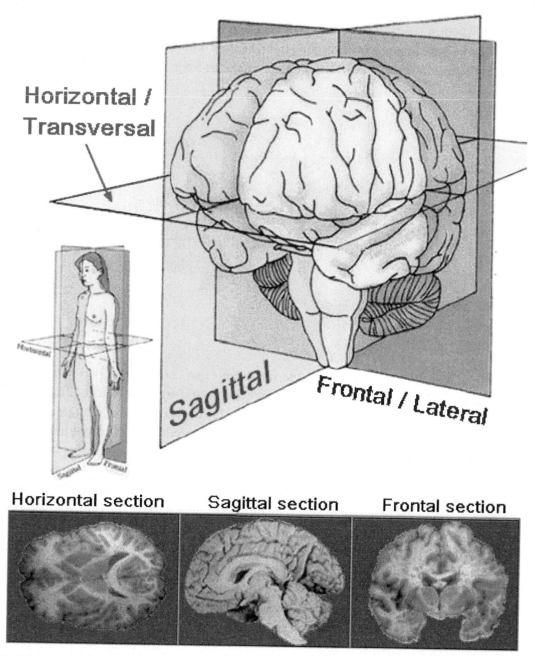

Figure 6-3 Viewing the brain from different aspects illustrates its numerous structural features. The left panel shows a section of the brain as viewed from the top. The middle panel shows a side view of the brain at its midline. The right panel shows a section of the brain as viewed from the front (or coronal) aspect.

The largest subdivision and the phylogenetically newest part of the brain is the cerebrum. The cerebrum is derived from the telencephalon (which arose from the forebrain). It is organized into two hemispheres which are separated by a groove called the medial longitudinal fissure. A bundle of nerve fibers, known as the corpus callosum, connects the left and right hemisphere enabling information transfer between the hemispheres. The left cerebral hemisphere responds to signals and controls movement on the right side of the body and vice versa. The cerebrum is composed of several interior components (such as the hippocampus, amygdala, basal ganglia, olfactory bulb, etc.) and the cerebral cortex. The cerebral cortex is the multilayered outermost neural tissue ranging from 2 millimeters (mm) to 4 mm thick in humans (Kandel et al., 2000). It is referred to as the grey matter (cell bodies) and it surrounds the white matter (axons; see Figure 5-6). In many animals, the cerebral cortex is highly foliated, thereby increasing total surface area. The cerebral cortex is divided into four lobes: the frontal, temporal, parietal, and occipital.

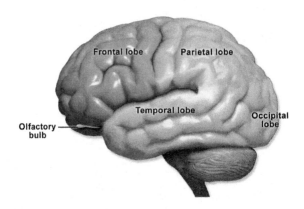

Figure 6-4 The lobes of the brain.

These lobes are further subdivided into specific regions that contribute to particular functions. In general, regions in the frontal lobes are involved in movement and executive functions such as planning, decision making, reasoning, judgment, and memory. The lower portion of the left frontal lobe contains Broca's area, which controls motor areas involved with speech production. Neurons in this area signal the intricate sequences of movement involving the mouth, tongue, jaw, etc. needed for speech. Damage to Broca's area often leads to a condition known as Broca's aphasia. This is characterized by difficulties expressing language and hesitant speech. Many other motor functions of the frontal lobes are carried out to a great extent in the premotor area and the primary motor cortex. The primary motor cortex is a localized band of tissue containing specialized neurons. It resides just anterior to the central sulcus. The primary motor cortex is organized into a type of "motor map," because overlapping subdivisions in the primary cortex correspond to specific parts of the body on the opposite side, controlling their movement.

The parietal lobe is involved in such processes as visual perception, spatial orientation, cognition, and speech, and includes the primary somatosensory area, which functions to integrate stimuli from the senses. The primary somatosensory area encompasses a band of neural tissue located just posterior to the primary motor area. It assimilates information regarding touch, pressure, temperature, and pain. It is comparable to the primary motor cortex in that stimulating certain portions of the primary somatosensory area causes sensation in the correlated body parts on the opposite side of the body.

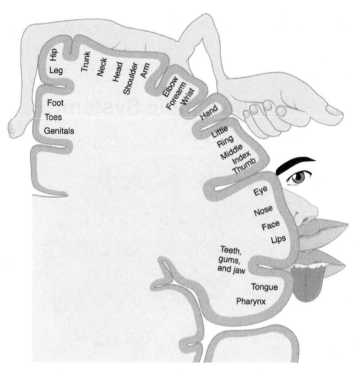

Figure 6-5 Sensory homunculus. The term, homunculus is Latin for "Little man" This diagram depicts the location of the brain cortex that corresponds with the region of the body where the sensory information is detected.

The occipital lobes are positioned in the posterior region of the brain and house the primary visual cortex, which is the principal center for visual processing. The temporal lobes are situated on each side of the brain, below the frontal and parietal lobes. Areas in the temporal lobes are involved in olfaction (smell), audition (hearing), and facial recognition (which is processed, in part, in the fusiform gyrus, a region that traverses both the temporal and occipital lobe). Part of Wernicke's area, which is necessary for understanding language and planning speech, is also located in the temporal lobe. Persons with damage to Wernicke's area often exhibit a type of receptive aphasia where they can speak, but their speech is often incoherent. It is believed that the plan for what an individual intends to say is developed in Wernickes's area. This information is then transmitted via white matter tracts to other parts of the brain, including Broca's area, where the instructions are carried out.

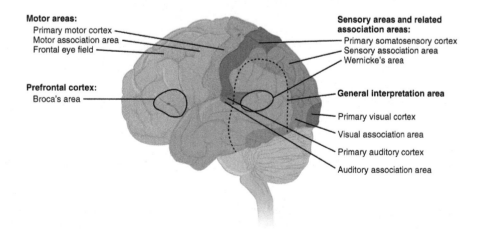

Figure 6-6 Examples of some essential cortical areas.

Other specialized regions in the temporal lobes include some of the components of the limbic system, which is often referred to as the "emotional brain". Limbic system structures are involved with the processing of feelings such as fear, anger, anxiety, pleasure, motivation, satisfaction, and memory.

The Limbic System

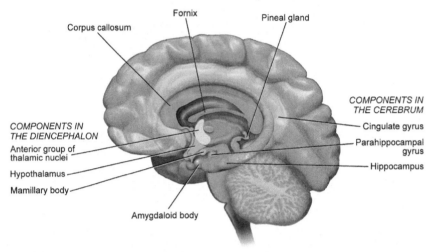

Figure 6-7 Location of limbic system structures.

Two main constituents of the limbic system are the amygdala and the hippocampus. The almond shaped amygdalae are found deep in the temporal lobes and are involved with configuring and retaining information associated with emotional events, thereby influencing how strong a memory is and how much emotion it provokes. The hippocampus, which is also located in the temporal lobe, is important for spatial navigation, learning new information, and the processing of short-term memory into long-term memory. Damage to the hippocampus can cause anterograde amnesia, which is the inability to form new memories from the recent past, leaving the recall of long-term memories unaffected.

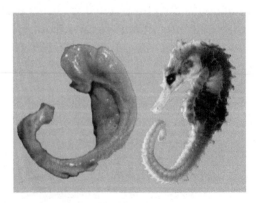

Figure 6-8 The hippocampus was so named due to its resemblance to a seahorse (from the Greek hippos meaning "horse" and kampos meaning "sea monster").

The limbic system includes a number of additional brain regions, such as the olfactory bulbs, the thalamus, and the hypothalamus. The olfactory bulbs transmit information pertaining to the sense of smell that is received from the olfactory receptor neurons in the nasal cavity. The centrally located thalamus serves as a major relay center, receiving and dispatching sensory and motor information to other brain areas, including the cerebral cortex. As a regulator of sensory transmission, the thalamus also influences sleep patterns and alertness. The hypothalamus, which is located below the thalamus, has a variety of essential functions. It is directly connected to the pituitary gland and produces neurohormones that control the secretion of hormones from the pituitary gland. It is involved in such mechanisms as the control of body temperature, appetite and satiety, water balance, and circadian rhythms.

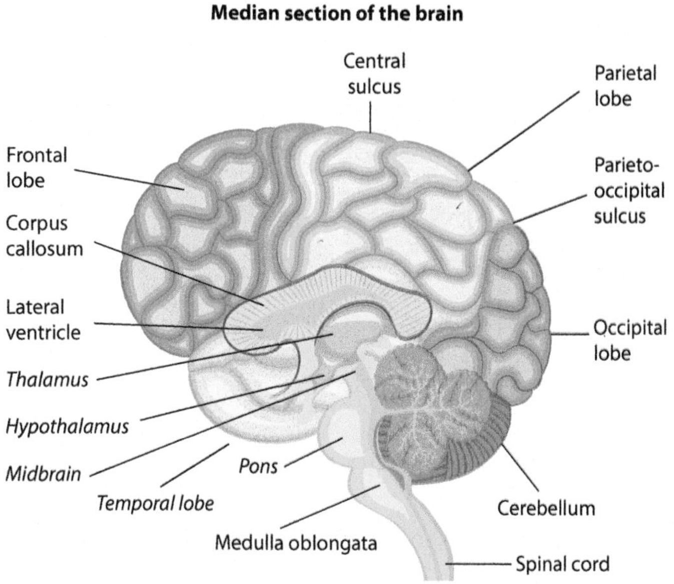

Median section of the brain

Figure 6-9 Major components of the brain.

The brain's interconnectedness

Structures in the limbic system are interconnected with many other brain regions. The hypothalamus, for example, exchanges information with the amygdala and the reticular formation. The reticular formation is a network of neurons found in the brain stem. It is composed of two divisions: the descending and the ascending reticular formation. The descending reticular formation receives information from the hypothalamus. It is involved with reflexive actions such as coughing, swallowing, and vomiting. It also plays a role in movement as it interacts with interneurons of the spinal cord that control skeletal muscle contraction. The ascending reticular formation (also called the activating reticular formation) produces altered levels of consciousness and alertness and plays an essential role in filtering incoming stimuli. It projects to the thalamus, which, in turn, conveys signals to the cerebral cortex. Abnormalities in the ascending reticular formation can result in a coma.

Limbic system components are also interconnected with regions in the basal ganglia. The basal ganglia are a group of functionally related brain structures in the cerebrum that are involved with many emotional and cognitive functions, such as routine learning (or habit formation). They are also involved in motor control, usually operating in an inhibitory capacity, whereby releasing inhibition enables motor system functioning. Main components of the basal ganglia include the nucleus accumbens and the substantia nigra. The nucleus accumbens plays an essential role in processing pleasurable experiences, including those involved with rewards and reinforcement. As such, it is also believed to have a central role in addiction. In addition to being involved in reward and addiction, the substantia nigra, a group of dark colored cells, has an essential role in movement, which has become better understood due to the elucidation of Parkinson's disease. This neurodegenerative disorder results from the death of dopaminergic neurons in the pars compacta region of the substantia nigra.

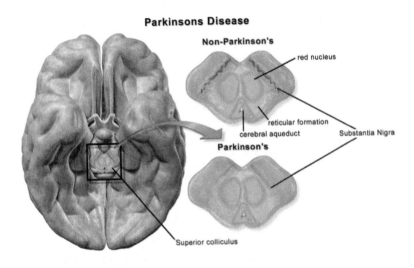

Figure 6-10 The neurons of the substantia nigra are affected in Parkinson's Disease.

Recognizable symptoms of Parkinson's include shaking, rigidity, slow movements, and difficulty walking. As the disease progresses, it leads to cognitive problems, such as dementia, depression, and sleep impairment. The substantia nigra is located in the region of the brain, above the hindbrain, known as the midbrain. The midbrain is part of the brain stem and serves many functions, such as relaying visual (via the superior colliculus) and auditory (via the inferior colliculus) information. It also contains the red nucleus, which is involved in motor coordination (such as is needed for normal gait when walking). It receives input from the motor cortex and sends output to the cerebellum, which is primarily involved in regulating the timing and precision of movements, thereby coordinating movement to be smooth and accurate.

Residing directly anterior to the cerebellum is the brainstem. In addition to housing the reticular formation and midbrain, the brainstem is also composed of the pons and medulla oblongata. The pons is positioned below the midbrain and above the medulla oblongata. The pontine respiratory group, which is involved in the regulation of the respiratory rate, is found in the pons. Areas in the pons are also involved in bladder control, facial expressions, and eye movement (in addition to a number of other functions). It also transmits signals from the cerebrum to the cerebellum. Directly below the pons is the medulla oblongata, which adjoins the spinal cord and has regions that regulate vital functions, such as heart rate, respiration, and blood pressure.

Protecting the brain

Other vital components of the brain worth noting include the ventricles, the blood brain barrier, and the meninges. The ventricles are open spaces in the brain filled with cerebral spinal fluid (CSF). The colorless cerebral spinal fluid is produced by the choroid plexuses, which are specialized structures found in the ventricles. The ventricular system provides support, protection (cushioning), and chemical balance for the brain tissue.

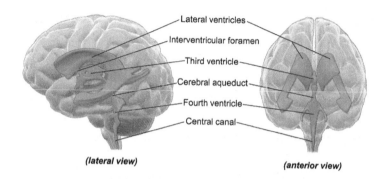

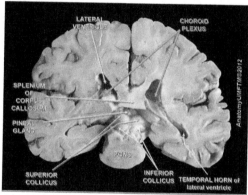

Figure 6-11 Top: The ventricles of the brain. Bottom: Frontal brain section showing the brain ventricles and choroid plexus.

The CSF that is distributed throughout the ventricular system exchanges chemical components and metabolic wastes with the blood to maintain homeostatic conditions in the brain. This exchange occurs by way of the blood–brain barrier (also called the blood–cerebrospinal fluid barrier), a partition created by endothelial cells of capillaries that separates the blood from the CSF.

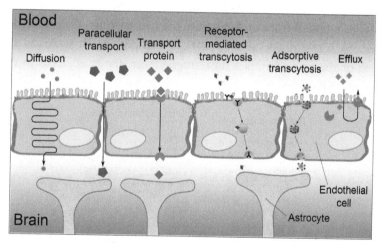

Figure 6-12 The blood–brain barrier.

Tight junctions formed between adjacent endothelial cells prohibit many substances (such as bacteria) from passing between the endothelial cells of the brain's capillaries. However, it is essential that some substances are consistently exchanged with the brain tissue. Specific transporter proteins on the plasma membrane are necessary to move hydrophilic molecules (i.e., amino acids and glucose) from the blood to the brain tissue. Lipid-soluble molecules, such as O_2, CO_2, hormones, ethanol, and nicotine, can readily diffuse through the plasma membrane and enter the brain tissue. Both the ventricular system and the blood–brain barrier play important roles in two widespread neurodegenerative disorders: Alzheimer's disease and Parkinson's disease. Hallmarks in the brains of patients with severe Alzheimer's disease include the substantial shrinkage of brain tissue accompanied by significant ventricular enlargement.

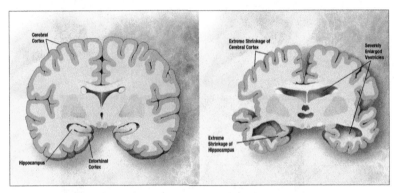

Figure 6-13 Brain shrinkage and ventricular enlargement are characteristics of severe Alzheimer's disease.

In Parkinson's disease, neurons that produce the neurotransmitter dopamine are adversely affected. This suggests that an effective treatment would be to administer dopamine to patients who suffer from this disease. However, dopamine will not traverse the blood–brain barrier. Fortunately, a dopamine precursor molecule, called levodopa (L-dopa) can cross the barrier and be taken up by neurons where it is converted into dopamine. As such, it is a highly useful treatment for the disease.

CSF is also found in the central canal of the spinal cord and in the subarachnoid space of the brain and spinal cord. The subarachnoid space is the area between the arachnoid membrane and the pia mater. These two membranes, along with the dura mater (Latin for "tough mother"), are the primary components of the meninges, layers of connective tissue enveloping the brain and spinal cord. Bordering the skull is the dura mater, a thick, durable membrane that contains blood vessels and supports sinuses where blood and CSF is emptied from the brain into the jugular vein. The middle layer is the arachnoid mater, so called, because it resembles the meshwork of a spider web. It serves as padding for the brain. The innermost layer, or the pia mater, is a thin, fragile layer that is adjacent to the brain surface and harbors capillaries that deliver vital nutrients to the brain tissue.

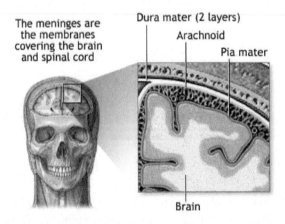

Figure 6-14 The meninges are membranes that cover the brain and spinal cord.

The central role of the brain in the nervous system

The brain, and the sum of all the integration of information that occurs within it, undoubtedly fulfills an integral role in the nervous system. But, its vital functioning certainly cannot be carried out independently. The brain and spinal cord comprise the central nervous system (CNS) and must exchange information with the peripheral nervous system (PNS) to function properly.

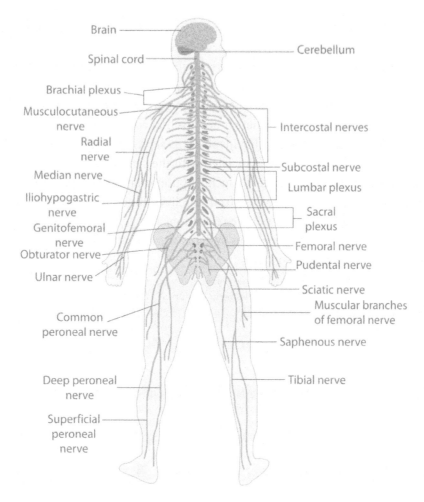

Figure 6-15 The CNS consists of the brain and the spinal cord. The PNS is composed of the nerves and ganglia (a cluster of neuronal cell bodies) located outside of the brain and spinal cord.

The PNS consists of the sensory receptors and nerves that reside outside of the CNS. It has two divisions: the afferent and efferent systems. The neurons of the afferent system transmit information from sensory receptors to the CNS, where it is integrated and understood, and if necessary, an appropriate response is generated. The efferent system (also called the motor division) transmits signals (action potentials) from the CNS to the muscles and glands to execute responses. The efferent system has two divisions: the somatic system and the autonomic division. The somatic system utilizes motor neurons that carry efferent signals from the CNS to the skeletal muscle. It is generally involved in the control of movements that are conscious (or voluntary). The autonomic nervous system (ANS) usually controls functions that are involuntary (below the level of consciousness). These functions include digestion, heart and respiratory rate, perspiration, salivation, pupil dilation, smooth muscle contractions, and the like.

The autonomic nervous system can be further divided into the parasympathetic and sympathetic nervous systems. The nerves of the parasympathetic nervous system are found at each end of the spinal cord and flank the sympathetic nerves. The parasympathetic nerves are generally used for housekeeping functions, which refer to the standard, maintenance-type activities that need to be performed on a regular basis and are in effect during quiet or low stress times. The phrase "rest and digest" is often associated with the parasympathetic nervous system. The most superior nerves of the parasympathetic nervous system include the optic nerve, which adjusts the eye and can constrict the pupil; and the cranial nerves, which can stimulate salivation. Another major nerve that has parasympathetic activity is the vagus nerve. The vagus nerve carries impulses for a number of functions, such as decreasing the heart rate, constricting airways, stimulating digestion, and inhibiting glucose release in the liver. Spinal nerves found at the inferior end of the spinal cord are involved in stimulating the bladder to contract and empty, as well as in stimulating arousal in the genitalia. The nerves of the sympathetic nervous system generally initiate functions that counteract those of the parasympathetic system. They are often used in situations that involve stress, physical activity, risk, and excitement. As such, the phrase "fight or flight" is often associated with the sympathetic system. Nerves in the sympathetic nervous system carry out functions such as pupil dilation, salivation inhibition, heart rate increase, bronchiole dilation, glucose release from the liver, blood vessel constriction to raise blood pressure, digestion inhibition, bladder muscle relaxation, and genitalia arousal inhibition. Together, the parasympathetic and sympathetic nervous systems work to up-regulate and down-regulate body functions in order to maintain homeostasis.

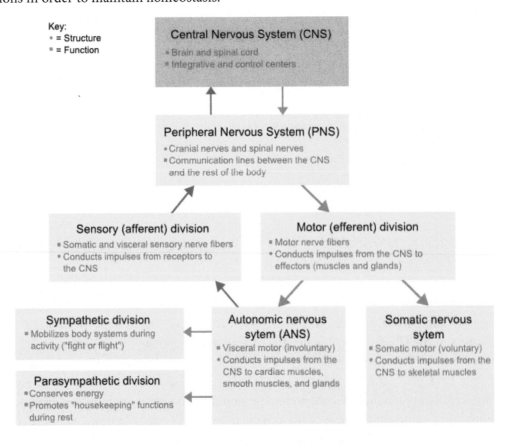

Figure 6-16 The components of the nervous system.

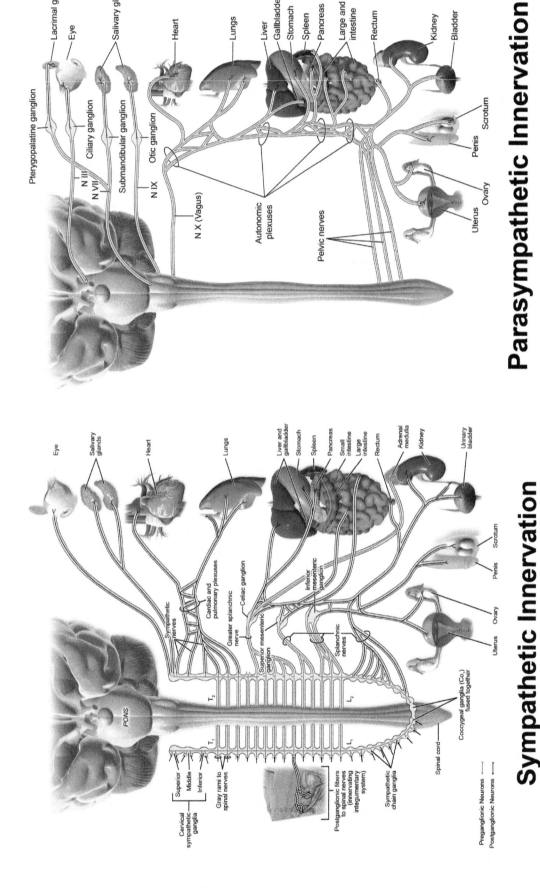

Parasympathetic Innervation

Figure 6-17B   The parasympathetic nervous system.

Sympathetic Innervation

Figure 6-17A   The sympathetic nervous system.

The patellar reflex serves as a familiar example of the interaction between the spinal cord of the CNS and nerves of the PNS. The spinal cord runs through an opening (the vertebral foramen) in the vertebrae. Pairs of spinal nerves emanate from each side of the spinal cord. Each spinal nerve has a dorsal root and a ventral root which unite to form a spinal nerve. The dorsal root contains the axons of afferent neurons, which transmit action potentials from receptors in the quadriceps muscle that are generated when the patella bone of the knee is struck. This signal is carried to the grey matter of the spinal cord where action potentials are transmitted (sometimes by way of interneurons) to the motor, or efferent, neurons of the ventral root. The efferent neurons synapse with the skeletal muscle cells of the quadriceps, causing contraction and resulting in a kick motion. Impulses are also transmitted to the brain, where the information is recognized and integrated resulting in an awareness of the activity.

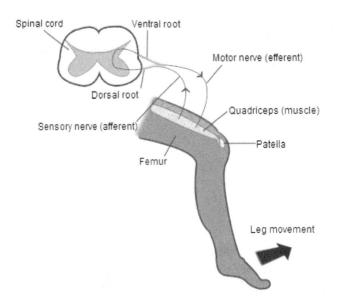

Figure 6-18 The patellar reflex.

The brain–mind connection

How does sensory information translate into physical responses, feelings, and memories?

Connections and integration

The patellar reflex serves as a simple example of how the CNS can interact directly with the PNS to elicit a physical action (kick) in response to a sensory stimulus (patellar strike). More complicated movements and reactions necessitate more complex interactions. For example, to carry out precise, goal- directed movements, various types information must be received and integrated with information from assorted regions in the brain. This information is used to identify the desired objective, recognize specific details about the body's position in space, and integrate with memories of past approaches, so that a plan of action can be formulated. The information is transmitted to the motor cortex, which will convey the specific directions (via action potentials) to the required body parts (such as certain muscles) to carry out the appropriate strategy for the desired movement. The brain's interconnectedness can also be illustrated by reviewing some of the key events that occur when a word is viewed and then spoken. When a word is first seen, photons of light reach the retinal neurons which formulate a topographic (ordered, map-like) projection. This information is transmitted by the optic nerve to the thalamus and then to the primary visual cortex of the occipital lobe. The visual association area recognizes the word and conveys this information to Wernicke's area, where the word is understood. Neuronal fibers connect Wernicke's to Broca's area, where the plan to speak the word is formulated. Action potentials are transmitted to the pre-motor area, where the movements are encoded, and then to the motor cortex, which sends signals to the necessary body parts (jaw, tongue, etc.) to initiate the speech.

These examples reiterate the principle that highly specialized regions in the brain, composed of unique neurons, are significantly interconnected. Indeed, the connectivity of the brain is currently an intense area of research. At present, The National Institutes of Health has allocated considerable funding for The Human Connectome Project (HCP), with the goal of elucidating brain interconnectivity by using state-of-the-art technologies such as functional magnetic resonance imaging (fMRI), diffusion magnetic resonance imaging (dMRI), and electroencephalography (EEG), etc.) to catalogue both anatomical and functional relationships in the human brain. Visit http://www.humanconnectomeproject. org/ for more details.

Emotion

As previously discussed, limbic system structures are generally associated with processing and initiating emotion. Cognitive scientists often categorize the generation of emotion as either "bottom up" or "top down" (McRae, 2012). Emotions generated by the bottom up theory are produced by a factor that is perceived as highly provocative, such as unexpectedly realizing a large spider is crawling on oneself. The amygdala is usually active during this type of emotional generation. Bottom up emotional generation is elicited in the laboratory setting by presenting subjects with visual stimuli (such as human faces expressing fear or anger or predatory animals) that are believed to communicate evolutionarily conserved emotional responses (Ohman & Mineka, 2001; Bar & Neta, 2007). Top down emotional generation usually incorporates thought and appraisal, such as feeling emotional discomfort by inferring, from a tersely worded memo from a superior, that termination of your employment is impending. In this case, activity in the dorsomedial prefrontal cortex, which is involved with making immediate judgments and evaluations, as well as activity in the amygdala, is apparent (Cooper et al., 2012). In addition to fear, other essential brain components interact to generate complex emotions, such as pleasure, moods, motivation, compulsion, etc. Release of specialized neurotransmitters, such as dopamine and serotonin, play important roles in the generation of emotions such as these. For example, the ventral tegmental area (VTA) has dopaminergic neurons that send projections to the nucleus accumbens and the prefrontal cortex and plays a fundamental role in the reward pathway and motivation. Serotonin has various functions in the body. Interestingly, most of the body's serotonin is found in the digestive tract, where it regulates intestinal movements. However, in the central nervous system, it is involved in regulating emotions related to mood. In fact, a number of successful pharmacological treatments for anxiety and depression function by modifying serotonin levels.

Dopamine Pathways
Serotonin Pathways
Frontal cortex
Striatum
Substantia nigra
Functions
• Reward (motivation)
• Pleasure, euphoria
• Motor function (fine tuning)
• Compulsion
• Perseveration
Nucleus accumbens
VTA
Hippocampus
Raphe nucleus
Functions
• Mood
• Memory processing
• Sleep
• Cognition

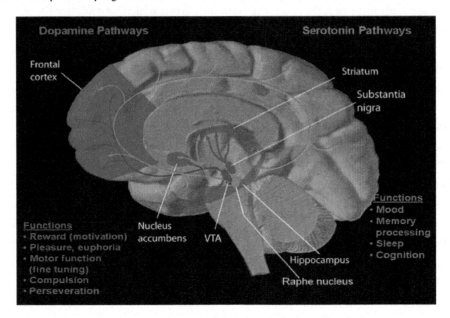

Figure 6-19 Dopamine and serotonin pathways in the brain.

The release of specialized hormones from the endocrine system (such as epinephrine and cortisol) bring about physiological and behavioral responses that are coupled with emotions. For example, the adrenal glands release epinephrine (also called adrenaline), which is involved in coordinating the "fight or flight" (sympathetic) response when a threat is encountered. Cortisol is released from the adrenal cortex and is involved in the body's response to stress. The prolonged exposure to cortisol due to long-term stress can contribute to a number of detrimental physiological conditions. In general, the intensity of the emotion that is evoked by the stimulus correlates with behavior response.

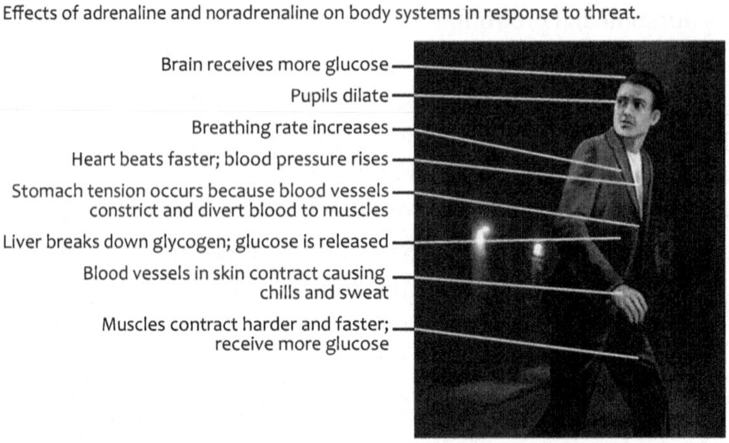

Effects of adrenaline and noradrenaline on body systems in response to threat.
Brain receives more glucose
Pupils dilate
Breathing rate increases
Heart beats faster; blood pressure rises
Stomach tension occurs because blood vessels constrict and divert blood to muscles
Liver breaks down glycogen; glucose is released
Blood vessels in skin contract causing chills and sweat
Muscles contract harder and faster; receive more glucose

Figure 6-20 A The fight or flight response.

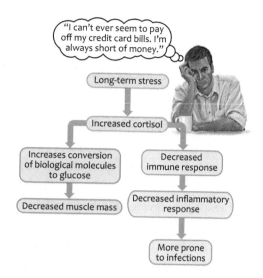

Figure 6-20B Effects of cortisol as a result of long-term stress.

Memory: early and late LTP

Information pertaining to emotional stimuli is often integrated with other brain regions including those involved with past memories and feelings, and this, of course, may augment or diminish one's emotional perception. Indeed memory: the encoding, retention and retrieval of a sensory or motor experience, is another absolutely vital function of the brain. In general, memory can be categorized as short term (sometimes also referred to as working memory) or long term. Short-term memory involves temporary and reversible alterations in neurons, such as changes in membrane potential caused by variations in EPSPs and IPSPS or by variation in ion transport caused by different neurotransmitters (i.e., stimulatory, inhibitory, modulatory). Functional imaging studies, EEGs, and studies of both animals and humans with brain injuries indicate that the prefrontal cortex and regions in the parietal lobe are primarily involved in processing information for short-term memory (Muller & Knight 2006; Linden, 2007).

Long-term memory involves the storage of memories for extended time periods (days, years) and is characterized by more permanent changes, such as increased dendritic outgrowth, thus establishing more long-lasting neuronal connections that are found throughout the brain. The hippocampus plays a central role in the conversion of types of short-term memory to long-term memory and, as such, is essential to the process of learning. Learning can be simply defined as the modification of a response based on information stored in memory. Specifically, the hippocampus tends to be involved in spatial and declarative learning (i.e., knowledge about something, such as knowing the name of the president). Although certain brain regions may be more or less involved in the establishment of particular types of memories, memories are not generally localized to a specific brain structure, but rather are embodied in neuronal connections dispersed widely throughout the brain. Both memory and learning result from differential activity at neuronal synapses. This activity includes such processes as long-term potentiation (LTP). LTP refers to an increase in the strength of a synapse that enhances the signal transmission between the involved neurons. It results from the generation of continuous action potentials from a presynaptic neuron to a postsynaptic neuron and occurs when an action potential is transmitted to a postsynaptic neuron that is already strongly depolarized. In 2000, Dr. Eric Kandel was awarded the Nobel Prize in Physiology or Medicine for his research on the molecular basis of long-term potentiation. Kandel postulated that early LTP is the basis for short-term memory. During the process of early LTP, the excitatory neurotransmitter, glutamate, is released from the presynaptic neurons. Normally, only the AMPA receptor on the post synaptic cell is operational, but continued stimuli (i.e., action potentials) from the presynaptic cell activates the NMDA receptor, resulting in the influx of Ca^{2+} into the postsynaptic cell. Calcium activates a second messenger cascade that results in the insertion of additional AMPA receptors into the post synaptic neuron's plasma membrane, thereby increasing its ion conductance and strengthening this synapse.

Late LTP brings about more long-lasting, structural changes in the neurons involved in particular pathways. In this case, repeated stimulation of the presynaptic cell causes the release of dopamine, which acts in a modulatory fashion to generate a signal transduction response involving cyclic AMP, protein kinases, and the cAMP response element-binding protein (CREB) transcription factor. This factor activates genes involved in generating dendritic outgrowth and the new synaptic connections.

Thus, it is clear that the nervous system is a highly complex integrative system that performs a multitude of essential functions in the body. We have seen how information can be encoded, processed, stored, and used to generate responses and learned about some of the varied, highly specialized regions in the brain and spinal cord that carry out these functions. How the nervous system acquires the essential information to fulfill its tasks is the next topic of our discussion.

Chapter 6 Review

I. Helpful and interesting animations

1. Development of the cerebral cortex:
   http://www.hhmi.org/biointeractive/development-cerebral-cortex
2. Development of the human embryonic brain:
   http://www.hhmi.org/biointeractive/development-human-embryonic-brain
3. Pain perception:
   http://www.youtube.com/watch?v=3VBOTYq2E8c&list=PLBC3B4C5B158840BF&index=13
4. Wernicke's aphasia:
   http://www.youtube.com/watch?v=dKTdMV6cOZw&feature=related
5. Broca's aphasia:
   http://www.youtube.com/watch?v=1aplTvEQ6ew&feature=fvw
   http://www.youtube.com/watch?v=6zNKz7YoUao&feature=fvw
   http://www.youtube.com/watch?v=1l9P4H1BKEU&feature=fvwrel
   http://www.youtube.com/watch?v=nS-aHz_8aMk&feature=related
6. Molecular basis of early LTP:
   http://www.hhmi.org/biointeractive/molecular-basis-early-ltp-short-term-memory
7. Molecular basis of late LTP:
   http://www.hhmi.org/biointeractive/molecular-basis-late-ltp-long-term-memory
8. Molecular activity during short term memory formation in the sea slug, Aplysia:
   http://www.hhmi.org/biointeractive/molecular-activity-aplysia-short-term-memory
9. Molecular activity during long term memory formation in the sea slug, Aplysia:
   http://www.hhmi.org/biointeractive/molecular-activity-aplysia-long-term-memory
10. The Human Connectome Project:
    http://humanconnectome.org/

II. Active Testing: Do you know the facts?

A. List the words in this chapter you would have printed in bold type.
Can you define these words?

B. What are the main, "take home" messages of this chapter?
Is your answer the same as your instructor's answer?

C. Some Questions:

1. Name the regions that the forebrain, midbrain and hindbrain develop into in a 5 week embryo and in an adult.

2. What is the general function of the midbrain in an adult?

3. What is another name for the cerebrum?

4. In a 5 week embryo, what is the most posterior brain region?

5. List 4 main functions of the brain.

6. What is the main function of the somatosensory cortex?

7. Illustrate and describe the blood brain barrier.

8. Illustrate and label the 3 components of the meninges. What is the function of the meninges?

9. Describe the function of the ventricles and the CSF.

10. Define: "cerebral cortex". Describe its role in the brain.

11. Identify the four brain lobes and their primary functions.

12. Describe the location the cerebellum and its primary functions.

13. What 3 structures compose the brain stem and what is the primary function of each?

14. Identify the location and function of the reticular formation.

16. Identify the location of the thalamus and hypothalamus and describe the function of each.

17. Which major disease is related to damage in the basal nuclei? Describe this relationship.

18. What structures comprise the limbic system and what is their function?

19. Name the division of the efferent system that sends signals to the somatic system and is involved with voluntary (and usually conscious) body movements.

20. List the bodily functions that the autonomic division of the nervous system regulates.

21. Name the nervous system division that is involved in such activities as decreasing the heart rate, inhibiting glucose release from the liver, and stimulating stomach activity.

22. Define the dorsal root ganglion and the ventral root of a spinal nerve.

23. Describe the process that is carried out in the brain in order to speak a word that you see.

24. Explain the potential ramifications of damage to Wernicke's area and Broca's area.

25. Describe LTP. Explain what it is, the molecular basis of the events that bring it about, and what biological changes it leads to in the brain.

III. Inquiring minds want to know…

Challenge Questions

1. How would: "Flashes of light show how memories are made?" To answer this question, go to: http://www.nature.com/news/flashes-of-light-show-how-memories-are-made-1.15330. To find out even more, read: Nabavi, S. et al. (2014). Engineering a Memory with LDP and LTP. Nature 13294.

2. Describe the concept of memory reconsolidation. How might an understanding of this topic facilitate the treatment of post-traumatic stress disorder (PTSD)?

References

Kandel, E.R., Schwartz, J.H., & Jessel, T.M. (2000). *Principles of Neural Science (4th edition)*. USA: McGraw-Hill.

McRae, K., Supriya, M., Prasad, A., Pereira, S., & Gross, J. 2012 (2012). *Bottom-up and top-down emotion generation: implications for emotion regulation.*

Ohman, A., & Mineka, S. (2001). Fears, phobias, and preparedness: Toward an evolved module of fear and fear learning. *Psychological Review,* 108 (3). 483-522. Retrieved from http://www.ncbi.nlm.nih.gov/pubmed/11488376

Bar, M., Maital, N. (2007). Visual elements of subjective preference modulate amygdala activation. *Neuropsychologia,* 45. doi 10.1016/j.neuropsychologia.2007.03.008

Cooper, J., Dunne, S., Furey, T., & O'Doherty, JP. Prefontal cortex mediates rapid evaluations predicting the outcome of romantic interactions. *The Journal of Neuroscience,* 32 (45). doi: 10.1523/JNEUROSCI.2558-12.2012

Müller, NG., & Knight, RT. (2006). The functional neuroanatomy of working memory: Contributions of human brain lesion studies. *Neuroscience,* 139 (1), 51-8. Retrieved from http://www.ncbi.nlm.nih.gov/pubmed/16352402

Linden, DE. (2007). The working memory networks of the human brain. *Neuroscientist,* 13, (3). doi 10.1177/1073858406298480

Chapter 7

The Sensory Systems

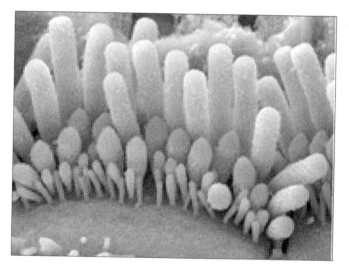

Figure 7-1 Steriocilia on hair cells (mice).

How is information obtained and delivered to the nervous system?

Sensory receptors and the special senses

Sensory perception is accomplished by the use of both the special and the general senses. The vestibular system, auditory system, visual system, olfaction, and gustation (i.e., balance, hearing, sight, smell, and taste) are known as the special senses. These special senses utilize specialized organs (such as the ear, eye, nose and tongue) to carry out their functions. This is in contrast to the general senses, which convey information from areas throughout the body, generally from the skin and internal organs. The general senses include: mechanoreception (pressure, proprioception and vibration), nociception (pain) and thermoreception (temperature). Both the special and general senses rely on sensory receptors.

Receptors can be classified as either specialized cells or the terminals of particular afferent neurons that respond to stimuli, such as light, heat, pressure, chemical substances, or mechanical tension. They function to acquire information from both the internal and external environment and communicate it to the body systems. Their response to stimuli usually results in a change in ion conductance, which, in turn, causes alteration in receptor (graded) potentials. If threshold is reached, action potentials are generated, and messages pertaining to the stimuli are transmitted to the CNS. This phenomenon is referred to as sensory transduction: the conversion of a stimulus to a change in membrane potential leading to the transmission of a signal. For example, bending the steriocilia on a specialized cell (such as a hair cell in the cochlea) in the auditory system causes potassium channels to open, which, in turn, depolarize the cell. This results in the release of neurotransmitters, which generate an action potential in the associated afferent neurons. These neurons transmit the resulting signal to the auditory centers in the brain.

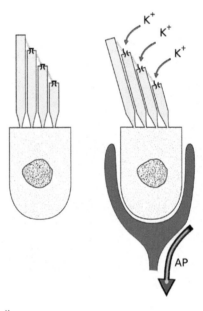

Figure 7-2 Sensory transduction by a hair cell.

The hair cell described above is classified as a mechanoreceptor. Mechanoreceptors detect changes in mechanical energy due to touch, pressure, vibration, and acceleration. The sensory hair cell transduces sound waves that result from changes in air pressure to electrical impulses (or action potentials). Other types of mechanoreceptors are found in the skin. These include Pacinian corpuscles, Meissner's corpuscles, Merkel discs, and Ruffini endings. In particular, on the human hand, Pacinian corpuscles detect vibration and are important for tool use. Meissner's corpuscles likewise detect vibration, and are essential for grip control. Merkel discs are important for the detection of points, edges and texture. Ruffuni endings are involved in the detection of hand shape and finger position.

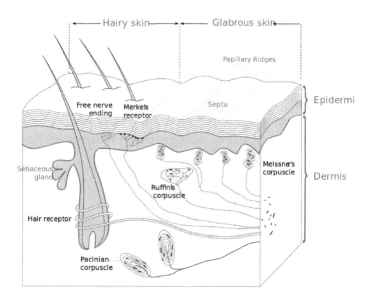

Figure 7-3 Sensory receptors in the skin.

Also found at the body surface and in particular locations of the body interior are thermoreceptors and nociceptors. Thermoreceptors consist of free nerve endings that detect changes in body temperature. Nocicpeptors detect noxious chemicals and chemicals released as a result of damaged tissue. Their activity leads to the perception of pain. In general, nociceptors transmit information to two kinds of sensory neruons: glutamate-releasing neurons, which communicate sharp, localized pain, and substance-p releasing neurons, which convey dull, aching pain that is generally not well localized.

Another type of sensory receptor is the stretch receptor (a mechanoreceptor). Stretch receptors can be found in a number of locations in the body including arm and leg muscles, certain tendons, the heart, and the carotid arteries. Stretch receptors located in muscle are called muscle spindles, which are composed of neuronal terminals that surround muscle cells. Stretch receptors in the tendon are known as golgi tendon organs (GTO) and consist of a neuronal terminals assembled with collagen. They can detect muscle tension. The stretch receptors of the arms and legs sense and regulate limb position and movement. When a muscle is expanded or contracted and force is generated, ion channels on associated afferent neuronal terminals open, resulting in depolarization and the generation of action potentials, which are then propagated to the CNS. The strength of the force generated by the muscle is encoded in the frequency of the action potentials. Together, the muscle spindles and golgi tendon organs detect changes in tension, which directly relates to body part position. This information is communicated to the CNS, where it is integrated with information from the vestibular system to generate the proprioceptive sense. Proprioception is an awareness of the relative positions of body parts. It functions to monitor and maintain appropriate body and limb positions.

The lateral line system in fish serves as an excellent example of proprioception. This system is composed of mechanoreceptors, which detect vibrations and currents in the surrounding aquatic environment. Sensory cells are situated in a lateral canal which extends along the length of the body. As water flows through the canal, the mechanical energy from the flow of the water shifts the gelatinous cupula, a structure that encases the steriocilia of sensory hair cells. This movement causes the steriocilia to bend, opening ion channels and resulting in the production of receptor potentials. When threshold is reached, action potentials are generated and transmitted via afferent neurons to the CNS. In fish, the lateral line system plays an important role in escaping from predators, seeking prey, and coordinating group movement (schooling).

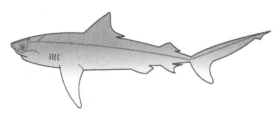

Figure 7-4A The lateral line as shown on a shark.

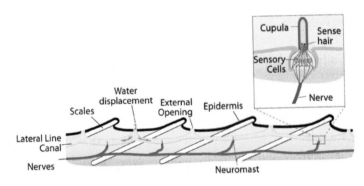

Figure 7-4B The fish lateral line system. Note that the neuromast is the mechanoreceptive organ (or functional unit) of the lateral line system.

How is balance maintained?

The vestibular system

The vestibular system of the inner ear utilizes many of the same features as the fish lateral line system (e.g., mechanoreceptors, cupula, hair cells, etc). It enables an organism to maintain proper balance by identifying and relating the position and motion of the head. The vestibular apparatus includes three semicircular canals and the two fluid filled chambers, the utricle and saccule. The utricle and saccule are housed in the vestibule of the inner ear.

The Internal Ear

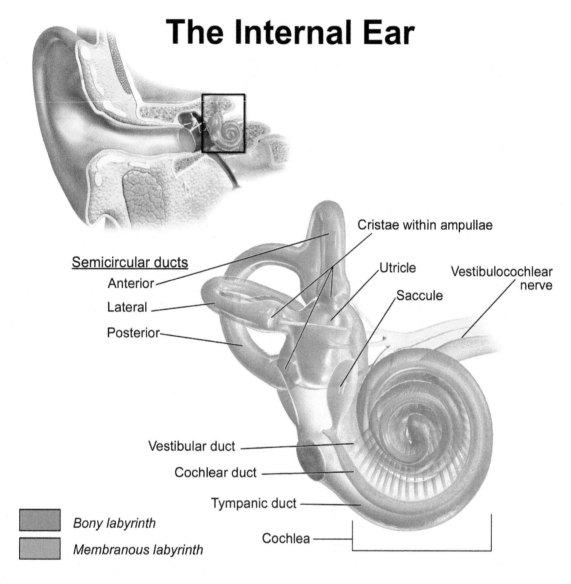

Cristae within ampullae

Semicircular ducts

Anterior

Lateral

Posterior

Utricle

Saccule

Vestibulocochlear nerve

Vestibular duct

Cochlear duct

Tympanic duct

Cochlea

Bony labyrinth

Membranous labyrinth

Figure 7-5 Components of the inner ear, which include the vestibular system.

The semicircular canals are involved in the detection of rotational movement. They are oriented perpendicularly and contain a fluid that is rich in potassium ions. At the widened base of each semicircular canal is the ampulla, a structure that houses sensory hair cells surrounded by a gelatinous cupula. Rotational movement of the head or body shifts the fluid in the semicircular canals, which displaces the cupula, bending the steriocilia of the sensory hairs cells, ultimately resulting in the transmission of a neural impulse (AP) along the vestibular nerve in an analogous manner to the lateral line system of the fish.

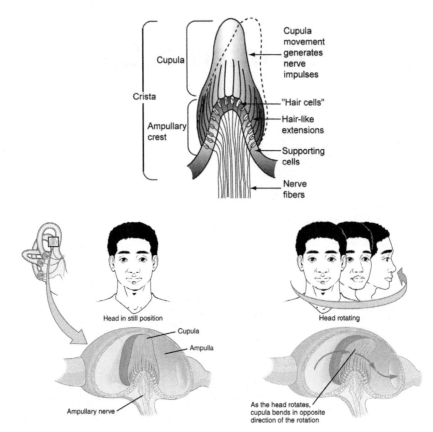

Figure 7-6A   Structures involved in sensory transduction for rotational movement in the vestibular system.

Figure 7-6B   Transduction of rotational movement in the vestibular system.

The utricle and saccule are chambers that reside at the base of the semicircular canals. They are responsible for the transmission of information pertaining to the linear and vertical motion of the body and the up/down movement of the head. They too have sensory hair cells, but instead of being housed in a cupula, the steriocilia of the hair cells found in these regions protrude into a structure, the otollithic membrane, that is filled with a viscous fluid–containing otoliths, or calcium carbonate crystals. When the head bends down, the otoliths respond to the gravitational pull, displacing the otolithic membrane and its contents. Similarly, acceleration of body movement in one direction results in a lag in the movement the otolithic membrane. Both of these activities shift contents housed in otolithic membrane, which, in turn, bend steriocilia of the sensory hair cells leading to the communication of information via action potentials to the CNS, generating perception of the particular movements.

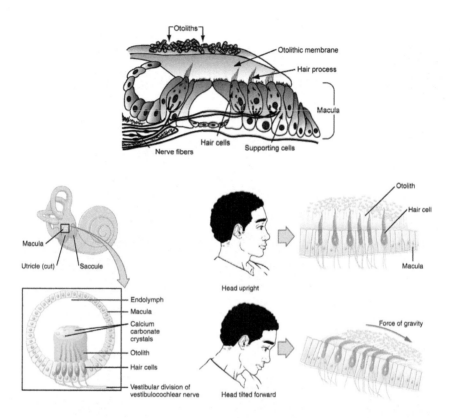

Figure 7-7A Structures involved in sensory transduction for linear and vertical motion in the vestibular system.

Figure 7-7B Transduction of information pertaining to the vertical movement.

How do we hear?

The auditory system

Mechanoreceptors are also essential components of the auditory system. The sense of hearing utilizes sensory hair cells that respond to the vibrations of sound waves. Sound waves are the product of pressure variation (i.e., more compressed air in comparison to less compressed air) caused by the vibration of an object in a medium, such as air. For example, the vibration of an object (such as a tuning fork or vocal cords) cause the surrounding air to vibrate. These vibrations produce sound waves. Volume (or loudness) is a reflection of sound wave amplitude, whereas pitch is a function of sound wave frequency.

The sound waves that move through the special structures of the ear transmit vibrations, which are transduced into action potentials by the bending of cilia on sensory hair cells. The action potentials are transmitted by the vesibulocochelar nerve to auditory centers in the brain. Initially, sound waves travel from the outer ear (the pinna) by way of the auditory canal to the tympanic membrane (or eardrum). Adjacent to the eardrum is the malleus, one of the three small bones (or ossicles) of the middle ear. The malleus bone adjoins the incus bone, which borders the stapes. These bones convey the mechanical vibration of the ear drum to the oval window, a membrane on the exterior side of the cochlea.

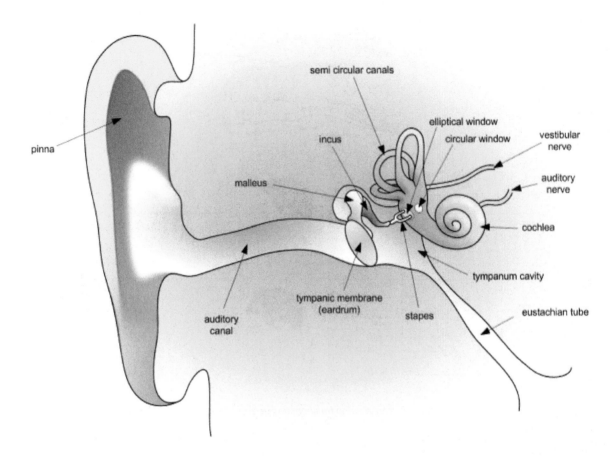

Figure 7-8 The anatomy of the human ear.

Vibrations from the oval window next pass into the cochlea, a hollow, spiral-shaped, fluid-filled tube made from bone. It has three fluid filled chambers: the scala vestibuli, scala tympani, and scala media. The scala media is also known as the cochlear duct, and is bordered superiorly by the Reissner's membrane and inferiorly by the basilar membrane. Above the scala media is the scala vestibuli and below it is the scala tympani. Both the scala vestibule and the scala tympani contain perilymph, a fluid rich in sodium ions (Na+) whereas the scala media contains endolymph, which is rich in potassium ions (K+). The cochlear duct contains the main component of hearing, the organ of Corti, which is distributed along the upper side of the basilar membrane and extends along the length of the cochlear duct. The organ of Corti is the main sensory organ of hearing. It contains the specialized hair cells that detect the sound vibrations transmitted into the cochlea. The uppermost structure in the organ of Corti is the tectorial membrane, which is in contact with the steriocilia of the hair cells.

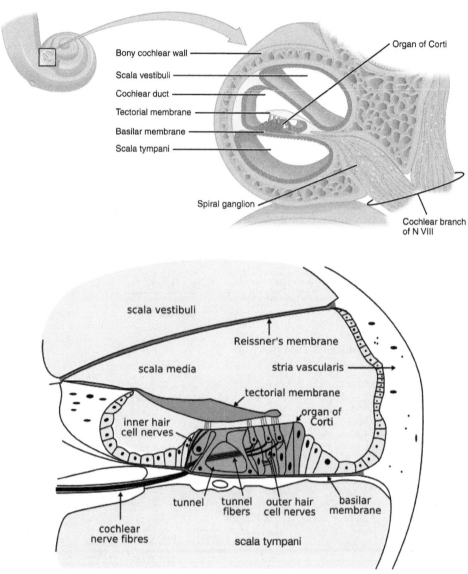

Figure 7-9A A cross-section of the cochlea.

Figure 7-9B The organ of Corti.

Vibrations from sound waves bend the steriocilia on the hair cells, opening mechanically gated ion channels by deflecting a tip link, which is a spring-like structure that attaches to ion channels on the steriocilia. Opening of the channels allows the passage of K+ into the hair cell. This depolarizes the cell and initiates the release of neurotransmitters, which generate APs in the neighboring afferent neurons.

The basilar membrane plays a significant role in the perception of sound. Near its beginning (at the oval window, where the ossicle bones transmit the vibrations coming from the eardrum) the basilar membrane is narrow in width and rigid (due to its thick composition). In this region, high-frequency vibrations (from high-pitched sounds) move the basilar membrane and, thus, deflect the steriocilia on the specific hair cells located in this area. Low-pitched sounds vibrate the basilar membrane near the wider, less stiff, and farther end. Hence, the cochlea is "tuned" as a result of the location and activation of specialized hair cells in the organ of Corti along the basilar membrane.

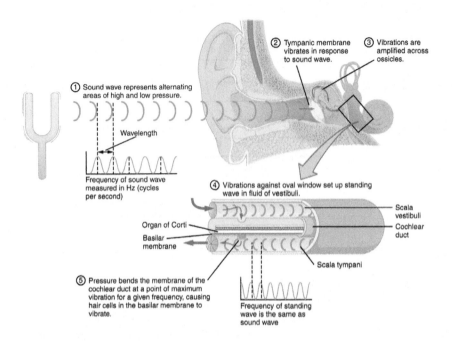

Figure 7-10A The path of sound waves in the ear.

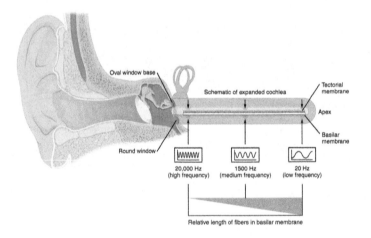

Figure 7-10B Cochlear structure enables the perception of high and low pitched sounds.

How do we see?

Photoreceptors and Vision

The specialized structures of the eye are well adapted to carry out its primary role in the visual system, which is to transmit and transduce light energy in order to enable visual processing and perception. Essential eye structures include the sclera (the white, protective outermost eye layer), the choroid (a layer composed of connective tissue and blood vessels), the posterior chamber (the small area at the sides of the eye located behind the iris but in front of the lens, which contains aqueous humor), the ciliary body (tissue near the suspensory ligaments that contains the ciliary muscle) and the suspensory ligaments, which help support the eye. Photons of light first pass through the cornea, the outermost, transparent part of the eye that encases the iris (which is the pigmented portion of the eye), the pupil (the opening at the center of the iris that controls the amount of light entry), and the anterior chamber (a compartment that resides between the iris and the cornea). The anterior chamber is also filled with aqueous humor. This watery fluid is important in maintaining the appropriate hydrostatic pressure inside the eye, maintaining the shape of the eye, and also circulates nutrients and removes wastes in this front region of the eye (which lacks blood vessels).

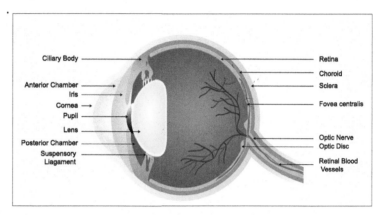

Figure 7-11 The anatomy of the eye.

Light then passes through the lens, a curved transparent structure that helps the eye focus by the process of accommodation. In this process, the lens flattens when a distant object is viewed, and becomes more rounded when viewing a nearby object. To flatten the lens, the ciliary muscles relax, which causes the ligaments that are attached to the lens to tighten, extending the lens. To make the lens more convex, the ciliary muscles contract, causing the ligaments to be less taut.

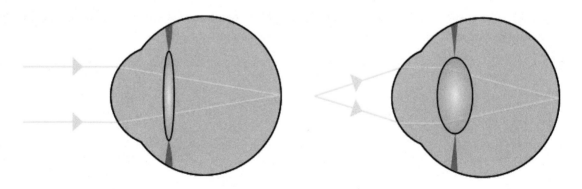

Figure 7-12 Lens shape during the process of visual accommodation. When a distant object is viewed, the lens flattens (as depicted on the left). When a near object is viewed, the lens rounds (as depicted on the right).

Light passes from the lens into the vitreous chamber, the area between the lens and retina that contains vitreous humor, a gelatinous substance that helps to refract light as well as hold the eye in place. Photons of light from the focused image then strike the retina. The retina is a layer of specialized tissue lining the interior surface of the eye. It is composed of light-sensitive photoreceptive cells (the rods and cones), bipolar cells, and ganglion cells, as well as various support cells, such as the horizontal, and amacrine cells. Bipolar cells transmit impulses from the photoreceptive cells to the ganglion neurons, whose axons comprise the optic nerve. Amacrine and horizontal cells function to integrate and regulate the transmission of the sensory input to the ganglion neurons.

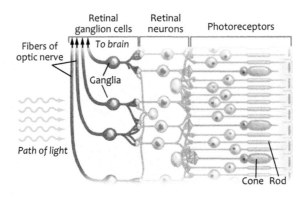

Figure 7-13 The cells of the retina.

In the retina, the rod cells are specialized for the detection of low-intensity light, whereas the cone cells are specialized for detecting light of different wavelengths (or colors). Rod cells are found throughout most of the retina, except in a region known as the fovea centralis. Cone cells are highly localized to the fovea centralis and the macula, with a few interspersed throughout the remainder of the retina. Both rod and cone cells have an outer segment with disc-like structures that contain photoreceptive molecules (or photopigments) that absorb light energy. In rods, the photoreceptive molecule is rhodopsin, in cones it is photopsin. Human cones cells each have one of three types of photopsin molecules that respond to wavelengths that correspond to red, green, or blue light. Perception of color gradations is achieved by overlapping responses to the wavelengths of each primary color.

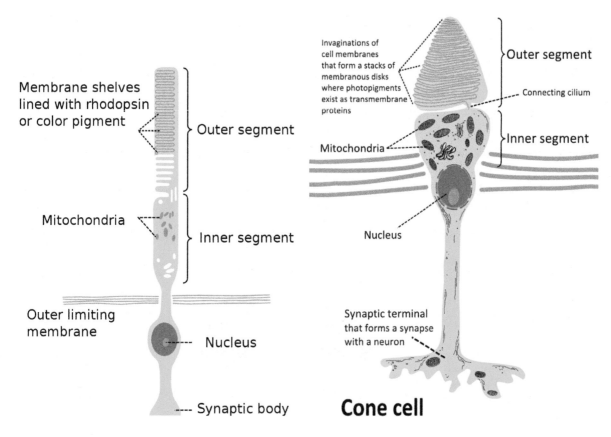

Figure 7-14A Rod cell of the retina.
Figure 7-14B Cone cell of the retina.

Phototransduction and visual processing

The conversion of light energy to action potential signals (or phototransduction) by the rod photoreceptor cell is well understood. The rhodopsin photopigments, which reside on the membrane of the rod cell disc, are composed of an opsin molecule with a retinal molecule bound to it. The opsin molecule is a membrane bound G protein coupled receptor (GPCR). Its associated retinal molecule (a form of vitamin A), undergoes a conformational change (from the *cis* to the *trans* conformation) when photons of light are encountered. However, in the dark, when the rhodopsin molecule is not activated by light, sodium channels on its membrane are open, permitting an influx of Na+ that depolarizes the rod cell. This depolarization causes the rod cell to release the neurotransmitter glutamate from its terminals into the synapse with an associated bipolar cell. The glutamate inhibits the bipolar cell from releasing neurotransmitters into its synapse with a ganglion cell, thereby prohibiting the ganglion cell from generating action potentials. When light energy strikes the retinal molecule, causing a conformational change, the rhodopsin is activated. This activates the associated G protein. The alpha subunit of the G protein activates phosphodiesterase, resulting in the conversion of cGMP to GMP, which causes the Na+ channels on the rod cell disc membrane to close. Because there is no longer an influx of cations (which would result in depolarization), the rod cell hyperpolarizes. This causes the release of glutamate into the synapse with the bipolar cell to cease, thereby removing the inhibition. The bipolar cell can now "fire" or releases neurotransmitters to initiate APs in the ganglion cells. These APs are transmitted via the optic nerve to the visual processing centers in the brain.

In humans, there are 120 million photoreceptor cells compared to only 1 million ganglion cells. Ganglion cells receive signals from specific bipolar cells that correlate to particular groups of photoreceptive cells (or rods and cones). The specific group of cells that is associated with a particular ganglion cell is referred to its receptive field. The receptive field facilitates the perception of an image's edges by enabling the detection of contrast. More defined images result from the activation of smaller receptive fields. In the figure below, the circles represent the receptive field for bipolar cells. Note that receptive fields are not two-dimensional, as depicted in the figure, but rather are cone shaped to facilitate depth perception. Bipolar cells can be characterized as "on center" or "off center." For example, if light hits the center of the receptive field for an "on center" type of bipolar cell, the bipolar cell depolarizes and initiates action potentials in an affiliated ganglion cell. However, if photons of light are transmitted to the area surrounding the center, the corresponding ganglion cells will not fire. Analogous results are found when light penetrates specific regions of receptive fields of "off center" center cells.

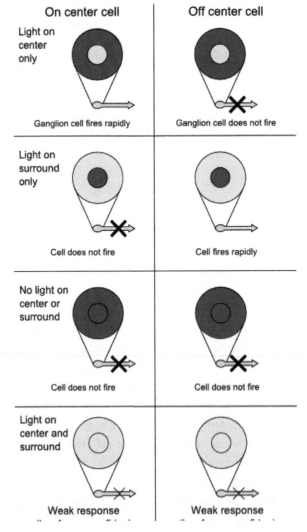

Figure 7-15 Receptive fields facilitate visual processing.

The location of a visual stimulus is encoded in the nervous system by comparing input from each eye as it moves horizontally and vertically. This assists in the determination of the relative lateral location (left/right) as well as the vertical location (up/down). Comparing input from each eye also facilitates depth perception. A map-like projection from the retina to the visual cortex in the brain relays the left/right location, up/down location, and distance (depth perception) information. Visual information is sent via the optic nerve through the lateral geniculate nuclei to the visual cortex in the brain.

Interestingly, information from a visual field (e.g., "right" visual field or "left" visual field) is processed in the opposite side of the brain. For example, the visual field to one's left is viewed by the right side of both eyes and is processed in the right visual cortex (and vice versa).

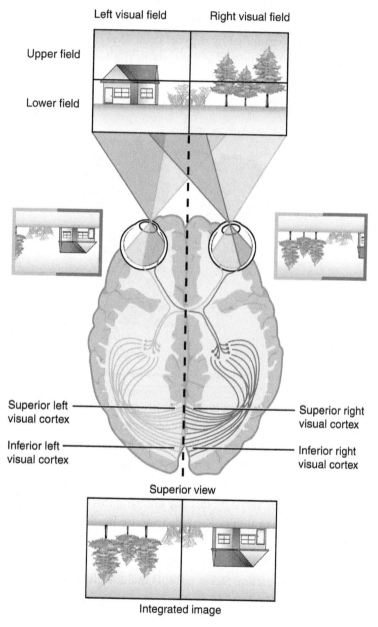

Figure 7-16 The visual projection pathway.

Gustation, olfaction, and chemoreceptors

Chemoreceptors respond to the presence of specific molecules in both the internal and external environment. They can be found in the special sense organs for taste (gustation) and smell (olfaction). The sensory structures for taste, the taste buds, are located on protuberances of the tongue (the papillae). There are four types of papillae. The filiform papillae are the most prevalent but do not contain taste buds. Rather, they provide a rough surface for food manipulation. The vallate papillae have taste buds. They are relatively large in size and are positioned in a "V" shape along the tongue. The fungiform (or mushroom shaped) papillae also have taste buds and are asymmetrically dispersed on the tongue surface. The foliate (leaf-shaped) pappilae contain the most sensitive taste buds and are located on the sides of the tongue. Interestingly, the number of foliate papillae tends to decrease with aging. Taste buds consist of sensory receptor cells surrounded by support cells. One end of the receptor cell synapses with afferent neurons, which transmit the signal for the taste to the brain cortex. The opposite end of the receptor cells have gustatory hairs that protrude into a pore where they come into contact with tastants, chemical substances that are dissolved in the salvia.

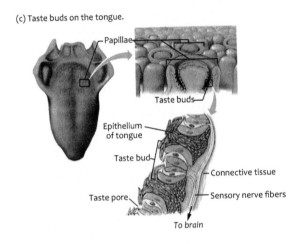

(c) Taste buds on the tongue.

Figure 7-17 Taste buds.

The taste sensory receptor cells found in taste buds are specific for each of the five kinds of tastants: sweet, sour, bitter, salty, and savory. Various molecular mechanisms are employed to cause depolarization in the sensory receptor cell, which results in the release of neurotransmitters into its synapse with the associated afferent neuron. For example, the most sensitive receptor cells for the acidic sour taste are localized to lateral areas of the tongue. The H+ ions associated with tastant cause depolarization of the sensory receptor cell in three ways: by directly entering through H+ channels; by binding to K+ channels, which closes them and prohibits K+ efflux; or by binding to cation channels, allowing an influx of positive ions. The sweet, bitter, and savory tastants bind to G protein coupled receptors, which activate a second messenger pathway (using such molecules as cAMP and kinases) to alter ion channel conductance, resulting in depolarization. Sweet tastants include glucose and other artificial sweeteners, and the receptors for this taste are localized to the taste buds on tip of the tongue. Taste buds that contain sensory receptor cells for the bitter taste respond to tastants that contain alkaloids and are located on the posterior part of the tongue. Savory tatants generally contain amino acids, such as glutamate. Receptors for this taste are usually dispersed on the tongue. Receptors for the salty taste are localized to the tip of the tongue and depolarize when Na+ ions pass through Na+ channels. Many of the axons that transmit information from the taste receptor cells enter the brainstem, where they synapse with neurons whose axons transmit impulses to the thalamus. From there, APs are sent to the nearby taste areas of the brain, where the particular taste is identified. Not surprisingly, the perception of taste is influenced by texture, temperature, and olfaction.

Olfaction, or the sense of smell, enables the average person to recognize over 4,000 different odors, as well as detect odorants from distant sources. This is significant since olfaction is used for a number of important objectives, such as communication, food identification, awareness of predators and prey, identication of kin and group members, and marking of trails and territories. Olfactory receptor cells are also chemoreceptors and each receptor may respond to more than one type of odor. The olfactory receptor cells have sensory hairs (or cilia) that protrude into the mucous of the nasal cavity.

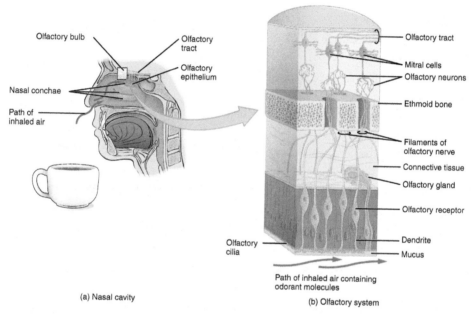

Figure 7-18 Components of the olfactory system.

Airborne odorant molecules that are dissolved in the mucous of the nasal cavity bind to G protein coupled receptors embedded in the sensory hair membrane. Binding of an odorant molecule to the G protein receptor activates adenylate cyclase, which converts ATP to cAMP and results in the opening of cation channels. This leads to the depolarization of the receptor cell and the transmission of action potentials to associated afferent neurons. The axons of these olfactory neurons are organized in clusters. Their cell bodies are located superior to the olfactory receptor cells in a structure known as the olfactory bulb. The olfactory bulb has multiple layers of distinct neurons, such as granule cells, mitral cells, and tufted cells. This neuronal variability and specific organization facilitates odor discrimination by filtering out certain odors to enhance sensitivity of other odors. The neurons of the olfactory bulb transmit information to three regions of the olfactory cortex in the frontal lobe. The lateral olfactory area is involved in the conscious perception of smell, whereas the intermediate olfactory area serves to modify and filter incoming information. The medial olfactory area is primarily involved with visceral and emotional responses to odor. In fact, information from the olfactory cortex, as well as from the neurons of the olfactory bulb, is often integrated and processed in limbic system structures.

Olfactory receptor cells are unique in that the olfactory epithelium is replenished about every two months as it deteriorates. This is somewhat unusual, because in general, most neurons are permanent cells that are not replaced. Also, as mentioned above, the sense of smell contributes to the sense taste. Often times, if the sense of smell is weakened (perhaps due to congestion caused by a cold), taste perception is likewise diminished. This is because vaporized molecules from foods are transmitted from the throat to the olfactory receptors in the nasal cavities, which, if unaffected, would contribute to the perception of the specific taste.

Chapter 7 Review

I. Helpful and Interesting Animations:

1. Stretch receptors in muscles:
   http://www.youtube.com/watch?v=4vgf0uVkg5U&list=PLBC3B4C5B158840BF&index=15
2. Auditory transduction:
   http://www.youtube.com/watch?v=PeTriGTENoc&index=17&list=PLBC3B4C5B158840BF
3. The cochlea:
   http://www.hhmi.org/biointeractive/cochlea
4. Summary of hearing:
   http://www.youtube.com/watch?v=xMUl5CCoW6Y
5. The eye:
   http://www.youtube.com/watch?v=RE1MvRmWg7I&feature=related
6. Anatomy of the eye:
   http://sites.sinauer.com/neuroscience5e/animations11.01.html
7. Phototransduction:
   http://sites.sinauer.com/neuroscience5e/animations11.02.html
8. Information processing in the retina:
   http://sites.sinauer.com/neuroscience5e/animations11.03.html
9. Visual pathways:
   http://sites.sinauer.com/neuroscience5e/animations12.01.html
10. The olfactory system:
    http://sites.sinauer.com/neuroscience5e/animations15.01.html

II. Active Testing: Do you know the facts?

A. List the words in this chapter you would have printed in bold type.
Can you define these words?

B. What are the main, "take home" messages of this chapter?
Is your answer the same as your instructor's answer?

C. Some Questions:

1. Define and give an example of sensory transduction.

2. Name 5 receptor types and give an example of each of their functions.

3. Describe the structure and functions of the body parts involved in maintaining balance.

4. Explain how rotational movement of the head and/or body is detected.

5. Explain how non-linear body movement and information about the head position (up/down) is detected.

6. Describe the structure and functions of the body parts involved in hearing.

7. Draw and label a diagram showing the anatomical features of the eye.

8. Describe how the eye "accommodates" in order to focus on a near object and on a distant object.

9. Draw and label a diagram showing the cells of the retina. Identify the direction of information processing.

10. Name the photoreceptive molecules (or photopigments) of the eye. Where are they found? Which are specialized for detecting light of different wavelengths? Which detect low intensity light?

11. Explain the sequence of events in a rod cell of the retina when light hits it.

12. What is the function of horizontal and amacrine cells in the retina?

13. What process occurs when an "Off Center" bipolar cell is illuminated in its center?

14. What side of the eyes is the left visual field viewed by? What side of the brain is the left visual field processed on?

15. Illustrate the components of a taste bud.

16. What type of receptors are utilized in olfaction?

III. Inquiring minds want to know...

Challenge Questions

1. It has been suggested that humans can discriminate several million different colors and almost a half a million different tones. Studies of olfaction suggest humans can discriminate more than 1 trillion olfactory stimuli! How would a scientist determine how many olfactory stimuli can be discriminated? [*Hint*-See: Bushdid, C. et al. (2014) Science. **343,** 1370-1372]

2. *Mal de debarquement* syndrome is a sensation of movement that continues after one has come ashore from a boating excursion. What are some of the common symptoms and the physiological (vestibular) basis for this syndrome? How is *Mal de debarquement* syndrome commonly treated?

Chapter 8

Muscles and Body Movement

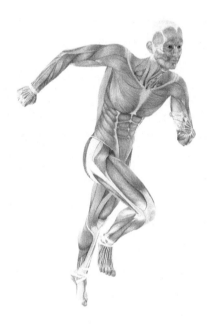

Figure 8-1 Muscle man running.

Why are muscles so useful?

The muscular system provides a number of vital functions. Muscles are necessary for such important tasks as body movement, communication, maintaining posture, respiration, heart contraction, organ compression, dilation and constriction of blood vessels, and production of body heat. Muscles have essential characteristics that are necessary for their proper function. These include contractility (muscle shortening to generate force or movement), excitability (response to stimuli from the nervous system), elasticity (natural recoil after being stretched), and extensibility (ability to be lengthened beyond resting state). There are three types of muscle tissue: skeletal, smooth, and cardiac. We begin our discussion of muscle tissue with the long, cylinder-shaped, striated skeletal muscle.

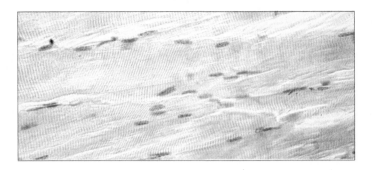

Figure 8-2 Skeletal muscle tissue.

Skeletal muscle cells have more than one nuclei per cell (multi-nucleated) and the nuclei generally reside on the periphery of the muscle cell. They are mostly under voluntary control (by the somatic nervous system); however, muscles involved in reflexes are under involuntary control. They are attached to bones (via tendons), and their primary function is for various types of movement, including body movement, locomotion, posture, breathing, and facial expressions. Individual skeletal muscles are composed of skeletal muscle cells (often called fibers), blood vessels, nerves, and connective tissue. As such, they are regarded as complete organs. Skeletal muscles have a highly organized structure.

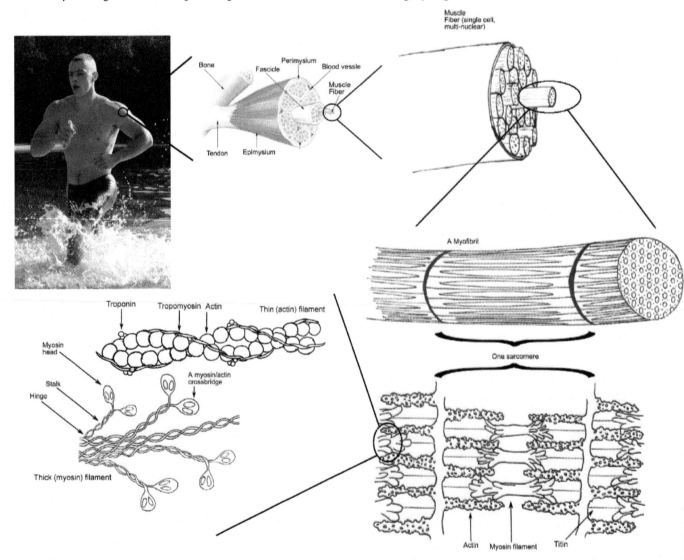

Figure 8-3 The structure of a skeletal muscle.

Long cylindrical muscle cells (or fibers) are bundled together by connective tissue. These bundles are known as fasiculi. Motor neuron axons and blood vessels are dispersed throughout the fasiculi. Individual fasculi are also grouped together in parallel and are encased by connective tissue. The plasma membrane of a muscle cell is referred to as the sarcolemma, and the cytoplasm is known as the sacroplasma. A muscle cell contains a number of contractile components called myofibrils. Myofibrils consist of thick filaments (made of myosin protein) and thin filaments (composed mainly of the actin protein).

The sarcomere

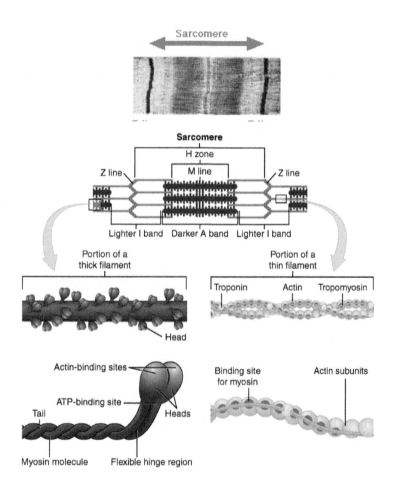

Figure 8.4 The structure of a sarcomere.

The thick and thin filaments of a myofibril, along with other associated proteins, constitute a sarcomere, the basic contractile unit of skeletal muscle. Thus sarcomeres align end to end to form a myofibril. The striation (or the alternating light and dark appearance of skeletal muscle tissue) results from the alternating bands of thick and thin filaments. Sarcomeres also have a well-defined structure, which includes the Z line (a filamentous protein complex that attaches to actin filaments and delimits a sarcomere), I bands (which constitute the region between the Z line to the end of the thick filaments and are light colored), the A bands (comprising the length of the thick filaments), the H zone (non-overlapping region between the thick and thin filaments), and the M line (composed of filaments that help secure myosin). The myosin protein consists of a tail and two head subunits. The thick filaments are large bipolar filaments formed from tail–tail interactions between myosin molecules and contain several hundred myosin heads oriented in opposite directions. The heads bind and hydrolyze ATP, which generates the force for muscle contraction by sliding oppositely oriented pairs of thin filaments toward each other. These thin filaments are composed of actin protein filaments that are associated with an elongated protein, tropomyosin, and a globular protein, troponin. The tropomyosin protein resides along the groove of the actin filament. The troponin protein contains three subunits: one that binds to actin, a second that binds to tropomyosin, and a third that binds to calcium ions. The tropomyosin/troponin complex regulates the interaction between active sites on actin and myosin.

The mechanism by which a sarcomere shortens in length, and thus, a muscle contracts, is described by the sliding filament model. When a muscle is stimulated to contract by a motor neuron, myosin heads on the thick filaments attach to binding sites on actin subunits of thin filaments. Movement of the myosin heads slides the thin filaments toward each other, which effectively shortens the sarcomeres and contracts the muscle.

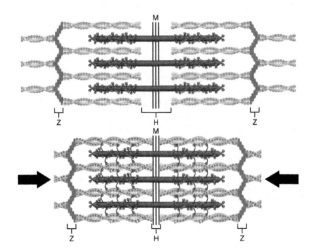

Figure 8.5 The sliding filament model of muscle contraction.

How is a skeletal muscle cell stimulated to contract?

A skeletal muscle contraction is initiated at the neuromuscular junction (also called the motor endplate). This is the region where a presynaptic terminal of an axon branch of a motor neuron forms a synapse with the postsynaptic membrane (sarcolemma) of the muscle cell. When an action potential reaches the axonal terminal of a motor neuron, voltage gated Ca^{2+} channels open, resulting in the influx of calcium ions. This causes the synaptic vesicles containing the neurotransmitter acetylcholine (ACh) to fuse with the presynaptic membrane and release ACh into the synaptic cleft, where it binds to and opens ligand gated Na+ channels on the sarcolemma. The resulting Na+ influx initiates a depolarization in the muscle cell. The sarcolemma of the muscle cell contains deep invaginations known as transverse tubules.

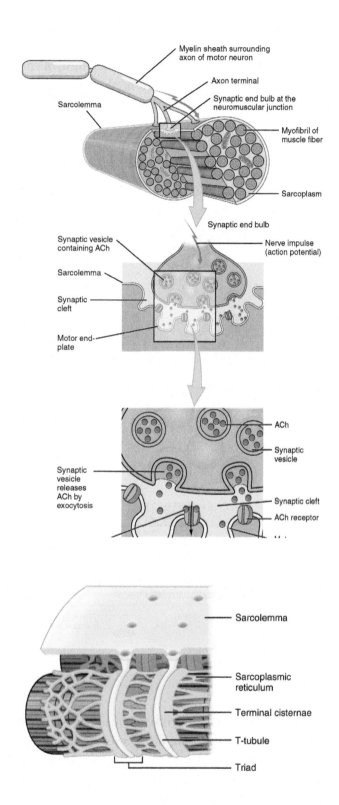

Figure 8.6A Signal propagation at the motor end plate.

Figure 8.6B The T-tubule.

These invaginations enable the rapid spread of the depolarization to the cell interior, which triggers the release of Ca^{2+} from the sarcoplasmic reticulum (a specialized form of endoplasmic reticulum found in muscle cells). Ca^{2+} ions bind to the troponin molecule on the actin filament. This association induces a conformational change, which causes the displacement of the tropomyosin molecule, thereby exposing binding sites on the actin molecule. These newly accessible sites are the locations where the myosin heads of the thick filaments contact the actin molecules of the thin filaments, forming an association known as a cross bridge. At this point, the myosin heads pull and release the thin filament in cycles powered by ATP hydrolysis.

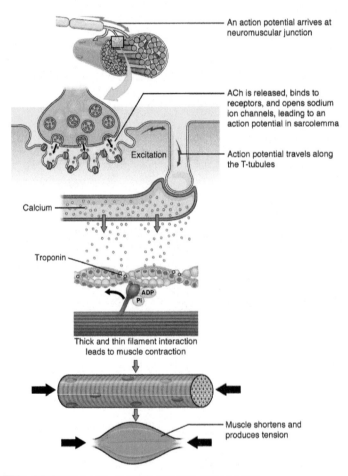

Figure 8-7 Skeletal muscle contraction.

When the cross bridge is initially formed, the myosin head has ADP and inorganic phosphate (Pi) bound to it. These molecules are released during the "power stroke:" the process in which the hinge region of the myosin head undergoes a conformational change causing the head to bend, sliding the actin filament in the opposite direction. At this point, a new ATP molecule binds to the myosin head causing it to detach from the actin filament. Subsequent hydrolysis of ATP to ADP and Pi repositions the myosin head in preparation for the next cycle of thin filament movement.

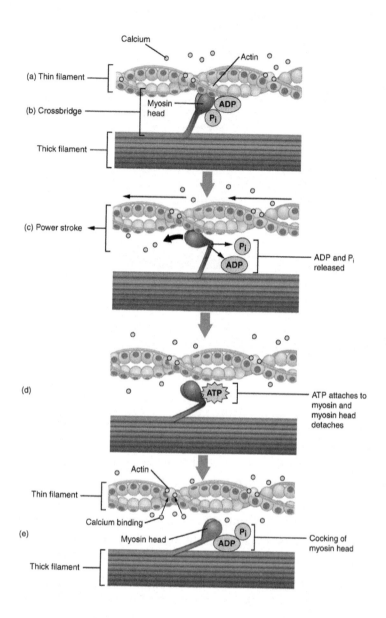

Figure 8-8 ATP hydrolysis powers the movement of actin filaments during a skeletal muscle contraction.

Once the contraction subsides and action potentials to the muscle cease, the entire system is reset. Ca^{2+} is removed from the troponin and actively transported (via Ca^{2+} pumps) back (from the cytosol) into the sarcoplasmic reticulum. Tropomyosin returns to its original location on the actin filament, blocking the myosin binding sites. The thin filaments passively slide back to their original position.

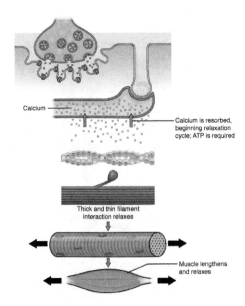

Figure 8-9 Skeletal muscle relaxation.

Muscle twitch

A muscle contraction in response to a stimulus that causes an action potential is referred to as a muscle twitch. A muscle twitch is composed of three phases: the lag phase, contraction phase, and relaxation phase. The lag phase of a muscle twitch consists of the events leading up to cross bridge formation, including the propagation of the action potential from the motor neuron to the muscle cell and the exposure of the binding sites on the actin molecule. The contraction phase includes the cross bridge cycle, in which the myosin head makes contact with the actin, shifts the actin, releases and rejoins numerous times, producing sarcomere shortening. During this cycle, ATP bound to the myosin head is broken down to ADP. Some of the energy from this reaction is used to release the cross bridges and enable the myosin heads to return to their resting position in preparation for the formation of a new cross bridge. Any remaining energy is released as heat. The relaxation period is characterized by the active transport of Ca^{2+} ions into the sarcoplasmic reticulum, the occlusion of the actin active sites by tropomyosin, and the passive lengthening of the muscle fibers.

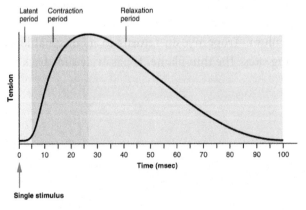

Figure 8-10 Stages of a muscle twitch.

In a skeletal muscle fiber, the duration of an action potential is short in comparison to the duration of contraction phase. If a muscle fiber is re-stimulated before it has completely relaxed, a second twitch occurs, which is added to the first (wave summation), resulting in a stronger contraction. The rapid arrival of threshold-level stimuli triggers action potentials that cause the summation of muscle twitches, resulting in a continuous contraction known as muscle tetanus. Incomplete tetanus occurs when muscle fibers partly relax between contractions. Complete tetanus occurs when there is no relaxation between the frequent action potentials, resulting in a smooth, sustained contraction and an increased tension. The basis for this effect is that the Ca^{2+} released in the sarcoplasm due to the first stimulus is not completely returned to the sarcoplasmic reticulum before the next stimulus arrives. More Ca^{2+} is available in the sarcoplasm to bind to troponin and enable additional cross bridge formation, resulting in a stronger contraction. Thus, an important feature of skeletal muscles is their capacity to produce contractions of varying strengths to match the necessary task. By the process of wave summation, (which can lead to tetanus) an increase in the frequency of muscle stimulation intensifies the strength of contraction. Motor unit recruitment is an additional means by which the degree of muscle contraction can be regulated. It will be discussed below.

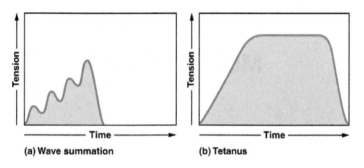

Figure 8-11 Muscle tetanus.

What makes one muscle different from another?

Muscle fiber types

A particular muscle is usually composed of different types of muscle fibers, each having unique properties. Slow twitch muscle fibers are relatively small in diameter, contract slowly, and produce weak contractions, but tend to resist fatigue, and therefore, can maintain contractions for long periods of time. The low intensity of the contraction is due to the slow rate of hydrolysis of the ATP molecules on the myosin head in the slow twitch type muscle cell. Slow twitch muscle fibers have many mitochondria and a high content of myoglobin (a specialized oxygen- and iron-binding protein). These types of muscle cells use oxygen efficiently to generate ATP and are often referred to as slow oxidative (SO) fibers. Postural muscles, which can sustain contractions for relatively long periods of time, have a high composition of slow oxidative muscle fibers. The two other muscle fiber types are known as the fast twitch oxidative-glycolytic (FOG) and the fast twitch glycolytic (FG) fibers. FOG fibers are intermediate in fiber diameter size and are characterized by an intermediate aerobic capacity and fatigue resistance (when compared to the slow oxidative fibers and the fast glycolytic fibers). Like the slow oxidative fibers, they have a high myoglobin content with many mitochondria, which facilitates their ability for aerobic metabolism. But, they also have a high glycogen content, which enables them to have a high capacity for anaerobic metabolism. Compared to slow oxidative fibers, they have more rapid myosin ATPase kinetics, and thus, can generate faster contractions. These types of fibers are generally found in the muscles of the lower limbs and are used for endurance type activities. The muscle fibers that have the largest diameter are the FG fibers. In contrast to both the slow oxidative and the FOG fibers, the FG fibers have a low myoglobin content, low resistance to fatigue, and a low aerobic capacity with few mitochondria. Their primary mechanism of metabolism is anaerobic, and thus, they have a high glycogen concentration. Muscles in the upper limbs contain many of this fiber type, which is well suited for brief but intense movements.

Most muscles are composed of both fast and slow twitch fibers. Stronger tasks require the progressive recruitment of larger fibers. For example, to generate gentle contractions that do not produce a large muscle tension, an organism will excite motor neurons that innervate smaller, slow oxidative type fibers in a particular muscle. To increase the force generated by the contracted muscle, action potentials can be transmitted to the medium sized, FOG fibers in the muscle. If a strong burst of force is needed, the largest muscle fibers (the FG) will be excited. Because motor neurons generally have a number of axonal branches, each motor neuron can excite more than one muscle fiber. A single motor neuron plus all the muscle cells (fibers) innervated by it is called a motor unit.

MOTOR NEURON

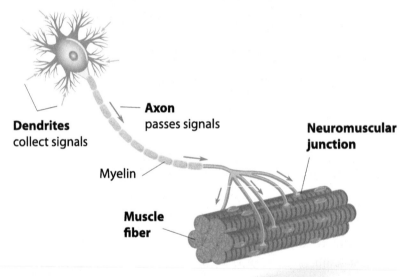

Figure 8-12 A motor unit.

Larger muscles that make forceful movements generally contain motor units with many muscle fibers. Smaller muscles that make delicate movements contain motor units with fewer muscle fibers. The strength of the overall muscle contraction can be increased by increasing both the number and type of motor units that are excited. The term recruitment refers to the effect of exciting more motor units so that more muscle fibers are contracting at the same time, thereby increasing the force of contraction that a muscle can generate. Another factor that influences the force of contraction of a muscle is its length. A muscle can generate its greatest tension when it is close to its ideal length, that is, not over or under stretched. The length-tension curve (also called the force-length relationship) compares the intensity of a contraction to muscle length when the contraction takes place.

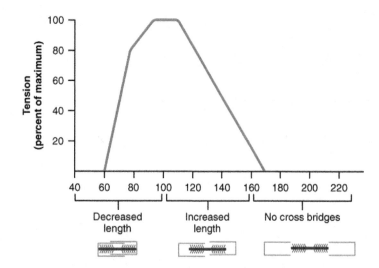

Figure 8-13 Optimal sarcomere length produces maximal muscle tension.

When a muscle is extended to its optimal length, the overlap between the thick and thin filaments is ideal, resulting in the availability of an optimal number of myosin binding sites on the actin filament. Thus, a maximal number of cross bridges can be formed to slide actin filaments, thereby producing an ideal contraction. If the muscle is extended to a longer length, then there is very little overlap between the thick and thin filaments, prohibiting ideal cross bridge formation and the ability to generate sufficient muscle tension. However, excessive overlap of the thin and thick filaments is a consequence of a slack muscle, where the sacomere length is shorter than optimal. This decreases the number of available myosin binding sites and cross bridge formation, resulting in greatly reduced muscle tension. Because muscles are attached to bone, it is not possible to change muscle length to a great extent. Generally, in the body, a muscle is at its optimal length when at its resting state.

Energy sources for muscle contraction and types of muscle movement

ATP provides immediate energy for muscle contractions and is produced from three sources: creatine phosphate, anaerobic respiration, and aerobic respiration. During resting conditions, creatine phosphate accumulates in muscle tissue, storing energy that can be used to synthesize ATP. At the beginning of a contraction (that is, for about the first 10 to 15 seconds), the ATP needed for a muscle contraction is produced from creatine phosphate. To provide additional ATP, the metabolic process of glycolysis is used to produce two ATP molecules and two pyruvate molecules per glucose molecule. If oxygen is not available (which may occur during strenuous exercise, when oxygen is depleted faster than it can be replenished), pyruvic acid can be converted to lactic acid. Aerobic respiration accounts for the production of the majority of ATP needed in muscles both when active and at rest. The breakdown of glucose, fatty acids and pyruvic acid generate up to 36 ATP molecules via glycolysis and the citric acid cycle. The energy produced by these aerobic mechanisms can sustain muscle activity for extended periods of time.

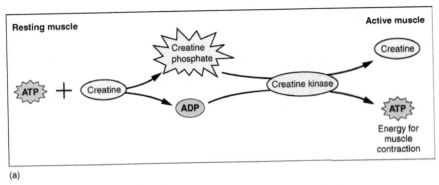

(a)

(b)

(c)

Figure 8-14 *Energy sources for muscle contractions.*

Skeletal muscle organization

Most skeletal muscles are arranged as antagonistic pairs. Members of a pair pull a bone in opposite directions. When one member of the pair contracts, the other member relaxes and is stretched. An excellent example of antagonistic coupling can be seen in the movement of the upper arm muscles.

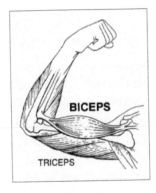

Figure 8-15 *The biceps and triceps are arranged as antagonistic pairs.*

When the bicep muscle of the upper arm contracts to pull the forearm upward, the triceps muscle relaxes. When the triceps muscle contracts to move the forearm down, the biceps muscle simultaneously relaxes. The bones moved by skeletal muscles often act as levers. The joint at one end of the associated bones forms the fulcrum of the lever with the load at the opposite end. The muscle is attached at a point between the ends and generates the force needed for a particular task. There are a variety of ways in which muscles connect to bones, producing different features that are specialized for various muscle activities. Muscle contraction can also be classified according to the type of length change in the muscle during a specific movement. In a concentric contraction, a muscle shortens as it contracts (e.g., lifting a load). In an eccentric contraction, the muscle lengthens as it contracts (e.g., lowering a load or slowing a movement). The muscle remains the same length in an isometric contraction (e.g., holding load).

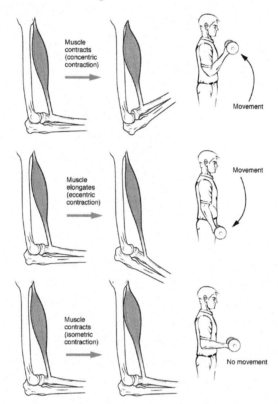

Figure 8-16 Types of muscle contraction.

How does smooth muscle compare to skeletal muscle?

Smooth muscle cells have specialized functions and characteristic structural features that are somewhat different from skeletal muscle cells. Smooth muscle can be found surrounding the bladder, reproductive tracts, gastrointestinal tract, respiratory tract, the eye, and blood vessels. Smooth muscle has a variety of functions, which include emptying the bladder, contracting the uterus, propelling food through the digestive system, regulating blood vessel diameter, and contracting glands. In general, contractions of smooth muscle tend to be slower than skeletal muscle and tend not to readily fatigue. For example, muscles that control the diameter of a blood vessel can maintain a contraction for a prolonged period of time. Smooth muscle cells are oval in shape with a single nucleus that is centrally located in the cell. Unlike both skeletal and cardiac muscle, they do not appear striated. Smooth muscle cells are under the control of the autonomic (involuntary) nervous system. Smooth muscle tissue in certain parts of the body (i.e., visceral smooth muscle) is classified as single unit and is associated by gap junctions. This enables action potential or ions (such as Ca^{2+}) to spread to adjacent cells so that the groups of cells contract in unison, creating coordinated movement. Autorhythmic contractions in the densely packed single-unit smooth muscle tissue are generated spontaneously by pacemaker cells. Multi-unit smooth muscle tissue does not have gap junctions, but rather is innervated by individual neuronal terminals from the parasympathetic and sympathetic nervous system.

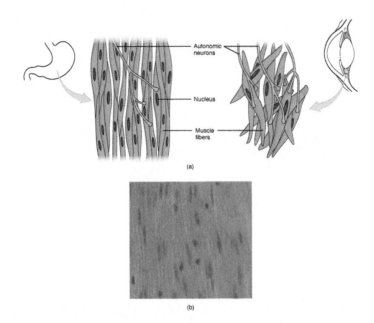

Figure 8-17 Examples of smooth muscle tissue.

Smooth muscle cells generally have less myosin protein than skeletal muscle, contain similar amounts of actin and tropomyosin, but do not contain troponin. Other thin filament-associated proteins, such as calponin and caldesmon, can be found in smooth muscle cells. The sarcoplasm of the spindle-shaped smooth muscle cells contain slanted filaments that are anchored by a structure called a dense body. This enables smooth muscle to contract in a non-linear fashion. Because there is more distance between thick and thin filaments in smooth muscle when compared to skeletal muscle, a smooth muscle has the capacity to shorten to a much greater extent than a skeletal muscle. These features are essential to the function of smooth muscle, as it often surrounds structures that change in diameter. Thus, it can relax and become quite elongated or significantly shorten when contracted, resulting in a bulging appearance.

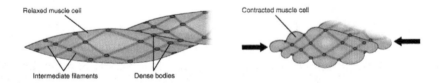

Figure 8-18 Relaxed and contracted smooth muscle.

The process of initiating a contraction in the smooth muscle cell varies significantly from that of skeletal muscle cells. There are no T tubules in smooth muscle cells to transmit action potentials into the interior of the muscle cell (as occurs in skeletal muscle cells). Instead, smooth muscle cells rely on ion channels and second messenger pathways to initiate Ca^{2+} release in the sarcoplasm. Both action potentials and hormones can trigger the opening of voltage or ligand gated Ca^{2+} channels on the smooth muscle cell membrane. A signal transduction pathway involving molecules, such as phospholipase C and inositol triphosphate (IP_3), cause the sarcoplasmic reticulum to release intracellular stores of Ca^{2+} into the sarcoplasma, where the Ca^{2+} combines with the protein calmodulin. This interaction activates myosin light chain kinase (MLCK). This kinase phosphorylates myosin, enabling cross bridge cycling with actin, generating smooth muscle cell contraction. Relaxation entails the removal of Ca^{2+} from the sarcoplasm by transporting it back to the sarcoplasmic reticulum or out of the cell, as well as cleaving the phosphate molecule from the myosin head by phosphatases. (For a comprehensive summary, see Webb RC, 2003.)

Why is cardiac muscle so unique?

Cardiac muscle is composed of branched, cylindrically shaped cells. It has a striated appearance, somewhat similar to skeletal muscle, but has a single, centrally located nucleus, as found in smooth muscle cells. It is controlled by the autonomic nervous system, capable of spontaneous contractions, and possesses intercalated discs found at the Z line of sarcomeres. These serve to physically join cardiomyocytes (using desmosomes) and enable ions to pass into adjacent cells (using gap junctions), resulting in coordinated contraction. Cardiac muscle is found in the heart and functions to propel blood into the pulmonary and systemic circulatory circuits.

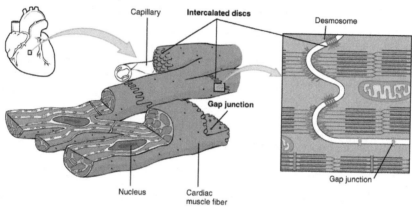

Figure 8-19 Cardiac muscle tissue.

The processes of excitation and contraction in cardiac muscle have some distinctive features, but also include mechanisms that are similar to those in skeletal muscle. In the heart, action potentials are normally initiated by the specialized pacemaker cells of the sinoatrial (SA) node found in the right atrium. (Note that action potentials may also be initiated in the heart atrioventricular (AV) node in certain circumstances.) Action potentials from the SA node are propagated throughout the heart cardiomyocytes via the gap junctions joining the cells. In an individual cardiac muscle cell (or cardiomyocyte) an action potential causes voltage gated Ca^{2+} channels in the T tubule membranes to open. This results in an influx of calcium from the extracellular fluid (Na+ ions may also enter). This increase in intracellular Ca^{2+} concentrations activates receptors (known as ryanodine receptors) on the sarcoplasmic reticulum, resulting in the further release of Ca^{2+} into the sarcoplasma. At this point, the contractile mechanism is essentially the same as that in skeletal muscle. Ca^{2+} binds troponin, displacing tropomyosin and exposing myosin binding sites on the actin filament. ATP-driven cross-bridge cycling results in cardiac muscle contraction.

It is important to note that the action potential in cardiac muscle cells lasts significantly longer than action potentials in neurons or skeletal muscle cells. Hence, a cardiac muscle cell has a relatively long refractory period. It cannot be re-stimulated to contract until the initial action potential has subsided. Thus, under normal conditions, tetanic contractions in the heart are not possible. The cardiac muscle in the heart contracts long enough to pump the blood, then relaxes to fill before being stimulated to contract (pump) again. This important concept will be further discussed in the next chapter.

Chapter 8 Review

I. Helpful and Interesting Animations

1. Skeletal muscle contraction:
   http://www.youtube.com/watch?v=BMT4PtXRCVA
2. Excitation-contraction coupling:
   http://www.youtube.com/watch?v=8wa04qYsaps
3. Smooth muscle contraction:
   http://www.springer.com/cda/content/document/cda_downloaddocument/4702s.swf

II. Active Testing: Do you know the facts?

A. List the words in this chapter you would have printed in bold type.
Can you define these words?

B. What are the main, "take home" messages of this chapter?
Is your answer the same as your instructor's answer?

C. Some Questions:

1. List some characteristics of muscles that distinguished one type from the others with regard to the following:

	Skeletal	Smooth	Cardiac
Location			
Appearance			
Cell Shape/ Striations?			
Nucleus			
Cell-cell attachments?			
Control/ Capable of spontaneous contractions?			
Function			

2. Draw a diagram of a skeletal muscle. Make sure you include the fasiculus, muscle fiber, vascularization, connective tissue, myofibrils and sarcomeres (with appropriate labels).

3. Define and describe each of the following terms as you illustrate the main components of the basic contractile unit of a skeletal muscle cell: sarcomere, actin, Z disk, M line, I band, troponin, A band, tropomyosin, H zone, myosin.

4. Draw, label and explain a diagram showing the process of how a skeletal muscle is stimulated to contract and the sliding filament model of muscle contraction.

5. Define skeletal muscle tetanus. Draw a graph depicting tetanus.

6. Fill in the chart below that describes the three types of muscle fibers:

	Slow Oxidative	Fast Aerobic(Oxidative Glycolytic: FOG)	Fast Anaerobic (Glycolytic: FG)
Fiber diameter			
Contraction Speed/Intensity			
Fatigue Resistance			
Myosin ATPase Activity			
Myoglobin content			
Location where abundant			
Function			

7. Describe how animals regulate their force of muscle contraction and the 3 sources of energy for contraction as well as the duration of the energy supply of each.

8. Describe the "length-tension" characteristic of muscle.

9. List the differences between various types of muscle contractions (i.e., isomeric, concentric).

10. List 5 characteristics of smooth muscle that differ from skeletal muscle.

III. Inquiring minds want to know…

Challenge Questions

1. Explain the biological basis of how botox, curare and the venom of a black widow spider affect muscle.

2. Dystrophin is cohesion protein that is found between myofilaments and the sarcolemma of muscle fiber cells. What major disease is caused by defects in dystrophin? Describe the symptoms of this disease. Explain the biological basis that underlies defects in dystrophin and this disease.

Reference

Webb, R.C. (2003). Smooth muscle contraction and relaxation. *Advances in Physiology Education, 27,* 201-206. Retrieved from http://advan.physiology.org/content/27/4/201

Chapter 9

The Circulatory System

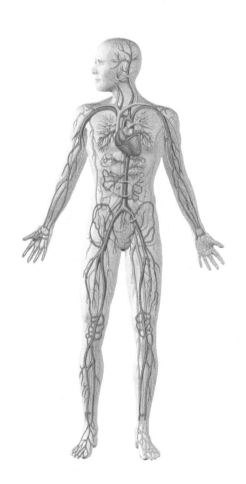

Figure 9-1 The Circulatory System

How is design optimized for function?

Animal circulatory systems share basic elements that include: circulating fluid, a pump, channels, and areas for the exchange of substances. Circulating fluid is usually in the form of blood or hemolymph. A pump, such as tubular or a chambered heart, is necessary to generate the pressure needed to propel the circulating fluid. Channels, such as blood vessels, are needed for the transport of the circulating fluid over distances; and areas for exchange, such as sinuses or capillary beds, are crucial for the exchange of gases (O_2, CO_2), nutrients, and waste. Very simple invertebrate animals, such as sponges and cnidarians (e.g., the hydra) use cilia to move water in their central cavity, thereby facilitating the exchange of nutrients and the diffusion of gas across a single cell layer or cells layers composed of just a few cells.

Figure 9-2 The hydra is an invertebrate that utilizes a simple circulatory system.

More complex animals often have many layers of multiple cells, and organs that are located deep in their bodies. In organisms such as these, substances cannot be exchanged with the environment by simple diffusion. Adaptations such as a muscular heart to pump specialized fluid (blood) through tubular vessels, and well developed respiratory and excretory systems (to facilitate the transfer of O_2 and nutrients to body tissues and the removal of CO_2 and wastes from the body) are necessary. Some circulatory systems, such as those found in most invertebrates and sedentary animals (i.e., mollusks), are classified as open circulatory systems. In this type of system, the heart pumps hemolymph into vessels that empty into body spaces (sinuses). Open circulatory systems provide less resistance to fluid flow, and thus necessitate less forceful pumps, which conserve energy and thus are well suited for animals with sedentary lifestyles. Closed circulatory systems are often found in some invertebrates and all vertebrates. In this type of system, blood is confined in vessels throughout the body and does not mix with interstitial fluid. Higher pressures can be maintained throughout the system, and blood can move rapidly throughout the body. Closed circulatory systems allow for a more precise control of blood distribution and flow rate, which can be regulated by simple adjustments to the diameter of the blood vessel

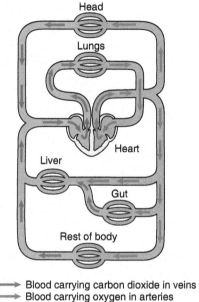

Figure 9-3 A double circuit, closed circulatory system.

Circulatory systems evolved from single circuits, using a heart with two chambers (found in animals such as fishes), to a double circuit type, composed of a heart with four chambers that pumps blood through separate pulmonary and systemic circuits (which are found in birds and mammals). Thus, as the complexity of organisms increased, the design of circulatory systems also became increasingly refined.

Circulating Fluid: Blood and its Components

Blood is a fluid connective tissue composed of blood cells (erythrocytes, leukocytes), platelets, and blood plasma, which contains water, plasma proteins, ions (such as: Na+, K+, Ca $^{2+}$, Cl-, HCO$_3^-$) dissolved gases (O$_2$ and CO$_2$), glucose, amino acids, lipids, vitamins, and some hormones.

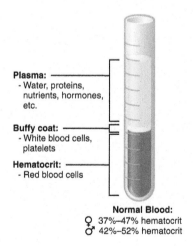

Figure 9-4 The composition of blood.

The blood cells and platelets develop in red bone marrow of specific bones which include the vertebrae, sternum, ribs, and the pelvis. They are generated from pluripotent stem cells that give rise to either myeloid or lymphoid progenitor cells during the process of haematopoiesis (or the formation of the cellular components of the blood: the red blood cells, white blood cells, and platelets).

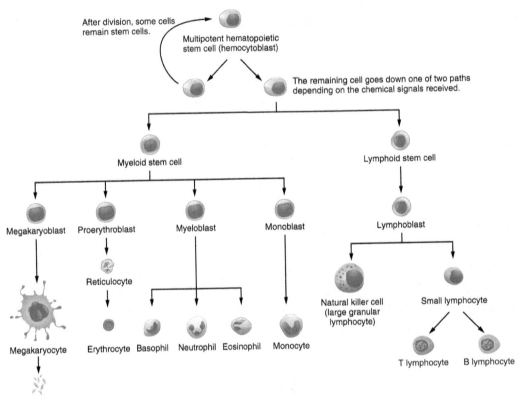

Figure 9-5 Haematopoiesis.

Erythrocytes (red blood cells) contain hemoglobin, a large globular protein which transports O_2 from the lungs to the body tissues. Hemoglobin comprises about one-third of the contents of the red blood cell. Oxygen binds to heme components (which include the Fe^{2+} ions). This binding (of O_2 to the hemoglobin protein) is enhanced by cooperativity.

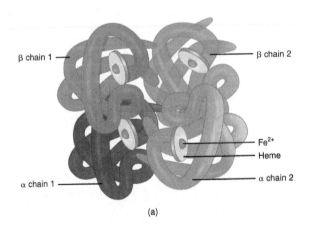

(a)

Figure 9-6 The hemoglobin protein.

Mature erythrocytes do not contain a nucleus or many organelles, and have a flexible plasma membrane which facilitates their transport through small diameter capillaries. They have a life span of about 4 months, at which time they are engulfed by macrophages and replaced by newly generated cells from the bone marrow. The primary role of white blood cells, or leukocytes, is to defend the body against infecting pathogens and eliminate dead and dying cells and cellular debris. The third component of the cellular fraction of blood is the platelets. These are cell fragments enclosed in a plasma membrane that initiate clotting by adhering to collagen protein that is exposed when blood vessels are damaged. During the clotting process, chemical factors are released which bring additional platelets to the impaired region, sealing off the damaged site.

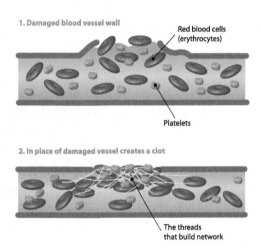

Figure 9-7 The formation of a blood clot.

The plasma portion of the blood is about 91% water, which serves as an excellent solvent for the other plasma components. Plasma proteins, such as albumin, fibrinogen, and globulins account for approximately 7% of the plasma volume. Albumins are important for maintaining osmotic homeostasis, blood pH, and for the transport of substances such as hormones. Fibrinogen is a glycoprotein that is essential for blood clot formation, and the globulin proteins are involved in such functions as lipid transport and the immune response (e.g., the gamma globulin protein is characterized as an immunoglobulin, IgG). Chemical components of the plasma comprise about 1% to 2% of the plasma and fulfill a number of vital functions. Ions (or electrolytes) are important for nerve and muscle function, maintaining pH and osmotic balance, and regulating hydration. Lipids in the blood are mainly fatty acids and cholesterol, which are important fuel sources and building blocks for a number of molecules, as well as cell membranes. Blood sugar is a crucial source of energy for the body cells, and blood is indispensable as a transporter for hormones, blood gases and other important molecules (such as vitamins and amino acids).

How is the blood pumped?

The heart-anatomy and the cardiac cycle

The human circulatory system uses a central, four chambered pump, the heart, to propel the blood through two separate body circuits: the pulmonary circuit and the systemic circuit. De-oxygenated blood enters the right atrium from the superior and inferior vena cava. At the same time, freshly oxygenated blood enters the left atrium from the right and left pulmonary veins. Once the atria are filled, the blood passes through the right and left atrioventricular (AV) valves into the ventricles. When both ventricles are filled, the deoxygenated blood is pumped from the right ventricle through the pulmonary (or semilunar) valve to the right and left pulmonary arteries into the lungs, and the oxygenated blood in the left ventricle is simultaneously pumped through the aortic valve to the aorta and into the systemic (or body) circuit.

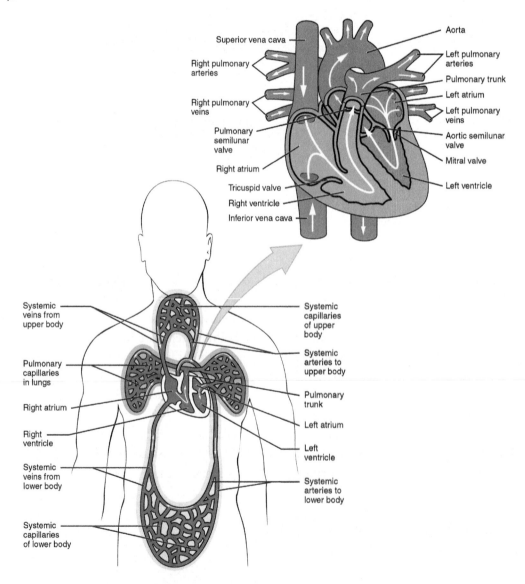

Figure 9-8 The path of blood flow through the heart and the body (including both the pulmonary and systemic circuits)

The sequence of events by which the heart pumps blood is known as the cardiac cycle. It is composed of two stages: diastole and systole. Diastole consists of the period of time when the ventricles are in a relaxed state and the chambers of the heart are filling with blood. It concludes with a brief period of atrial contraction to propel blood into the ventricles. Systole is the period of time when the ventricles are contracting.

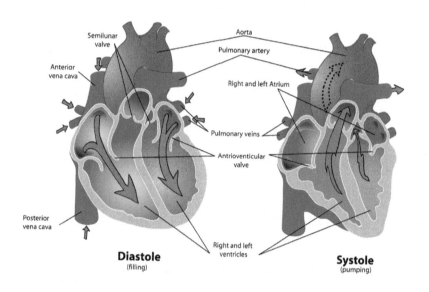

Figure 9-9 Diastole and systole.

At rest, a normal diastolic blood pressure ranges between 60 mmHg to 90 mmHg and a typical systolic blood pressure ranges from 110 mmHg to 140 mmHg. Generally, blood pressure readings are given as systolic pressure over diastolic pressure (e.g., 120/80). During the cardiac cycle, deoxygenated blood from the body tissues (part of the systemic circuit) enters the right atrium by way of the superior and inferior vena cava. At the same time, oxygenated blood, returning from the lungs (part of the pulmonary circuit) enters the left atrium. The period of time when the atria and ventricles are relaxed and the AV valves are closed is known as the isovolumetric ventricular relaxation stage of diastole. Pressure builds as the atria fill with blood, causing the opening of the tricuspid, (an atrioventricular, AV) valve, which is located between the right atrium and right ventricle and the bicuspid (or mitral) AV valve, which is located between the left atrium and left ventricle. Both ventricles fill as blood moves into them. The period of time when the atria and ventricles are relaxed and the AV valves are open is known as the ventricular filling stage of diastole. In the next phase, which is the isovolumetric ventricular contraction stage of systole, the AV valves close, and the ventricles begin to contract. The contraction results in an increased pressure in the ventricles, which causes the valve between the right ventricle and the pulmonary artery (known as the pulmonary semilunar valve) to open, allowing deoxygenated blood to flow to the lungs (part of the pulmonary circuit). At the same time, pressure due to the contraction of the left ventricle drives the aortic semilunar valve open, propelling oxygenated blood to the aorta and into the systemic circulation. This period is known as the ventricular ejection phase of systole.

The figure below compares the aortic, ventricular and atrial pressures during the cardiac cycle, in addition to indicating the timing of the heart sounds. Note that the atrial pressure remains relatively low throughout the cardiac cycle. A notable change in atrial pressure occurs as the AV valves close at the end of diastole (when the pressure is about 80 mmHg) and blood flow from the atria to the ventricles is temporarily terminated. As systole ensues, both the pressure in the ventricles and in the aorta increases rapidly, then decreases as blood is ejected, followed by the closing of the semilunar valves. The "lub-dup" heart sounds are known as the first heart sound (S1) and the second heart sound (S2). These normal heart sounds correlate to the reverberation of the blood upon the closing of the atrioventricular and semilunar valves.

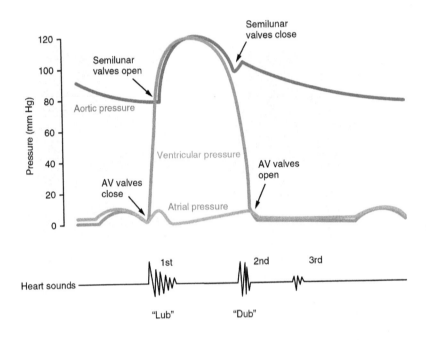

Figure 9-10 Pressure changes during the cardiac cycle.

The heart-cardiac cells and conduction

The heart wall is arranged in three layers: the pericardium (outermost layer consisting of the sac that encases the heart), the myocardium (the thickest layer that is made of cardiac muscle cells), and the endocardium (the thin inner lining that houses the cardiac conduction system). Cardiac muscle cells can be categorized into two main groups: myocardial contractile cells and myocardial conducting cells. The vast majority of cells in the atria and ventricles are the contractile type. These can both transmit impulses and generate the contractions that drive the pumping action of the heart. The *conducting cells* are a specialized type of cardiac muscle cell with a function similar to that of neurons. They generate and transmit action potentials that consistently initiate the synchronized atrial and ventricular contractions of the cardiac cycle. The myocardial conducting cells comprise the heart's conduction system, which produces the stereotypical pattern of electrical activity in the heart that generates the normal contraction. The cardiac conduction system of the heart is composed of the sinoatrial (SA) node, the atrioventricular (AV) node, the atrioventricular bundle (Bundle of His), the atrioventricular bundle branches, and the Purkinje cells. Thus, the mammalian heart is classified as myogenic (or auto-rhythmic), which indicates that contractions are initiated within the heart at regular intervals.

In the heart, action potentials are initiated by the spontaneous depolarization of pacemaker cells in the SA node located in the upper region of the right atrium. The SA node functions as a pacemaker, generating the sinus rhythm, or the normal pattern of impulses that trigger heart contraction. Pacemaker cells are electrically excitable cells, with a specialized plasma membrane possessing numerous Na+, K+, and Ca^{2+} channels. The conductance of ions in the cells of the SA node to generate the action potential differs somewhat from that of the action potential of a skeletal muscle cell or neuron.

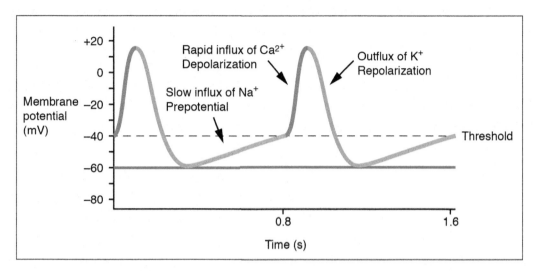

Figure 9-11 The action potential in the pacemaker cells of the SA node.

In the cells of the SA node, the rise in membrane potential toward threshold (or the depolarization) is initially due to a gradual decline in permeability to potassium ions, slowing the outflow of K+ and the slow influx of sodium ions. P_F represents the permeability of the so-called "funny channels". These channels are open at a low membrane potential and subsequently close as the membrane potential rises. These particularly unusual channels allow passage of a mixed current of both Na+ and K+ ions. As the funny channels close, transient Ca^{2+} (T-type Ca^{2+} channels) open, bringing positive charges into the cell and further contributing to depolarization. Thus the initial, gradual rise in membrane potential is due to the continuous decrease in permeability to potassium (diminished outward flow of K+). The first portion of this depolarization is due to an influx of sodium, and the later part is due to an influx of calcium (via transient, T -type Ca^{2+} channels). Once threshold is achieved, of the action potential is due to calcium flowing in through the long-lasting, or L type, calcium channels (also called slow Ca^{2+} channels). Note that these two types of voltage gated calcium channels play essential roles in this unique action potential. The L-type channels act in response to higher membrane potentials, open more gradually, and persist in the open state longer than T type channels. Thus, the T type channels are important for the initiation of action potentials, while the L-type channels are essential for sustaining the action potential. The repolarization is due to potassium channels opening and K+ ions flowing out of the cell.

The action potential generated in the SA nodes spreads through the atria via internodal pathways to the atrial cardiac muscle cells (cardiomyoytes) en route to the AV node. Recall that intercalated disks (which are found within the gap junctions that adjoin cardiac muscle cells) facilitate the flow of Na+, K+, and Ca^{2+} ions between adjacent cells, thereby propagating the action potential and providing for co-ordinated contractions. The cardiac muscle cells also have a unique action potential with characteristics that are quite different from both the action potentials generated in the pacemaker cells of the SA node, neurons, and skeletal muscle cells.

In the cardiac muscle cell action potential, the sudden rise to the peak of the action potential is due to the rapid opening of sodium channels and the resulting influx of Na+ ions. The next segment, the plateau phase, is a recognizable characteristic of the cardiac muscle cell action potential. It is primarily caused by the sustained opening of L-type (or slow) Ca^{2+} channels. Subsequent repolarization is due to the opening of K+ channels and the efflux of K+ ions out of the cell. As mentioned previously, the adaptive significance of a sustained action potential is that it creates a long period of time when the muscle cell is refractory to another stimulus. Thus, under normal conditions, tetanus (or a sustained contraction) is not possible. The heart contracts, pumps the blood, and then relaxes to fill its chambers prior to the next contraction. Under normal circumstances, the cardiac cells do not re-excite themselves to cause another AP. Rather, the pacemaker cells in the SA node set the rate of action potential firing and, thus, the normal beating of the heart (also called the sinus rhythm).

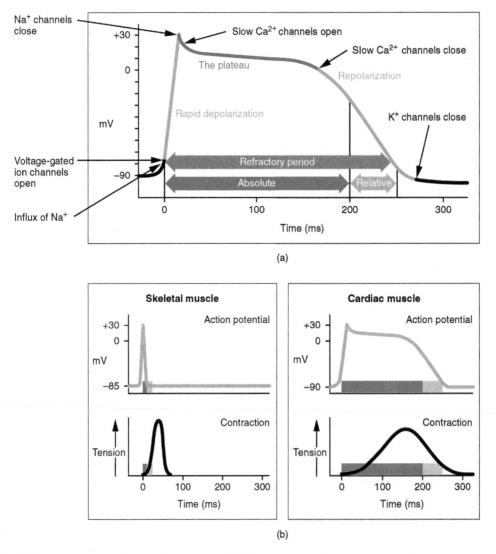

Figure 9-12 (a) The action potential in a cardiac muscle cell. (b) A comparison of an action potential in a skeletal muscle cell and a cardiac muscle cell.

APs that have been generated in the SA node and have spread rapidly through the atria next reach the AV node, which is located near the junction between the right atrium and ventricle, and provides an electrical conduit for the impulse to travel from the atrium to the ventricle. Transmission through the AV node slows due to the small diameter of the conducting fibers in this region. Impulses are then transmitted to the larger conducting fibers, the Bundle of His, which splits into left and right bundle branches, rapidly conducting the action potentials the Purkinje fibers. The Purkinje fibers quickly spread the electrical signal throughout the ventricles causing ventricular contraction.

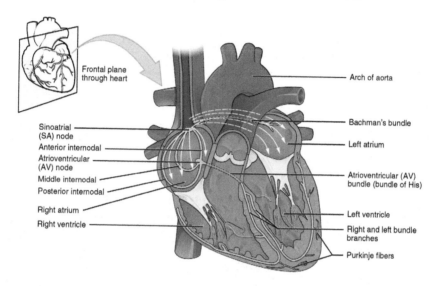

Figure 9-13 The conduction system of the heart.

The electrocardiogram (EKG or ECG) provides a standard graph that illustrates the location of the electrical activity of the heart during the cardiac cycle. To generate an electrocardiogram, electrodes are placed on the surface of the body to measure and transmit electrical signals to a device that produces a graph of the activity.

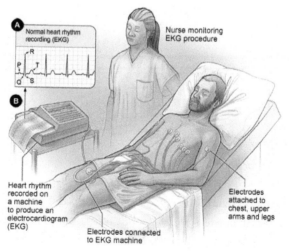

Figure 9-14 A An electrocardiogram.

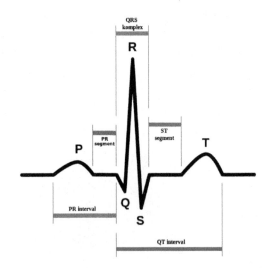

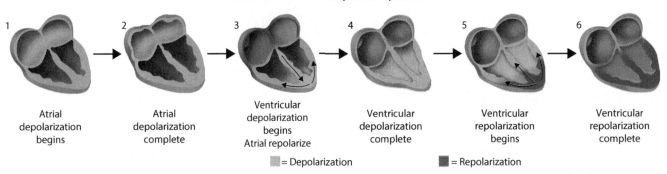

ECG and electrical activity of the myocardium

1	2	3	4	5	6
Atrial depolarization begins	Atrial depolarization complete	Ventricular depolarization begins Atrial repolarize	Ventricular depolarization complete	Ventricular repolarization begins	Ventricular repolarization complete

= Depolarization   = Repolarization

Connection between ECG and electrical activity of the myocardium, eps8

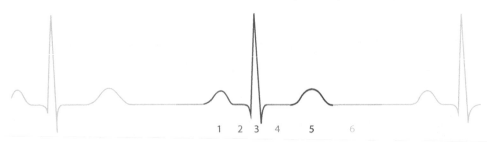

Figure 9-14B   Location of electrical current during an EKG.

Figure 9-14C   The standard read-out for a normal EKG.

During the P wave, the depolarization is spreading through the atria following the initiation of APs generated in the SA node. The atria will repolarize, but this is not apparent on the graph as it is masked by the rapid spread of the excitation and the resulting ventricular depolarization. As the depolarization moves from the atria to the ventricles, it is delayed at the AV node, which allows the atria to contract, emptying as much blood as possible into the ventricles prior to their contraction. Much of the PR segment is representative of the slowing of the impulse at the AV node. The excitation then spreads very rapidly via the right and left bundle branches to the Purkinje fibers, which are composed of specialized cells localized in the ventricular walls that can quickly and efficiently conduct action potentials to the ventricular cardiac muscle cells, stimulating them to contract. On the EKG, the spread of the excitation through the ventricles is represented by the QRS complex. The peak of the QRS wave is high due to the large amount of current flowing in the ventricles. It is also of short duration, due to its rapid transmission. Ventricular repolarization occurs next, as indicated by the T wave. The figure below illustrates the correspondence between the electrical conductivity of the heart as represented on an EKG and the cardiac cycle.

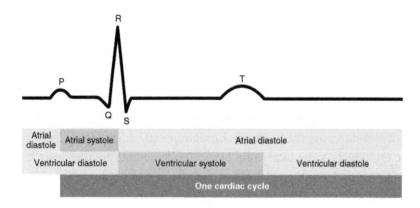

Figure 9-15 *Correspondence between the electrical conductivity of the heart (as indicated by the EKG) and the cardiac cycle.*

The heart

What factors affect contraction strength and heart rate?

A feature that influences the strength of the heart contraction is the amount of stretch (contractility) of the cardiac tissue. During normal heartbeats, the sarcomeres in cardiac muscle are not at their optimal length. An increase in the volume of the blood filling the heart (known as the end diastolic volume) will stretch the walls of the ventricles. The degree of increased stretch in the ventricular walls is termed the preload. An increased preload results in a more powerful contraction of the cardiac muscle, which in turn, increases the stroke volume (SV). The SV is defined as the amount of blood ejected per beat from the left ventricle. It is equivalent to the volume of blood in the ventricle at the end of the filling phase (end diastolic volume, or EDV) minus the volume of the blood left in the ventricle after the contraction (end systolic volume, or ESV). Thus: SV=EDV-ESV. This process, by which the stroke volume rises in response to an increase in the end diastolic volume, is referred to as the Frank-Starling mechanism of the heart. A representation of the Frank-Starling curve is shown in Figure 9-16. It indicates that for a given volume of blood that returns to the heart (select a point on x axis; note, this is also represented as the left ventricle end diastolic pressure, or LVEDP), the stroke volume will be greater when the heart muscle contractility is increased.

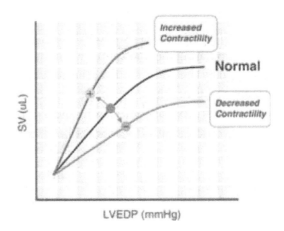

Figure 9-16 The Frank-Starling Curve.

By increasing the venous return and stretching the heart muscle, the force of the heart contraction and the amount of blood leaving the heart can be significantly augmented. This, in turn, increases the cardiac output (CO), which is the total volume of blood pumped by the heart in 1 minute. It is the product of the SV (measured as ml/ beat) and heart rate (HR, beats/minute), or CO=SVxHR. Increasing the amount of blood leaving the heart per beat (SV) and/or increasing the number of beats per minute (heartbeat) will increase the cardiac output. Exercise also results in an increase in cardiac output. During exercise, venous return to the heart increases, increasing the preload. This is because exercise causes blood vessels to dilate in order to bring more nutrients and oxygen to active skeletal muscles. Additionally, contracting skeletal muscles compress veins, increasing blood flow to the heart.

In contrast to the preload, the term "afterload" refers to the amount of pressure needed in the ventricles to surmount the aortic and pulmonary pressure and, thus, propel blood into the aorta and lungs. Because the pressure in the ventricles must be greater than the systemic and pulmonary pressure to initiate the opening the semilunar valves, illnesses such as hypertension (high blood pressure) cause increased afterload. When afterload increases, there is a corresponding increase in ESV, which in turn, decreases SV and cardiac output.

The heart - sympathetic and parasympathetic stimulation

The force of the contraction of the heart can also be affected by sympathetic and parasympathetic activity. The nerves that conduct impulses to the heart regulate (but do not generate) the rate of the heartbeat. Parasympathetic and sympathetic nerve fibers influence the pumping action of the heart by affecting both the heart rate and stroke volume. This regulation is necessary to maintain homeostasis with regard to blood pressure, blood O_2 and CO_2 levels, and blood pH. For example, baroreceptors are sensory receptors found in such locations as the walls of the aorta, atria, and carotid artery. They are sensitive to stretch in the walls of these vessels, which is indicative of blood pressure changes. Chemoreceptors in the carotid body are sensitive to changes in the constitution of arterial blood and can detect variations in the partial pressure of O_2 and CO_2, as well as changes in pH. Information from the baroreceptors and chemoreceptors is transmitted to the cardioregulatory center in the medulla oblongata of the brainstem.

The cardioregulatory center controls the action potential frequency in both parasympathetic and sympathetic nerves to the heart. The vagus nerve carries parasympathetic neuronal fibers to the heart and innervates the SA node and atrial muscle. Parasympathetic nerve stimulation has an inhibitory effect, resulting in a reduced heart rate. Parasympathetic neurons release the neurotransmitter acetylcholine (ACh). ACh binds to muscarinic receptors on the sinoatrial node cellular membrane causing an efflux of K+ and decreased permeability to Na+ and Ca^{2+}. This collectively hyperpolarizes the cell, slowing depolarization and increasing the amount of time needed to reach threshold, generate an AP and stimulate a contraction, thereby decreasing heart rate. Parasympathetic nerves also decrease the contractility of the cardiac cells in the atria, but have no significant effect on ventricular contraction. Sympathetic stimulation to the heart includes the release the neurotransmitter norepinephrine from nerves that directly innervate cardiac cells, thereby increasing heart rate, contractility, and stroke volume. Sympathetic stimulation also triggers the secretion of epinephrine (also known as adrenaline) from the adrenal gland into the general circulation. Norepinephrine and epinephrine bind to β adrenergic receptors on the cardiac cell membrane, which increases permeability to Na+ and Ca^{2+}, increasing the rate of depolarization and thus the velocity of the contraction.

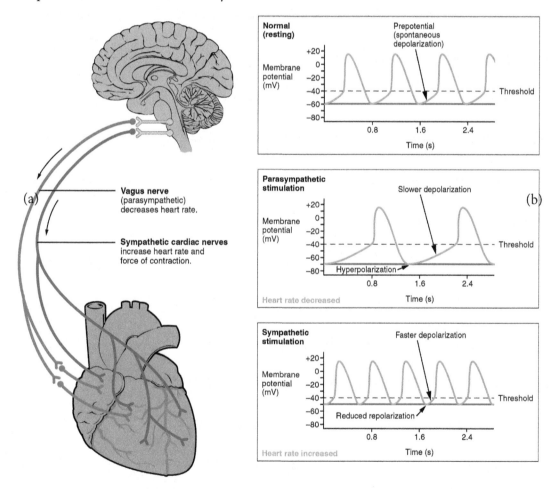

Figure 9-17A Autonomic innervation to the heart.

Figure 9-17B The effects of parasympathetic and sympathetic stimulation on action potentials in the heart.

Sympathetic stimulation to the heart also increases the force of heart muscle contraction (contractility). Activation of β adrenergic receptors on cardiac muscle cells causes G-protein-mediated synthesis and accumulation of cAMP, resulting in activation of cAMP-dependent protein kinase. This process not only assists in the opening Na+ and Ca^{2+} channels (increasing the cell's ability to depolarize), but also affects ryanodine receptors on the sarcoplasmic reticulum, facilitating Ca²⁺ release. Additionally, activation of cAMP-dependent protein kinase enhances the interaction of troponin and Ca²⁺, facilitating thin filament activation and improving cross-bridge cycling. It also facilitates the reuptake of calcium into the sarcoplasmic reticulum.

Improving the various steps involved in generating a muscle contraction enables the entire muscle contraction and relaxation process to occur more rapidly and, thus, generate more heartbeats per unit time. It also increases the contractility of the cardiac muscle. Therefore, for a given amount of blood in the heart (i.e., ventricular end diastolic volume), more of the blood that is present will be pumped out as a result of sympathetic stimulation.

In addition to sympathetic and parasympathetic stimulation, there are numerous factors that can affect stroke volume, heart rate, and cardiac output. The figures below concisely summarize many of these factors.

	Factors Affecting Stroke Volume (SV)		
	Preload	**Contractility**	**Afterload**
Raised due to:	• fast filling time • increased venous return **Increases end diastolic volume,** Increases stroke volume	• sympathetic stimulation • epinephrine and norepinephrine • high intracellular calcium ions • high blood calcium level • thyroid hormones • glucagon **Decreases end systolic volume,** Increases stroke volume	• increased vascular restistance • semilunar valve damage **Increases end systolic volume** Decreases stroke volume
Lowered due to:	• decreased thyroid hormones • decreased calcium ions • high or low potassium ions • high or low sodium • low body temperature • hypoxia • abnormal pH balance • drugs (i.e., calcium channel blockers) **Decreases end diastolic volume,** Decreases stroke volume	• parasympathetic stimulation • acetylcholine • hypoxia • hyperkalemia **Increases end systolic volume** Decreases stroke volume	• decreased vascular resistance **Decreases end systolic volume** Increases stroke volume

Figure 9-18 Factors affecting stroke volume.

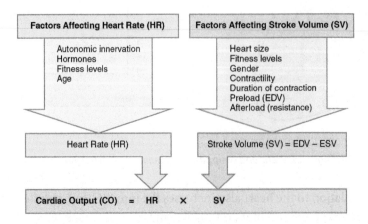

Figure 9-19 Factors affecting cardiac output.

Circulation

For optimal function, the circulatory system includes two distinct components: the systemic system and the pulmonary system. Although the volume of the blood should be relatively complementary in the two systems (otherwise blood would pool in one or the other), the pressures can be different.

This is essential, for exceedingly high pulmonary pressures could cause fluid leakage in the lungs. However, higher pressures in the systemic circuit are necessary for the sustained blood flow needed to maintain physiological activity. The pressure in the arteries is pulsatile. On the upward rise of each pulse, the heart is contracting, and on the slope down, the heart is relaxing. Note that in the arteries, the pressure remains above zero, even during relaxation.

The design of the circulatory system enables its proper function. Large diameter vessels are utilized for bulk transport over greater distances. The fluid flow is equal to the change in pressure divided by the resistance (or $F=\Delta P/R$). When the heart beats, a much higher pressure is generated at the large diameter aorta than at distant vessels (because the aorta is nearest to the forceful contraction of the ventricle). This difference accounts for the ΔP in the equation above. The resistance is influenced by the length and diameter of the vessel, as well as the viscosity of the blood. The equation for resistance is given by $R= 8L\eta/\pi r^4$, where L is the length of the vessel, η is the fluid viscosity, and r is the inside radius of the vessel. With regard to these relationships ($F=\Delta P/R$ and $R= 8L\eta/\pi r^4$), changing the radius of blood vessel (via dilation or constriction) has a dramatic effect on blood flow. Consider, for example the increase in flow (which would correspond to a factor of 16) when the radius is only increased by a factor of 2.

The blood vessels of the circulatory system include the arteries, arterioles, capillaries, veins, and venules, each having their own qualities. The arteries carry blood away from the heart. They are thick walled to withstand high pressure and stretch in response to increases in pressure generated immediately after a heartbeat. While the heart is relaxing, arterial walls rebound, giving blood an extra push to maintain blood flow. Arteries have relatively large diameters and low resistance to flow, enabling rapid, bulk movement of blood. Arterioles are the smaller branches of arteries that deliver blood to capillaries. Capillaries have thin walls made from a single layer of endothelial cells, providing short distances for the diffusion and exchange of substances such as O_2, CO_2, ions, and nutrients with the interstitial fluid. The branching of capillaries from arterioles results in a large surface area at the site of exchange. The flow rate of blood through capillary beds is adjusted by precapillary sphincters, or bands of smooth muscle at the arteriole end of capillaries that can constrict to obstruct flow, or relax to permit flow, into a capillary.

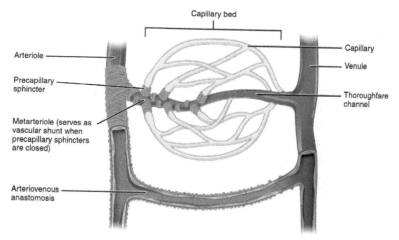

Figure 9-20 A capillary bed.

The regulation of blood flow at the capillary bed allows for the optimization of the time allotted for the exchange of substances between blood and tissues and, as such, is considered a major mechanism driving the exchange of substances. Diffusion down concentration gradients is another critical factor for the productive exchange of substances. Materials are exchanged by various means. O_2 and CO_2 can move from the capillary lumen and readily diffuse across the endothelial cell membrane. Polar substances move through fused vesicle channels in endothelial cell membranes. Water soluble substances diffuse through intercellular clefts between the endothelial cells of the capillary wall. At the arteriole end of a capillary bed, pressure of the blood is higher than the pressure of the interstitial fluid. This hydrostatic pressure difference results in water and very small solutes being forced out of the capillaries. At the venous end of the capillary bed, the hydrostatic pressure in the blood has dropped considerably, creating a net force that draws fluid back into the blood. This mechanism allows for the continuous distribution of fluid between the blood and interstitial fluid at the site of exchange in the capillary bed.

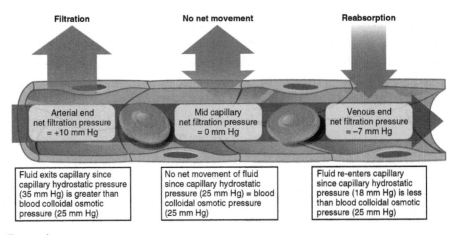

Figure 9-21 Capillary exchange.

Venules are small blood vessels that collect blood from the capillary bed, depositing it into the larger veins, which return blood to the heart. The walls of veins are thinner than arterial walls, but are still able to expand and contract in response to blood volume.

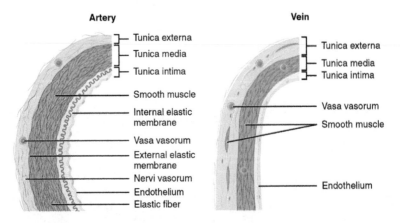

Figure 9-22 Comparison of an artery and a vein.

Unlike arteries, veins have one-way valves to prevent blood from flowing in reverse. In veins that run through skeletal muscle, contraction of the skeletal muscle compress the veins, creating pressure to increase the flow back to the heart. This mechanism is often referred to as the skeletal muscle vein pump.

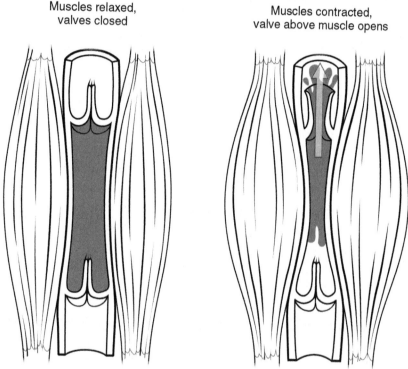

Muscles relaxed,
valves closed

Muscles contracted,
valve above muscle opens

Figure 9-23 The skeletal muscle vein pump.

Contractions of the smooth muscles in the walls of veins will decrease the diameter of the vein, creating additional pressure and aiding in the movement of blood. Note that vasoconstriction in arteries reduces the forward flow of blood through the systemic circuit, whereas the vasoconstriction of veins increases forward flow (driving more blood back to the heart), increasing circulation. Furthermore, veins act as blood reservoirs, as well as conduits. At rest, the venous system holds about 65% of the circulating blood. Constriction of peripheral veins can direct blood flow to the central veins that return blood to the heart, thereby increasing end diastolic volume. The veins also collect excess interstitial fluid that has been acquired by the lymphatic system. Normally, not all the fluid from the tissues can be reabsorbed into the blood plasma. The vessels of the lymphatic system, which extend throughout most of the body, collect excess interstitial fluid and transport it to lymph ducts that empty into veins.

Local and central control of circulation

Arterioles respond to both local and central (or extrinsic) signals to regulate blood flow in response to physiological changes. Local controls meet the needs of a particular tissue, such as an active muscle, whereas central control systems are essential for the needs of the whole body, such as maintaining systemic blood pressure. Two examples of local control include active hyperemia and flow auto-regulation. Active hyperemia is the increased blood flow to active tissues due to vasodilation. The increased metabolic activity of the tissue causes a decrease in O_2 and pH levels, an increase in metabolites (such as CO_2), and a temperature increase. Some of the metabolites (such as CO_2, H+, and lactate) function as vasodilators, expanding local arterioles thereby increasing the blood supply to the active tissue. Flow autoregulation is a response to a drop pressure in the arterioles to a particular organ or tissue that restores normal blood flow. For example, if an arteriole to an organ is partially occluded, blood flow and local pressure initially decrease (recall $F=\Delta P/R$). Low blood flow results in a relative decrease in O_2 and increase in metabolites that trigger vasodilation in the organ's arterioles. The dilation restores normal blood flow to the organ. Organs such as the brain, heart, and kidney have well-developed flow autoregulatory capabilities in comparison to the skeletal muscle, viscera, and skin.

Both active hyperemia and flow autoregulation are deemed "local" responses, as they do not incorporate extrinsic (central) hormonal or neuronal influences. However, there are a number of factors that regulate arteriolar smooth muscle and, thus, affect arteriolar radius. Examples of extrinsic vasoconstrictors include sympathetic nerves that release norepinephrine and the hormones angiotensin II and vasopressin. Vasodilators include neurons that release nitric oxide and the hormones: epinephrine and atrial natriuretic peptide. Note that epinephrine can function as both a vasodilator and vasoconstrictor depending on the type of receptor it activates. For example, epinephrine binding to the α_1-andrenergic receptors that are present on smooth muscle of blood vessels in the skin would cause vasoconstriction during the body's flight or fight (sympathetic) response. Interestingly, the pale color of the skin results from this response when an individual is frightened. In contrast, epinephrine binding to β-2 andrenergic receptors results in the dilatation of arteries to skeletal muscles, effectively increasing blood flow to skeletal muscles during the sympathetic response.

The circulatory system must be well regulated for ideal function, thereby enabling the optimal exchange of nutrients, wastes, and gases. In particular, to facilitate the appropriate exchange of oxygen and carbon dioxide with the body tissues and the lungs, the functioning of the circulatory system must be well aligned with the functioning of the respiratory system, which is the focus of the next chapter.

Chapter 9 Review

I. Helpful and Interesting Animations:

1. Action potentials and contraction in cardiac cells:
   http://www.youtube.com/watch?v=DSDf_dbWy_I
2. Heart contraction and blood flow:
   http://www.nhlbi.nih.gov/health/health-topics/topics/hhw/contraction.html
3. The heart electrical system:
   http://www.nhlbi.nih.gov/health/health-topics/topics/hhw/electrical.html
4. The ECG:
   http://www.youtube.com/watch?v=v3b-YhZmQu8
5. How a heart attack occurs:
   http://www.hhmi.org/biointeractive/how-heart-attack-occurs

II. Active Testing: Do you know the facts?

A. List the words in this chapter you would have printed in bold type.
Can you define these words?

B. What are the main, "take home" messages of this chapter?
 Is your answer the same as your instructor's answer?

C. Some Questions:

1. Distinguish between an open and closed circulatory system. List the benefits of each.

2. List 4 components of blood.

3. Name 3 plasma proteins and describe their function.

4. Draw and label a diagram of the human heart, indicating the direction of blood flow and the oxygenated and deoxygenated blood.

5. With regard to blood vessels, explain the relationship between flow, pressure, and resistance; and resistance, length and radius.

6. What would be the effect on fluid flow if the radius of a blood vessel was increased by a factor of 3?

7. During the cardiac cycle, what is defined as the period when the atria are contracting, the ventricles are relaxing and filling, and the blood pressure in the arteries falls to a minimum pressure?

8. Define stroke volume and cardiac output and describe the relationship between them.

9. Describe the Frank Starling mechanism.

10. Give an example of parasympathetic and sympathetic influence on the heart.

11. Define the terms: neurogenic and myogenic. Which term relates to mammals?

12. Describe the unique electrical properties if cardiac muscle and their relevance to the cardiac conduction cycle.

13. Draw and label a diagram describing the path of electrical potential through the heart.

14. Draw and label a graphical representation of the action potential in the SA node. Describe the conductance of ions in relationship to the graph. Next, draw and label a graphical representation of the action potential in the cardiac muscle. Describe the conductance of ions in relationship to the graph.

15. Draw and label 2 graphs that describe: the action potential in relation to the muscle contraction in skeletal muscle, and the action potential in relation to the muscle contraction in cardiac muscle. What is the adaptive significance of the longer action potential in cardiac muscle?

16. Draw, label and explain an EKG diagram.

17. Draw, label and explain an illustration depicting the pressure (in mmHg) in the pulmonary and systemic circulation as it relates to the body's blood vessels (i.e., arteries, arterioles, capillaries, venules, and veins)

18. Name a structure found in capillaries. Name a structure found in veins. What are their purposes?

19. Finish this sentence: Blood moves through veins in response to _____.

20. Define and differentiate between local and central control of blood vessels.

III. Inquiring minds want to know…

Challenge Questions

1. What is an arrhythmia? Describe the EKG recording and explain the underlying abnormalities of the following arrhythmias: atrial fibrillation, supraventricular tachycardia, first degree heart block, and premature ventricular complex.

2. Previously, cardiovascular and related non-communicable diseases were thought to be a primary health care problem only in affluent, industrialized nations. It has recently been reported that these diseases now rank as the number one cause of death globally, with more than 80% occurring in low and middle-income countries [Fuster, V. et. Al. (2014)]. In addition to the profound effect on human health, cardiovascular related illnesses, such as heart attack, stroke, diabetes etc., have a far-reaching economic impact, affecting not only individuals, but also straining the finances of nations. The U.S. Institute of Medicine (http://www.iom.edu/) has issued a report entitled: "Promoting Cardiovascular Health Worldwide" that details tangible recommendations to address this serious global health care problem. What are these recommendations? Do you think the goals outlined in the report are attainable?

Reference

Fuster, V., Narula, J., Vedanthan, R., & Kelly, B. (Eds.).(2014). Promoting cardiovascular health worldwide: Perspective on the 12 Recommendations of The Institute of Medicine. [Special Issue]. *Scientific American.* Retrieved from http://www.scientificamerican.com/products/cardiovascular-health/

Chapter 10

Gas Exchange

The Respiratory System

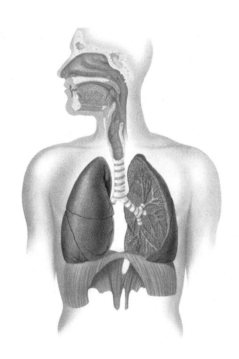

Figure 10-1 The respiratory system.

Why do we need to exchange gases, and how is it accomplished?

Physiological respiration, that is, the exchange of oxygen and carbon dioxide from a respiratory medium (such as air or water) with a respiratory surface (such as lungs, gills, or the body surface) is essential for cellular respiration and the generation of ATP, as molecular oxygen plays a primary role as an electron acceptor in this vital process. Common features of respiratory surfaces enable the respiration process to function efficiently. These include a surface area that is large (to maximize the quantity of diffused gases), thin (short diffusion distances), and moist (gases must be dissolved in interstitial fluid for intercellular transport). Features such as these increase the total amount of gas that can be exchanged by the process of simple diffusion, in which molecules move from regions of higher concentration to regions of lower concentration. Ventilation and perfusion are two primary processes of respiration that incorporate these features. Ventilation is the flow of the respiratory medium (air, water) over the external side of the respiratory surface. Perfusion is the flow of blood or other body fluids on the internal side of the respiratory surface.

The unique design of respiratory systems facilitate their specialized function. For example, moisture is added to inhaled air in the mouth and nasal passages, and lungs are often invaginated (like pockets) to prevent them from drying out. In animals who reside in aquatic habitats, respiratory surfaces are wetted by direct exposure to the environment. However, in comparison to air-breathers, a significant expenditure of energy is required by water-breathers to keep respiratory surfaces ventilated due to the high density and viscosity of water and the relatively low O_2 content. Additionally, as temperature and the amount of solute (i.e., in sea water) increases, the amount of gas that can dissolve in water decreases, which is a distinct disadvantage to water-breathers. Because air has a high O_2 content and low viscosity, the diffusion rate of gas molecules through air is significantly greater than through water. However, air-breathers are disadvantaged in that, during respiration, water is constantly being evaporated.

Many water breathers have gills that are uniquely adapted for efficient gas exchange by employing a counter-current exchange mechanism. In animals such as sharks, bony fishes, and some crabs, water moves in a one-way direction over the gills, which maximizes the exchange of gases over the respiratory surface because, at any point along the gill filament, the water is significantly more oxygenated than the blood, thereby maintaining a substantial concentration gradient.

The counter current exchange mechanism in the gills of fish results in removal of approximately 80% to 90% of the O_2 content of water as it flows over the gills. In comparison, mammals remove ~25% of the O_2 content of air. However, air has a much higher concentration of O_2 and a lower density and viscosity than water. This enables air-breathers to ventilate respiratory surfaces with relatively little energy and to maintain higher metabolic levels than water-breathers. Many insects have very high energy demands to facilitate flight and rapid terrestrial movement. In insects such as these, air-conducting tubes (trachea) lead from the body surface openings (spiracles) and branch to all body cells. Gas exchange takes place in fluid-filled tips (tracheoles) at the ends of branches. Insects ventilate their tracheal system by periodic body movements, such as alternating contraction and relaxation of flight muscles. This movement compresses and expands body structures, pumping air through the trachea. Insect flight muscles contain large amounts of mitochondria, which generate ATP when supplied with oxygen from the air.

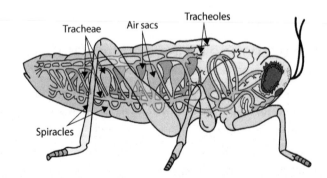

Figure 10-2 The insect gas exchange system.

Likewise, many birds also have high energy demands to facilitate flight, and utilize a well-designed respiratory system that incorporates both a continuous flow mechanism and the counter-current exchange of gases with blood.

The lungs are superbly adapted for the respiratory process. Ventilation of the lungs occurs primarily by one of two mechanisms: positive pressure breathing or negative pressure breathing. In positive pressure breathing, air is forced (or pushed) into the lungs by muscle contractions. For example, when on land, frogs utilize positive pressure breathing by using local muscles to lower the floor of their oral cavity as they draw air in through their mouth or nostrils (which causes their throat to puff out). Keeping their mouth and nostrils closed, they then elevate the floor of their mouth, which forces air into their trachea, bronchi, and lungs. Animals such as reptiles and mammals use a negative pressure mechanism of breathing. In this mechanism, air is pulled into the lungs. As respiratory muscles contract to expand the lungs during inhalation, the air pressure inside the lungs becomes lower relative to the pressure of the air taken into the mouth, trachea and, bronchi. This results in a negative pressure that causes air to be drawn into the lungs. Humans are negative pressure breathers with an extremely well adapted respiratory system. Let us now explore the highly functional design of the human respiratory system and the overall process of physiological respiration.

The human respiratory system - design and functioning

Air enters the respiratory system by way of the nose and mouth, where it gains hydration, is filtered, and is warmed. It next travels through the pharynx (the throat region), larynx ("voice box"), and trachea ("windpipe"). The trachea separates into two bronchi that further branch in each lung. The larynx, trachea, and large bronchi are non-muscular tubes that are supported by rings of cartilage that encircle them. The bronchi have cilia and specialized mucus secreting cells. Mucus functions to entrap substances such as dust, pollen, and bacteria. The cilia serve to propel unwanted material to the throat where it can be expelled. Smaller bronchi and brochioles contain smooth muscle cells that can control their diameter and regulate air flow. In general, very little resistance to flow is encountered in the airways of the respiratory system.

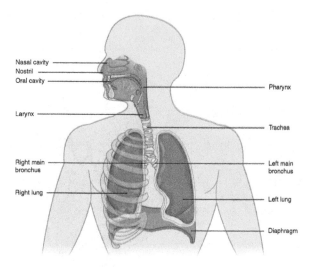

Figure 10-3A The major respiratory organs.

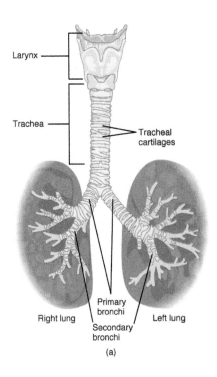

Figure 10-3B Airways in the respiratory system.

Within the lungs, the bronchi branch into bronchioles, which connect to alveoli (air sacs) surrounded by networks of blood vessels (i.e., pulmonary capillaries). The numerous alveoli (air sacs) that are enveloped by the blood vessels comprise the respiratory surface. The invaginated lungs help to maintain the water saturation of the air before it reaches the respiratory surface. This greatly reduces water loss by evaporation.

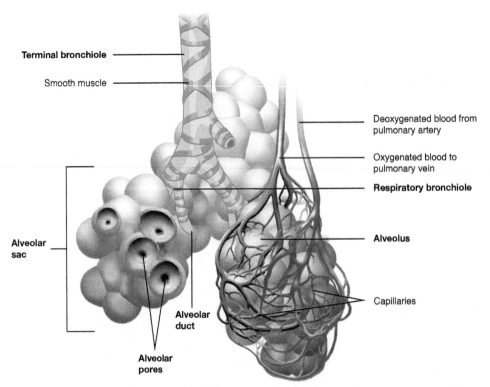

Figure 10-4 The alveoli.

A double-layered membrane of epithelial tissue, known as the pleura, encases and separates the lungs from the wall of the thoracic cavity. The inner pleural membrane layer is termed the visceral layer, and is adjacent to the lung surface. The outer layer (parietal) is in contact with the surface of the chest cavity (or the thoracic wall). The intrapleural space is a fluid-filled area between the visceral and parietal layers that reduces abrasion when the lungs expand and contract, because the two layers can slide past each other. The lower pressure of the intrapleural space relative to the surrounding areas gives rise to a negative pressure, which keeps the lungs in contact with the chest wall.

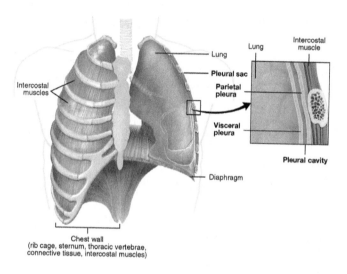

Figure 10-5 The lung pleura.

Contraction and relaxation of the intercostal skeletal muscles that reside between the ribs is necessary to lift the rib cage upward and outward as the lung volume expands during inhalation. The diaphragm (the sheet of skeletal muscle between the abdominal cavity and the chest cavity) must also contract, but as it contracts, it moves downward to accommodate lung expansion during inhalation.

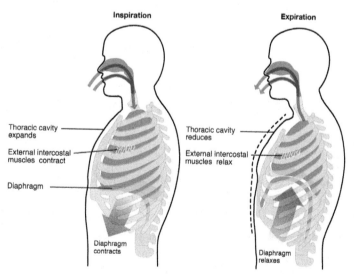

Figure 10-6 Inspiration and expiration

The lungs are naturally elastic and will recoil upon exhalation. Healthy lungs are also described as compliant, meaning they have the ability to stretch. The stretched lungs store potential energy that is released when air is expelled. During normal breathing at rest, air is exhaled passively; the diaphragm and the external intercostal muscles between the ribs relax and the lungs naturally recoil. However, during deep and rapid breathing, the forceful expulsion of air from the lungs is driven primarily by the contraction of the internal intercostal muscles.

Pressure changes during lung ventilation

Air flows in response to differences in air pressure. The ideal gas law describes the condition of a gas by taking into consideration such parameters as pressure, volume, and temperature. Mathematically, it is described as PV=nRT, where P=pressure, V=volume, n=number of molecules of a gas, R=universal gas constant (1.987 cal/K-mol), and T=temperature. Another way to express the Ideal Gas Law is P=nRT/V. Thus, at a constant T, the pressure of a gas is inversely proportional to its volume. This is referred to as Boyle's Law and is expressed as PV=k, meaning that at a constant temperature, the product of the pressure and volume of a gas is a constant. The equation for Boyle's Law can be expressed in a different form in order to compare the same substance under alternative conditions of pressure and volume: $P_1V_1 = P_2V_2$. Thus, in a given system, a decrease in volume will result in an increase in pressure, and an increase in volume will result in a decrease in pressure.

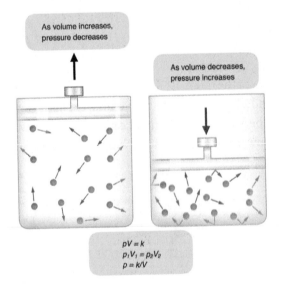

Figure 10-7 Boyle's law.

The significance of Boyle's law for respiratory physiology is that air flows from areas of higher pressure to areas of lower pressure. Ventilation refers to the exchange of air between the atmosphere and alveoli in the lungs. During ventilation, air moves into and out of the lungs, because the alveolar pressure is alternatively less than and greater than the atmospheric pressure. Air flow is given by the mathematical equation:

$$F = \frac{\Delta P}{R} = \frac{Palv - Patm}{R}$$

Where F=flow, R=resistance, Palv=alveolar pressure, Patm=atmospheric pressure. When the pressure in the alveoli is less than the atmospheric pressure, air will flow into lungs (inspiration). When the pressure in the alveoli is greater than the atmospheric pressure, air will flow out of lungs (expiration). In general, ventilation can be summarized by the following. During inhalation, the diaphragm contracts and moves downward, and the rib cage expands. This leads to an increase in lung volume, which brings about a decrease in alveolar pressure in comparison to the air pressure in the airways (which is equivalent to atmospheric pressure). Because air flows from areas of higher pressure to areas of lower pressure, air is drawn into the lungs. During exhalation, the diaphragm relaxes and moves upward, and the rib cage retracts, resulting in a decrease in lung volume and increase in pressure, causing air to be expelled.

Pressure changes during ventilation are well understood, and can be described more specifically, taking into account precise changes in alveolar pressure (Palv), transpulmonary pressure (Ptp), and intra-pleural pressure (Pip). Transpulmonary pressure refers to the difference in pressure between the inside and outside of lungs. Mathematically, it can be expressed as: Ptp= Palv-Pip. Alveolar pressure is the pressure in the alveoli. Intra-pleural pressure is the pressure in the pleural space, which holds the lungs open and opposes the natural elastic recoil inward of the lungs. The atmospheric pressure is the pressure in the nose, mouth, and airways. Under normal conditions the transpulmonary pressure is positive, intrapleural pressure is negative, and alveolar pressure alternates between a negative pressure and a positive pressure as a person breathes. Figure 10-8 illustrates the pressure changes that occur during ventilation.

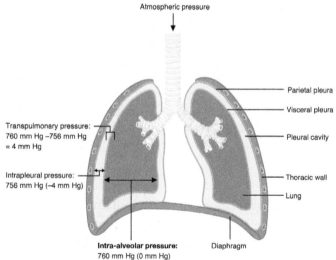

Figure 10-8 Pressures in the lungs.

The lungs always have air in them, but for an instant at the end of an expiration, before the next inspiration begins, there is no air flow; thus, Palv-Patm=0 and the alveolar pressure (Palv)=atmospheric pressure (Patm). Because the lungs always have air in them, the transpulmonary pressure is positive. Due to the equation Ptp=Palv-Pip, it follows that the pressure in the pleural space (Pip, or intrapleural pressure) must be negative. This negative intra pleural pressure helps to "hold" the lungs open, keeping them partially expanded. Initially, there is no air flow at the instant between breaths. Here, the alveolar pressure is equal to the atmospheric pressure at 0, and the intrapleural pressure is negative. The transpulmonary pressure is Ptp=Palv-Pip 0 − [-4]= 4mmHg. As a breath is taken, the chest wall expands, thereby lowering the Pip, which expands the lungs and increases their volume. The Palv drops, becoming less than the Patm, which draws air into the lungs. At mid-cycle (i.e., the peak of an inhalation), there is an instant where the net air flow is 0 (Palv=Patm). At this point, the chest wall is no longer expanding, but it has not yet begun to contract. The lung size is not changing and the epiglottis is open to the atmosphere. Due to the expansion of the chest wall (and corresponding increase in volume) at the end of inspiration (mid-cycle), the Pip has dropped from -4 to -7 mmHg. Expiration now begins as the respiratory muscles relax, the chest wall contracts, and the lungs recoil. The resulting decrease in volume causes an increase in the alveolar pressure to above the atmospheric pressure, and air is expelled. As expiration continues, the intrapleural pressure returns to the -4 mmHg value. In short, during the process of ventilation, the transpulmonary (Ptp) pressure increases to expand the lungs (and the lungs fill with air) by actively decreasing the pressure surrounding the lungs (or the Pip, intrapleural pressure) relative to the pressure inside the lungs (or the Palv, alveolar pressure). Further, if the transpulmonary pressure that normally assists in holding a lung open is disrupted, the lung will collapse. This condition is known as pneumothorax and can result from a number of conditions, including a puncture wound that allows air to enter into the intrapleural space. When atmospheric air rushes in, the intra-pleural pressure rises from its negative value to 0 mmHg, disrupting the normal pressure variations that hold the lung open.

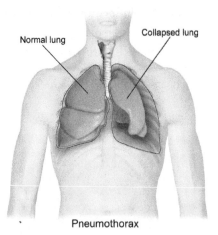

Normal lung

Collapsed lung

Pneumothorax

Figure 10-9 Pneumothorax.

Important parameters of lung ventilation can be assessed using a spirometer, a device that measures the volume and rate of air flow when an individual breathes into it. Some of the major parameters that can be calculated with a spirometer include the tidal volume, vital capacity, residual volume and force expired volume. The tidal volume is the amount of air moved in and out of lungs during an inhalation and exhalation. In healthy individuals at rest, it is ~500 ml. The vital capacity is the total volume of air a person can inhale and exhale by breathing as deeply as possible (maximum male: 4800 ml; female: 3400 ml). The residual volume is the air remaining in the lungs after as much air as possible is exhaled (males: 1200 ml; females: 1000 ml). The force expired volume (FEV) is the maximum amount of air that can be expelled during a forced exhalation. Comparison of these parameters provides valuable information that is used to evaluate pulmonary dysfunction.

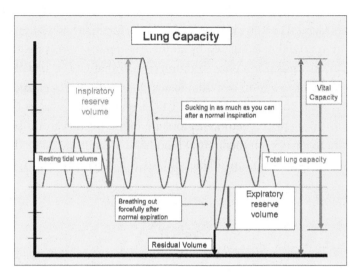

Figure 10-10 Lung capacity.

Spirometry is one of the most common tests to assess asthma, which occurs when airways are constricted due to inflammation. Another widespread lung disease is chronic obstructive pulmonary disease (COPD). Major symptoms of COPD include shortness of breath and a chronic cough with mucous. Emphysema is a type of COPD that occurs when the walls of the alveoli lose their ability to stretch and recoil, eventually weakening and breaking. This disrupts the normal exchange of oxygen and carbon dioxide. Smoking tobacco is a primary cause of emphysema, as toxins found in tobacco products damage the lungs and impair respiration. Complications that affect lung compliance (a measure of the ease of expansion of the lungs) may also occur in premature babies and in individuals with occupations such as coal mining. One determinant of the degree of lung compliance is the "stretchability" of the lungs. Thus, the greater the lung compliance, the easier it is to expand the lungs at any given change in transpulmonary pressure. Lung compliance is also dependent on surface tension, or the attractive forces between water molecules in the layer of fluid that lines the alveoli. Type II pnuemocytes are alveolar cells that produce and secrete surfactant, a mixture containing phospholipid molecules that forms a monolayer over the surface of the water molecules within the alveoli. Surfactant (or "surface acting agent") reduces the cohesive forces between water molecules on the surface of the alveoli, decreasing surface tension, which increases lung compliance. Because sufficient amounts of surfactant are not produced until approximately 35 weeks of gestation, some premature babies suffer from respiratory distress syndrome and need to make a strenuous effort to breathe in order to compensate for reduced lung compliance. Diminished lung compliance in coal miners is often caused by the formation of inelastic scar tissue in the lungs that result from inhalation of coal dust.

How is breathing controlled?

Respiratory control is executed both locally and centrally. For example, if air flow to the lungs is less than capillary blood flow, blood oxygen levels will fall. To compensate, smooth muscles in the walls of lung arterioles will contract, effectively reducing blood flow and allowing more time for oxygen to diffuse into the blood. A local control such as this provides for consistency between ventilation and perfusion rates. Centralized respiratory control centers are composed of distinct groups of cells in the medulla and pons regions of the brainstem. These centers receive and integrate neural signals from central and peripheral chemoreceptors and transmit signals to respiratory muscles to adjust ventilation rates in order to maintain homeostatic conditions. Central chemoreceptors reside in the medulla and respond to changes in the brain extracellular fluid. They are usually stimulated by an increased partial pressure of carbon dioxide (PCO_2) via associated changes in hydrogen ion concentration. Recall that CO_2 is usually stored in the blood as bicarbonate ions due to the dissociation of carbonic acid to bicarbonate ions and H+ ions: $CO_2 + H_2O \Leftrightarrow H_2CO_3 \Leftrightarrow HCO_3^- + H^+$. Thus, the accumulation of CO_2 drives this reaction to the right, resulting in an accumulation of H+. The peripheral chemoreceptors are found in the carotid bodies and aortic bodies. In general, they respond to changes in the arterial blood and are stimulated by decreased PO_2 (hypoxia), increased hydrogen ion concentration (metabolic acidosis), and increased PCO_2 (respiratory acidosis).

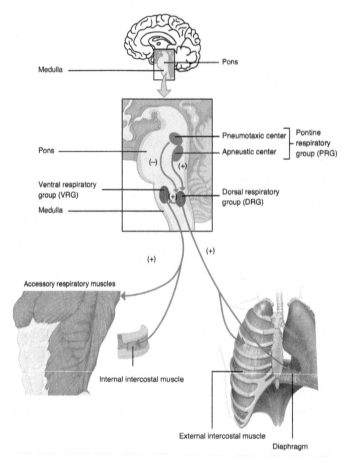

Figure 10-11 Respiratory centers of the brain.

The dorsal respiratory control group (DRG) is located in the medulla, and is primarily involved with inspiration. Neurons of the DRG transmit impulses to spinal motor neurons (specifically, the phrenic and intercostal nerves) that activate muscles involved in inspiration (the diaphragm and the intercostal muscles). Inspiration is initiated by a burst of action potentials in these spinal motor nerves to the inspiratory muscles. When action potentials cease, inspiratory muscles relax, and expiration occurs as the elastic lungs recoil. Neurons of the ventral respiratory group regulate the rhythm of inspiration and expiration. Specialized neurons in the upper part of the ventral respiratory control group (VRG), known as the Pre-Botzinger complex, are believed to comprise the respiratory rhythm generator (which establishes the basic rhythm of respiration). VRG neurons are also involved in augmenting the rate and depth of breathing by stimulating forceful exhalation and by adding to the signals that stimulate inhalation.

This may occur during exercise, when more vigorous respiration is necessary. The pneumotaxic and apneustic centers are located in the pons. The pneumaotaxic center modulates the rate of respiration by coordinating the rate of inhalation and exhalation. It also can transmit inhibitory responses to the DRG. The apneustic center is also involved in the breathing synchronization and can initiate long, deep breaths by sending stimulatory impulses to the DRG. Indeed, modifying respiration rates is an essential mechanism for regulating the blood gases and maintaining homeostasis.

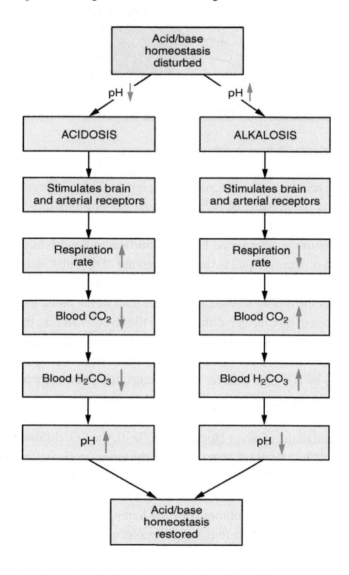

$$CO_2 + H_2O \Leftrightarrow H_2CO_3 \Leftrightarrow HCO_3^- + H^+$$

Figure 10-12 Maintaining acid/base homeostasis by adjusting respiration rate.

Gas transport - why and how?

Oxygen and carbon dioxide can readily diffuse through air and water and across cellular membranes.

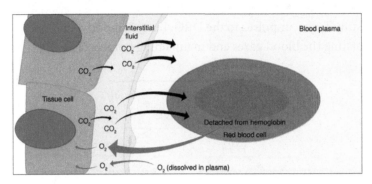

Figure 10-13 Gas exchange between the tissues and the blood.

Gas diffuses from one area to another because of differences in partial pressure. The partial pressure of a gas can be defined as the pressure of each individual gas in a mixture. The partial pressure of a particular gas in a mixture is independent of other gases in the mixture (Dalton's law). The partial pressure of a gas in a mixture is determined by its proportion in the mixture. The sum of the partial pressures of the gases in a mixture is equal to the total pressure of the substance. For example, 21% of air is composed of oxygen. Thus, the PO_2 in air = 21% of 760 mmHg, or 160 mmHg. In the body, the partial pressure of O_2 is higher in the freshly inhaled alveolar air than in the blood located in the surrounding capillary networks. Because of this, oxygen diffuses from the alveolar air into the blood. However, in the body tissues, the partial pressure of oxygen is greater in the capillaries entering the tissue than in the metabolically active tissue cells. As a result, oxygen will diffuse from the blood into the tissue. Carbon dioxide exchange occurs by a similar process. In the lungs, the pulmonary arteries that are carrying deoxygenated blood into the lungs have a higher PCO_2 than is present in the in the alveoli. As a result, CO_2 diffuses into the alveolar sacs and is exhaled out of the lungs. In the cells of active tissues, the PCO_2 is higher in the tissues than in the adjacent blood vessels. Thus, the CO_2 diffuses from the tissue into the local venules (which empty into veins) to be returned to the lungs for expiration. Therefore, as a general rule, gases will diffuse from an area of higher partial pressure to an area of lower partial pressure.

Most oxygen entering the blood combines with the hemoglobin protein inside erythrocytes. One hemoglobin molecule can combine with four oxygen molecules (See figure 9-6). Hemoglobin in the blood can carry approximately 60 times more oxygen than if the oxygen was simply dissolved in the plasma. Large quantities of oxygen combined with hemoglobin give rise to a considerable partial pressure gradient between the oxygen content in blood, tissues, and alveolar air. The partial pressure of oxygen can be correlated to the percent saturation of hemoglobin by the following reaction:

$$Hb + O_2 \Leftrightarrow HbO_2$$

When fresh air enters the lungs, the partial pressure of oxygen (PO_2) is high, which drives the reaction above to the right, promoting the binding of O_2 to hemoglobin. The PO_2 in active tissues is normally lower that the PO_2 of the blood, which would drive the above reaction to the left, releasing oxygen from the hemoglobin, so it can diffuse into the tissues. The state of hemoglobin saturation in lungs, when compared to the body tissues, is illustrated by the standard "S" shaped hemoglobin saturation curve shown in Figure 10-14.

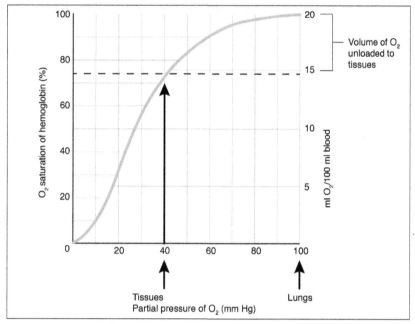

(a) Partial pressure of oxygen and hemoglobin saturation

Figure 10-14A Oxygen-hemoglobin dissociation curve.

In the arterial blood of the lungs (at the right side of the graph), the PO_2 of oxygen is about 100 mmHg, and most hemoglobin molecules are 100% saturated (that is, all four of their binding sites are bound with O_2 molecules). In the venous blood of the tissues, the partial pressure of oxygen is considerably lower, and most hemoglobin molecules are not completely saturated. Some interesting observations can be discerned from this graph. First, viewing the right side of the graph, we see that it takes a decline in the partial pressure of the O_2 in the blood from 100 mmHg down to about 60 mmHg for the percent saturation hemoglobin to drop only 10% (from 100% to 90% saturated). This provides for a significant safety factor. That is, the hemoglobin in the blood can remain almost totally saturated (and oxygen is still accessible) if less oxygen were to be available. Thus, at slightly higher altitude or in those who have a minor lung condition, the majority of the hemoglobin in the blood can still be almost completely saturated with O_2. Second, in the blood returning from the tissues, the partial pressure of oxygen is approximately 40 mmHg, and the hemoglobin has only released a little more than 20% of its oxygen (as it is still just under 80% saturated). At this point, there is a reserve of oxygen (more oxygen is available, if needed). Therefore, if body tissues are exceedingly active and more oxygen is needed, more can be released from the hemoglobin. Third, notice that the curve is quite steep between 0 mmHg and about 40 mmHg (left side of the graph). A relatively small change in the partial pressure of oxygen results in a significant release of oxygen from hemoglobin. Thus, a considerable amount of oxygen can be released without delay when needed.

Active tissues take up oxygen, which creates a gradient that favors the release of more oxygen from hemoglobin. (Recall $HbO_2 \rightarrow Hb + O_2$. Removing oxygen will shift this reaction to the right.) Factors produced by active tissues affect the affinity of hemoglobin for oxygen. Oxygen affinity is reduced by an increase in CO_2 and temperature and a decrease in pH. CO_2 production is generally increased in metabolically active tissues. A decrease in pH may result from an increased production CO_2 by shifting the reaction $CO_2 + H_2O \Leftrightarrow H_2CO_3 \Leftrightarrow HCO_3^- + H+$ to the right producing more H+ or by the accumulation of lactic acid in active tissues. Actively contracting muscles generate heat, resulting in an increase in temperature. Both CO_2 and protons can bind directly to hemoglobin, and an increase in all three of these factors (CO_2, H+, and temperature) can cause a conformational change in the hemoglobin protein that facilitates oxygen release.

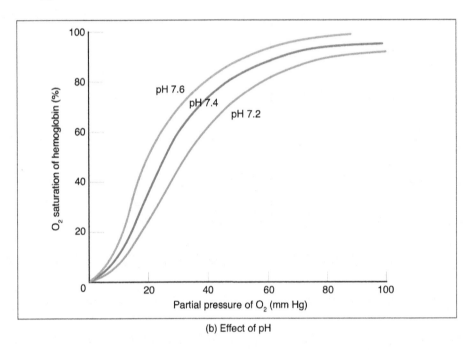

(b) Effect of pH

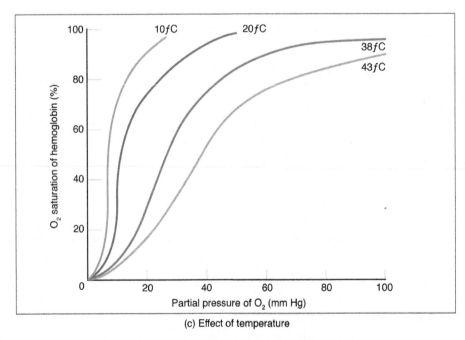

(c) Effect of temperature

Figure 10-14B Effect of pH on the oxygen-hemoglobin dissociation curve.

Figure 10-14C Effect of temperature on the oxygen-hemoglobin dissociation curve

Carbon dioxide transfer

Carbon dioxide is produced by cellular oxidation in active tissues. This results in a higher partial pressure of CO_2 in the tissues than in the blood, which facilitates the diffusion of CO_2 from cells, to the interstitial fluid, to the blood plasma. Some of the CO_2 released from the body tissues into the blood combines with water in the blood plasma to form bicarbonate (HCO_3^-) and H+. However, most of the CO_2 diffuses into the erythrocytes, where some binds directly to hemoglobin and some combines with water to form HCO_3^- and H+. The bicarbonate (HCO_3^-) formed from this reaction returns to the blood plasma, whereas the H+ from this reaction may bind to hemoglobin.

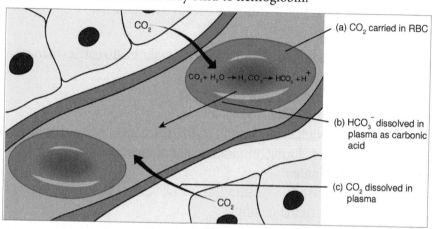

Figure 10-15 Carbon dioxide transport from the tissues.

In the lungs, the partial pressure of CO_2 is higher in blood than in alveolar air. Thus, the reactions that pack CO_2 into the blood are reversed and CO_2 diffuses into the alveoli, where it is removed from the body by exhalation. Specifically, some of the bicarbonate (HCO_3^-) in the blood plasma combines with H+ to form CO_2 and water. However, most of the HCO_3^- moves into the erythrocytes where it combines with H+ released from hemoglobin to form CO_2 and H_2O. CO_2 that was bound to hemoglobin is released. The CO_2 from both sources diffuses from the erythrocytes into the blood plasma. This CO_2, as well as the CO_2 generated from the reaction noted above (HCO_3^- + H+), diffuses from the blood plasma into the air of the alveoli.

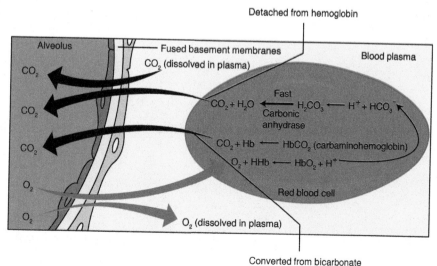

Figure 10-16 Gas exchange in the lungs.

In addition to carbon dioxide, other metabolites and waste products must be tightly regulated and removed from the body to maintain proper homeostasis. With this in mind, we next turn our attention to the processes of osmoregulation and excretion.

Chapter 10 Review

I. Helpful and Interesting Animations:

1. An overview of gas exchange:
   https://massasoit.instructure.com/courses/902776/wiki/bioflix-gas-exchange

2. Three different ways to breathe: human, bird, insect
   http://tabletopwhale.com/img/posts/10-24-14.gif

3. Pressure changes during inspiration and expiration:
   http://highered.mcgrawhill.com/sites/0072507470/student_view0/chapter23/animation__alveolar_pressure_changes_during_inspiration_and_expiration.html

4. Gas exchange during respiration:
   https://highered.mcgrawhill.com/sites/0072495855/student_view0/chapter25/animation__gas_exchange_during_respiration.html

5. Changes in partial pressure of oxygen and carbon dioxide:
   http://highered.mcgrawhill.com/sites/0072507470/student_view0/chapter23/animation__changes_in_the_partial_pressures_of_oxygen_and_carbon_dioxide.html

6. Movement of oxygen and carbon dioxide:
   http://highered.mcgrawhill.com/sites/0072507470/student_view0/chapter23/animation__movement_of_oxygen_and_carbon_dioxide.html

II. Active Testing: Do you know the facts?

A. List the words in this chapter you would have printed in bold type.
Can you define these words?

B. What are the main, "take home" messages of this chapter?
Is your answer the same as your instructor's answer?

C. Some Questions:

1. Distinguish between the terms: perfusion and ventilation.

2. Compare and contrast the advantages and disadvantages of water breathers and air breathers.

3. What term refers to the exchange of a substance or heat between two fluids flowing in opposite directions? Give an example of where this might occur and draw a diagram of it.

4. What type of respiratory system do insects have? What are some key features of it? Why is this a beneficial adaptation for insects?

5. What results when the external intercostal muscles and the diaphragm contract?

6. Differentiate between lung compliance and lung elasticity.

7. Name the events that occur when there is a drop in the Pip.

8. Describe how the Palv, Ptp, Pip, and chest cavity are affected during inspiration and during expiration.

9. What is surfactant and how does it function in the body?

10. List the two main tenets of Dalton's Law. Describe an example of Dalton's Law in Physiology.

11. Describe a local control to breathing that is chemical in nature.

12. Describe respiratory control in the brain. Include the contribution of the pons, medulla, chemoreceptors, etc.

13. List 3 locations in the pulmonary or systemic circuit where you would expect the partial pressure of oxygen to be 100mmHg. List 3 locations where you would expect the partial pressure of CO_2 to be 46mmHg.

14. Draw an illustration of both the systemic and pulmonary circuit. Show the direction of blood flow and label the partial pressures of O_2 and CO_2 at various locations. Distinguish between deoxygenated and oxygenated blood. Include: capillary beds and cells in the tissues surrounding the lungs, pulmonary veins and arteries, capillary beds and cells in a body tissue, the heart, the lungs.

15. Draw and explain the 3 key features of the Oxygen-hemoglobin dissociation curve, making the y axis the % hemoglobin saturation and the x axis the partial pressure of oxygen. Be sure to indicate the systemic arterial partial pressure of O_2 and the system venous partial pressure of O_2.

16. What three factors can decrease the affinity of hemoglobin for oxygen? What might bring about these changes in tissues? For each of these factors, how would the oxygen-hemoglobin saturation curves shift?

17. Describe the distribution of CO_2 in tissues.

18. Explain in detail the chemicals reactions which occur during
    A. the CO_2 transfer in the body tissues
    B. the CO_2 transfer in the lungs

Include an illustration of each for clarity.

III. Inquiring minds want to know…

Challenge Questions

1. Lung ventilation in animals can occur by a positive or a negative pressure mechanism. Similarly, the ventilation systems in some patient hospital rooms are designed with a positive or a negative pressure air flow mechanism. Would you expect patients who have a highly infectious disease, such as tuberculosis, to be placed in rooms with a positive pressure air flow system or negative air flow system? Why? What type of room should be given to patients with a severely compromised immune system? Why?

2. Severe respiratory difficulties result from airway collapse in newborns with Tracheobronchomalacia. How could a 3D printer be used to help treat this disease? [*Hint*: Zopf, D. et al. (2013) N. Engl J Med 368: 21] or: http://www.nejm.org/doi/full/10.1056/NEJMc1206319

Chapter 11

Osmoregulation and Excretion

Figure 11-1 Ship on an ocean.

Day after day, day after day,
We stuck, nor breath nor motion;
As idle as a painted ship
Upon a painted ocean.
Water, water, everywhere,
And all the boards did shrink;
Water, water, everywhere,
Nor any drop to drink.

—English poet Samuel Taylor Coleridge, written in 1797–98,
from *The Rime of the Ancient Mariner*

Why is it a bad idea to drink seawater?

Osmoregulation

Simply stated, if two solutions are separated from each other by a selectively permeable membrane that allows water to cross, but not solute, water will flow from the area where there is more "free" water (that is, not associated with solute) to where there is less. This passive movement of water through a selectively permeable membrane in response to solute concentration, pressure gradients, or both is known as osmosis. Osmolarity is a measure of solute concentration and is expressed as milliosmoles per liter of solution (mOsm/L). A solution can be comparatively hypoosmotic, hyperosmotic, or isoosmotic to another solution. A hypoosmotic solution will have less solute, but comparatively more free water than the solution it is being compared to. A hyperosmotic solution will have a higher concentration of solute when compared to another solution. If two solutions are separated by a semipermeable membrane that allows water to pass through but not solute, water will flow from the hypoosmotic solution (where there are comparatively more unassociated water molecules and less solute) to the hyperosmotic solution.

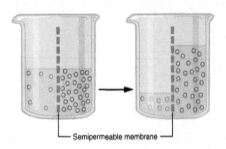

Figure 11-2 Osmosis.

Osmotic pressure is a force produced by the net movement of water when this movement is driven by differences in solute concentration. It can contribute to the shrinking or swelling of animal cells. For example, if an animal cell is placed in a hypertonic solution, it will likely shrink. This is because the solution outside the cell has a comparatively higher solute concentration, but less water than the cell's cytoplasm. Due to osmosis, water will move from inside of the cell (where there is more of it in comparison to the outside of the cell) to the cell exterior. Similarly, if an animal cell is placed in a hypotonic solution, due to osmosis, it will likely swell. Water molecules cannot directly diffuse across the lipid bilayer of cell membranes. Rather, water crosses cell membranes through specialized protein channels, known as aquaporins, by the process of facilitated diffusion.

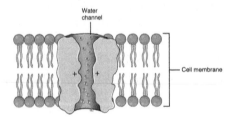

Figure 11-3 An aquaporin channel.

The facilitated diffusion of water will continue to occur from an area of higher water concentration to lower water concentration until equilibrium is reached, at which point there is no more net movement. Animals utilize the process of osmoregulation to maintain the physiologically appropriate osmolarity of body fluids. When cellular and extracellular fluids are isosmotic, cells will not experience the damaging effects of shrinkage or swelling.

Various animals have unique approaches to osmoregulation. Osmoregulators maintain a body fluid osmolarity that is well adapted to their physiological needs, and it is usually different from that of the external environment. In contrast, osmoconformers allow the osmolarity of their body fluids to match that of the environment. Examples of osmoconformers are sharks and marine invertebrates (such as squids). Animals such as these can regulate diffusion by adjusting the net flow of water in or out of their bodies. Osmoregulators have specially adapted structures (such as the kidney and excretory structures, which can actively filter and remove substances from the body) to tightly regulate the osmolarity of body fluids. These process help to maintain appropriate solute concentrations and preserve homeostasis.

Indeed, in osmoregulators, excretion and osmoregulation are inherently coupled. Molecules, ions and wastes are eliminated from the body to keep cellular and extracellular fluids isosmotic. In most animals, extracellular fluids are filtered through tubular structures with walls formed from a specialized layer of cells (transport epithelium) that contain transport proteins in their membrane. By the process of secretion, excess ions, unneeded byproducts of metabolic reactions and toxins are selectively transported from the blood and body fluids into the excretory tubule. These unessential molecules and waste products (such as nitrogen compounds, phosphates, sulfates, etc.) can then be excreted (or released) to the external environment. At the same time, molecules that are needed in the body are retained via the process of reabsorption. In this process, nutrient molecules (such as glucose and amino acids), water, and useful ions (such as Na+, K+, Cl-, and HCO_3-) are returned from the excretory tubule to the body fluids.

The breakdown of proteins to amino acids and nucleic acids to nitrogenous bases produce waste products containing amino groups (NH_2). In general, animals eliminate nitrogenous wastes as water solutes in one of three main forms: as ammonia (NH_3), urea [$CO(NH_2)_2$], or uric acid ($C_5H_4N_4O_3$).

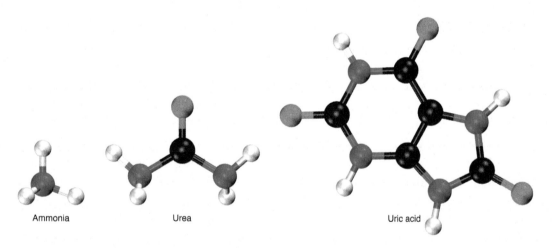

Ammonia   Urea   Uric acid

Figure 11-4 Nitrogenous wastes.

The availability of water primarily determines the mode of nitrogen excretion. A significant amount of water is necessary for the excretion of ammonia (NH_3), which is formed by the oxidation of NH_2 groups. If ammonia is allowed to accumulate in the body, the pH of cells may increase to toxic levels. Because water is readily available, most aquatic animals release nitrogenous wastes directly into their surrounding marine environment in the form of ammonia. Terrestrial organisms, such as mammals and amphibians, convert ammonia to the less toxic compound, urea. Birds utilize a unique form of nitrogen metabolism that requires less water and eliminate nitrogenous wastes in the form of uric acid.

Specialized excretory tubules are found throughout the animal kingdom. One of the most basic types of excretory tubules, the protonephridia, is used by the simple invertebrate, the flatworm. The protonephrida consists of a branching network of tubules. A specialized cell, the flame cell, is found at the end of the tubules. Hemolymph enters the tubule near the junction of the flame cell and tubule. Cilia in the flame cell propel the hemolymph into the protonephridia, where useful molecules are reabsorbed into body fluid and waste molecules are released through openings of the tubules that form pores at the body surface. Annelids (such as the earthworm) and adult mollusks have a somewhat more sophisticated excretory system than the flatworm. Their excretory tubule (known as a metanephridium) is rather convoluted, is surrounded by a capillary network, and empties into a bladder. Hemolymph enters through openings at the proximal ends of metanephridia, where it is propelled by cilia into the tubule. Needed molecules and ions are reabsorbed into the bloodstream. Excess ions and nitrogenous wastes are secreted into the tubule, collect in the bladder, and are then excreted from the body. The specialized excretory tubules of insects are known as malpighian tubules. They are located just posterior to the midgut. The distal end of these branched and convoluted tubules is closed, but the proximal end empties into the insect's digestive tract, where any non-essential molecules, ions and wastes will pass though the hindgut, rectum, and anus to be released as uric acid. Essential ions, such as Na+ and K+, nutrient molecules, and water will be reabsorbed.

Osmoregulation and excretion in mammals

Many vertebrates produce urine that is hypoosmotic to their body fluids. However, in order to conserve water, mammals use their kidneys to produce urine that is hyperosmotic to their body fluids. The kidneys are highly specialized, essential organs that function not only in the reabsorption of water and nutrients (such as glucose and amino acids) but also to balance salts and water (which is essential for blood pressure regulation), help control pH, and concentrate wastes for excretion. They also produce the hormone erythropoietin which stimulates the production of red blood cells, and the enzyme renin, a key factor in blood pressure homeostasis.

The kidneys reside in the abdominal cavity and have a unique structure that is well designed for their function. The kidneys are surrounded by a fibrous tissue layer known as the renal capsule. The outer (superficial) region of the kidney comprises the renal cortex, and the inner region is the renal medulla. Renal pyramids (also known as Malpighi's pyramids) are prominent funnel shaped structures separated by expansions of the cortex known as renal columns. Nephrons are specialized tubules that extend from the cortex into the pyramids. They are the functional units of the kidney. Wastes and excess ions are secreted into them to be released as urine, and needed substances are reabsorbed from these tubules back into the blood stream. The renal corpuscle comprises the initial filtering portion of the nephron (known as the Bowman's capsule) that surrounds a network of blood vessels known as the glomerulus. The renal corpuscle resides in the cortex, whereas the tubular segments of the nephron (such as the collecting ducts) protrude into the renal pyramids. The terminal end of the nephron transports filtrate (at this point, the filtrate is often referred to as urine) to linear collecting tubes that extend from the cortex to the medulla. The collecting tubes converge to form a larger duct which connects to the renal papilla of the medullary pyramids. Urine from the renal papilla drain into branches (or calyces ; singular calyx) of the renal pelvis. Two to three minor calyces, located at the bottom of each pyramid, converge to form a major calyx. Urine is delivered from the major calyces into the renal pelvis, which narrows and elongates to form the ureter. Ureters from each kidney transport urine to the urinary bladder where it is eliminated by way of the urethra to the exterior of the body. The renal hilum is a central depression where the ureter, renal nerve, and blood vessels pass into the kidney.

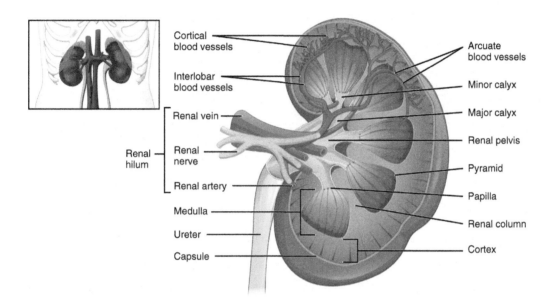

Figure 11-5 Anatomy of the kidney.

Blood flow in the kidney

Blood enters the kidney by way of the renal arteries, which directly split off from the abdominal aorta. The renal arteries branch into smaller vessels (such as the interlobar arteries, which pass through the renal columns, and the arcuate arteries that reside at the junction of the cortex and medulla), eventually delivering blood to the afferent arterioles. The afferent arterioles supply blood to the glomeruli (the network of capillaries encapsulated by the initial portion of the nephron (known as the Bowman's capsule) where the filtration process begins. Blood drains from the glomerulus into an efferent arteriole, which branches into capillaries that surround the tubules of the nephron. These peritubular capillaries take up the water and solutes that have been reabsorbed from the filtrate in the nephron. Blood vessels that surround the portion of the nephron known as the Loop of Henle are called the vasa recta, and are important for maintaining the ion concentration gradient of the medulla. The capillaries of the kidney branch and connect to venules, which deliver blood to the venous system of the kidney (including the arcuate and interlobar veins). These vessels transport blood to the renal vein, where blood exits the kidney to the inferior vena cava.

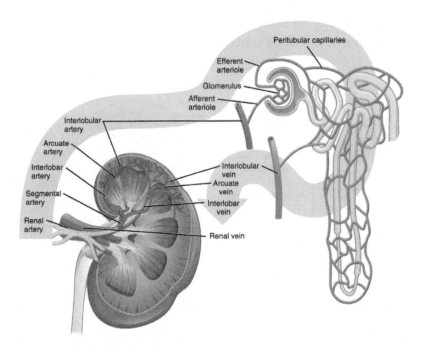

Figure 11-6 Blood flow in the kidneys.

Urine formation

There are three primary processes that result in urine production: filtration, reabsorption, and secretion, as summarized in Figure 11-7 below.

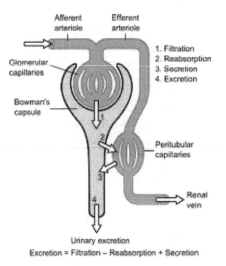

Figure 11-7 Urine production in the kidneys.

During the filtration stage, water, amino acids, ions, glucose, and nitrogenous waste molecules pass from the blood in the vessels of the glomerulus into the Bowman's capsule of the nephron to form the filtrate. Reabsorption occurs when substances pass from the filtrate through the cells of the nephron wall to the interstitial fluid, returning to the bloodstream by way of the peritubular capillaries. Secretion is the process by which specific small molecules, ions, and wastes are transported from the blood into the tubules of the nephron, adding to the filtrate. The filtrate will then pass to the renal pelvis (where it is often referred to as urine), ureters, and bladder, to be eliminated as urine.

The highly specialized functional unit of the kidney, the nephron, is a primary structure that is vital to these processes. Each human kidney has greater than 1 million nephrons. Differences in permeability along the length of nephrons are established by the specific transport proteins embedded in the membranes of the cells that comprise the nephron wall. This selective permeability, as well as differential concentration gradients of molecules and ions in the interstitial fluid that surrounds the nephrons of the kidney, facilitate the secretion of substances into the nephron and the reabsorption of substances from the nephron back into the circulation. Major components of the nephron include the Bowman's Capsule, the proximal convoluted tubule, the descending loop of Henle, the ascending loop of Henle, the distal convoluted tubule, and the collecting duct. About 80% of nephrons are classified as cortical nephrons. These have shorter loops, and primarily reside in the cortex. Juxtamedullary nephrons have longer loops that extend well into the medulla.

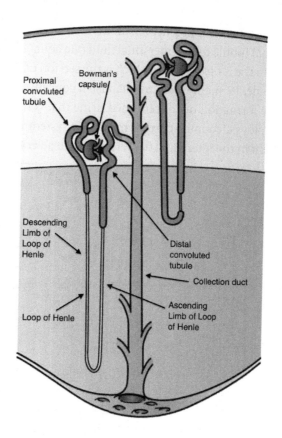

Figure 11-8 Nephron types.

Filtration

Approximately 47.5 gallons of fluid are filtered in the Bowman's capsules of nephrons each day. Afferent arterioles deliver blood to the glomerulus. Small spaces between the endothelial cells of the glomerular capillaries and the cells of the Bowman's capsule permit the transfer of smaller molecules (such as water, glucose, amino acids, sodium chloride, and urea) while restricting the passage of larger substances (such as proteins and blood cells) into the Bowman's capsule. The diameters of the afferent arteriole and glomerular capillaries are relatively large, which lowers the resistance in these vessels. However, the diameter of efferent arterioles is smaller. This creates a pressure differential that maintains a relatively high pressure in this region. This high pressure forces small molecules from the blood in the glomerulus into the Bowman's capsule of the nephron, thereby forming the glomerular filtrate. The filtrate then moves into the proximal tubule of the nephron. The main function of the proximal tubule is the reabsorption of water, ions, and nutrients back to the interstitial fluid. In this region, bicarbonate (HCO_3^-), water, and potassium (K+) are passively transported, and nutrients (such as glucose and amino acids) are actively transported (by specific membrane proteins) out of the nephron so that they can be reabsorbed back into the bloodstream. Na+/K+ pumps in the epithelium of the proximal tubule also move Na+ from the filtrate into the interstitial fluid. Movement of these positive ions results in a voltage gradient, which causes Cl- ions to follow (that is, move from the filtrate into the interstitial fluid and get reabsorbed). Ammonia (NH_3) is secreted into the proximal tubule by passive transport, whereas H+ is secreted into the tubule by active transport mechanisms. Due to the secretion and subsequent reabsorption of solutes, the filtrate in the proximal tubule becomes hypoosmotic to the surrounding interstitial fluid. Thus, water moves from the proximal tubule to the interstitial fluid (via aquaporins) by the process of osmosis.

The filtrate then passes into the loop of Henle, which is the section of the nephron between the proximal tubule and the distal tubule. Its main role is to establish a concentration gradient in the medulla of the kidney that facilitates the formation of concentrated urine that is hyperosmotic to the blood. In so doing, the loop of Henle employs a counter-current multiplier system in which ion pumps are used to create a concentration gradient in the interstitial fluid, resulting in a very high solute concentration deep the medulla.

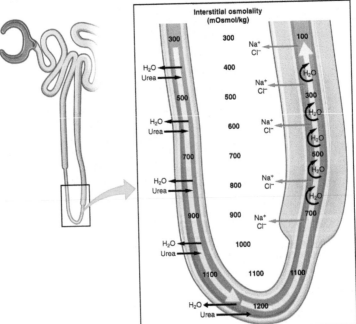

Figure 11-9 The loop of Henle.

As the descending loop of Henle passes through increasingly higher regions of solute concentrations in the interstitial fluid of the medulla, water moves out from the tubule. This concentrates the filtrate in the tubule. At the bottom of the loop of Henle tubule, the osmolarity of the filtrate in tubule is approximately equal to the osmolarity of interstitial fluid at this region of the medulla. As the loop of Henle ascends, Na+ and Cl- are actively transported out of the tubule, effectively decreasing the osmolarity of the filtrate in the tubule as it rises toward the cortex and enters the next segment of the nephron, the distal tubule. Here, Na+, Cl- , H_2O, and HCO_3- are reabsorbed, and K+ and H+ are secreted. Next, the filtrate enters the collecting duct, which further concentrates the urine. As the collecting duct descends into the increasing solute gradient of the medulla, water present in the collecting duct filtrate will pass through aquaporin channels into the interstitial fluid to be reabsorbed into the circulation, and the remaining filtrate (urine) will be concentrated. See Figure 11-10 below for a summary of reabsorption and secretion in the nephron.

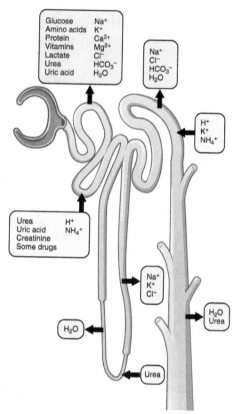

Figure 11-10 A summary of secretion and reabsorption in the nephron.

Water reabsorption in the collecting duct can be regulated by antidiuretic hormone (ADH). ADH is released from the posterior pituitary gland when osmoreceptors (in the hypothalamus) detect an increase in the osmolarity of body fluids. ADH stimulates the production of aquaporin channels in the collecting duct, thereby facilitating water reabsorption. Additionally, when necessary, H+ can also be secreted into the collecting duct, and some urea may diffuse passively out of the collecting duct.

In summary, then, some main functions of the kidney are to control osmolarity (mainly by adjusting water loss), to control total fluid volume (mainly by adjusting Na+ loss), and to regulate pH (mainly by adjusting bicarbonate loss or gain). It also plays a major role in blood pressure regulation, which we shall investigate next.

Renin-angiotensin-aldosterone system

Blood pressure changes in the body can occur for a number of reasons, such as when the body loses or gains Na+. Loss of Na+ reduces the osmolarity of the body fluids, causing a decrease in the water that is reabsorbed in the kidneys. This can lead to a lower blood volume, which can cause a drop in blood pressure. Contrarily, a gain of Na+ (perhaps by the excessive intake of salty food), can have an opposite effect and lead to an increase the water that is reabsorbed in the kidneys and a higher blood volume. When blood volume and blood pressure drop, components of the renin-angiotensin-aldosterone system (RAAS) act to raise blood pressure. The site of blood pressure/blood volume regulation in the kidney is the juxtaglomerular apparatus (JGA). This specific group of cells is located near the glomerulus and is primarily composed of specialized smooth muscle cells (the juxtaglomerular cells), which are located in the wall of the afferent arterioles, and the macula densa cells, which make up part of the distal tubule.

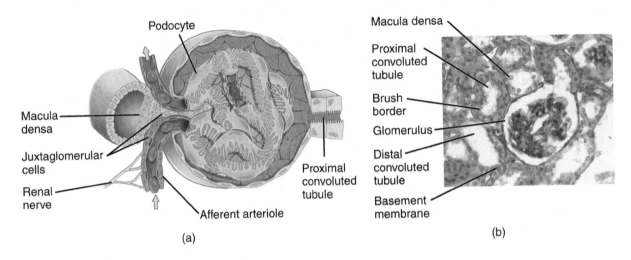

Figure 11-11 The juxtaglomerular apparatus.

The JGA cells function as a type of intra-renal baroreceptors that can detect a decrease in blood pressure. In response to a blood pressure decrease, these cells synthesize and release an enzyme called renin (also known as angiotensinogenase), which acts on the protein angiotensinogen, that is produced in the liver and secreted into the bloodstream. When renin is released from the JGA cells, it converts angiotensinogen to angiotensin I. Angiotensin converting enzyme (ACE) converts angiotensin I to angiotensin II. Angiotensin II elicits a number of significant downstream effects. It promotes the vasoconstriction of blood vessels, which directly acts to increase blood pressure. It also stimulates the secretion of the hormone aldosterone from the adrenal cortex, which increases the reabsorption of sodium and water in the kidney, thereby increasing the volume of fluid in the body (which in turn, increases blood pressure). See Figure 11-12 below for a summary of RAAS.

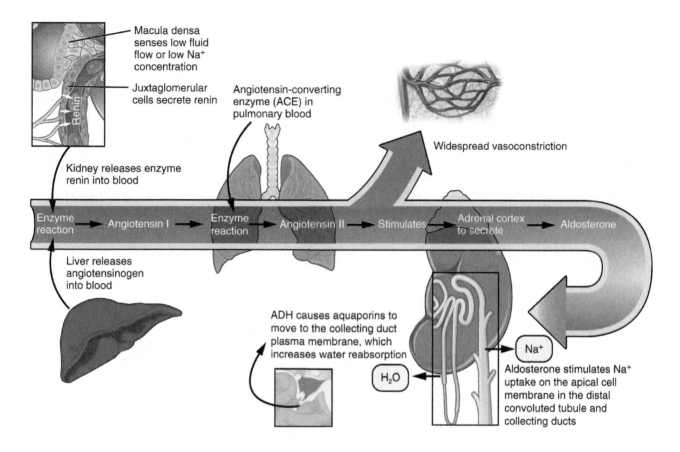

Figure 11-12 RAAS.

The macula densa cells also play an important role in blood pressure regulation. These cells monitor the Na+ concentration in the filtrate and regulate the release of renin via paracrine signals to the adjacent juxtaglomerular cells.

If RAAS acts to raise blood pressure, what acts to lower blood pressure?

Atrial natriuretic peptide (ANP; also known as ANF, atrial natriuretic factor) is synthesized, stored, and released from myocytes in the atria when stretch receptors are activated in response to an increase in blood pressure. ANP is a protein hormone that inhibits renin release, stimulates vasodilation, and promotes natriuresis (which is the loss of sodium) by prohibiting Na+ reabsorption in the kidney. Thus, the actions of ANP have the opposite effect of renin and aldosterone. ANP also causes the dilation of the afferent arteriole (which brings blood to the glomerulus) and the constriction of the efferent arteriole (which drains the glomerulus). Dilatation of the afferent arteriole increases the blood flow into the glomerulus, whereas constriction of the efferent arteriole impedes the outflow. The net effect is an increase in the glomerular filtration rate (GFR) which is a measure of the flow rate of fluid that is filtered in the kidney. An increase in the GFR (or the faster the flow of fluids in the nephron) leads to an increase in the overall urine production and a decrease in the reabsorption of water and Na+. Collectively, the actions of ANP result in a decrease in the plasma fluid volume, which amounts to a decrease in cardiac output. This will lower the blood pressure, returning it back to normal in situations when the blood pressure is too high.

pH regulation in the kidneys

The primary mechanism for pH regulation in the kidneys is the bicarbonate buffering system, as indicated by the equation: $CO_2 + H_2O \Leftrightarrow H_2CO_3 \Leftrightarrow HCO_3^- + H^+$. The enzyme, carbonic anhydrase (CA) is an important catalyst for this reversible reaction. Recall that bicarbonate (HCO_3^-) is initially filtered from the blood into the tubular lumen of the nephron and that H+ can be secreted into the tubular lumen in exchange for Na^+. When a bicarbonate ion encounters a H+ ion in the tubular lumen, the H^+ combines with the filtered HCO_3^- to form H_2CO_3 (carbonic acid), which dissociates into H_2O and CO_2. The CO_2 can then diffuse into the tubular epithelial cell. In the cytoplasm of the tubular epithelial cell, CO_2 reacts with H_2O to produce bicarbonate (HCO_3^-) and H+. Bicarbonate is transported across the tubular epithelial cell membrane by a $Na+/HCO_3^-$ symporter to the interstitial fluid, where it is reabsorbed into the bloodstream. In sum then, a filtered bicarbonate ion is reabsorbed for every H^+ ion that is secreted. In this manner, the kidneys remove acid from the body while retaining an effective buffer.

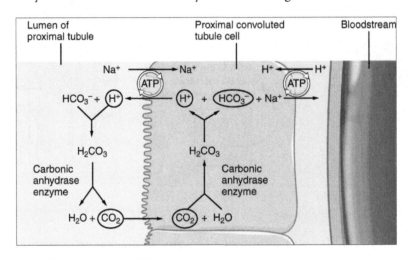

Figure 11-14 Reabsorption of bicarbonate in the kidney.

When the pH of the body fluids is too high and the blood is more basic than usual, there is not a sufficient amount of H+ ions being secreted into the lumen of the nephron tubule to react with all the filtered bicarbonate (a base). Excessive bicarbonate in the tubular lumen will then be excreted in the urine. By the law of mass actions, loss of HCO_3^- will drive the reaction: $CO_2 + H_2O \Leftrightarrow H_2CO_3 \Leftrightarrow HCO_3^- + H^+$ to the right, thereby increasing the amount of H+ ions, restoring the pH to normal values. When the blood is too acidic, the H+ ions are secreted into the nephron as expected. In the tubular lumen, the excess H+ ions tend to associate with other weak basis, such as phosphates and are then excreted in the urine. However, due to the reaction of $CO_2 + H_2O$ that is catalyzed by carbonic anhydrase in the cytoplasm of the tubule cell, a filtered bicarbonate ion is reabsorbed into the blood and serves to buffer the acidic conditions, restoring normal pH.

Drinking sea water will not restore hydration

Although the kidneys are capable of successfully regulating the body's sodium levels under normal circumstances, the sodium concentration in seawater is well above the kidney's maximum ability to concentrate the urine. More water will be excreted in an attempt to eliminate the excess sodium via urine than the amount of water that is gained from drinking the seawater. The blood's sodium concentration will increase to toxic levels. Due to osmosis, water will diffuse from cells, disrupting cellular function. Additional physiological mechanisms, such as neuronal conduction (which relies on appropriate Na+ concentrations) will likely also be affected. This can cause serious abnormalities, such as seizures and heart arrhythmias, that can be fatal.

Chapter 11 Review

I. Helpful and Interesting Animations:

1. Osmosis:
   http://www.youtube.com/watch?v=c0xswdNwPLg&list=PLXwnjgs_UWpLcVHARCbbglQJPwFl-kD_v&index=2
2. The urinary system:
   http://www.youtube.com/watch?v=hiNEShg6JTI
3. Concentrating urine in the kidneys:
   http://www.youtube.com/watch?v=3THZeaMfuSw&list=PLBC3B4C5B158840BF&index=42
4. RAAS:
   http://www.youtube.com/watch?v=bY6IWVgFCrQ
5. Acid/base balance:
   http://www.youtube.com/watch?v=i_pTaTveCCo
6. Kidney stones:
   http://www.nlm.nih.gov/medlineplus/ency/anatomyvideos/000075.htm

II. Active Testing: Do you know the facts?

A. List the words in this chapter you would have printed in bold type.
Can you define these words?

B. What are the main, "take home" messages of this chapter?
Is your answer the same as your instructor's answer?

C. Some Questions:

1. Two compartments: A and B are filled with solution and separated by a semi-permeable membrane that allows water to pass, but not solute. If water flows from A to B, which solution is hypertonic and which is hypotonic? Why

2. Of the following, put an "S" by those components that are usually is secreted, an "E" by those that are usually excreted and an "R" by those that are usually reabsorbed. Some may have both.

Glucose $Cl-$
H+ NH_3
Amino acids   K+
Na+ H_2O
HCO_3^-

3. Give an example of an animal that excretes each of the following:

Urea-

Ammonia-

Uric acid-

4. Compare and contrast the structure and functioning of: protonephridia, metanephridia and malpighian tubules.

5. What is unique about urine in mammals in comparison to almost all other vertebrates? Why is this important?

6. List 4 key functions of the kidney.

7. List the 6 structures urine goes through starting from its initial production to its release.

8. Why would one consider the production of urine to be a two-step process? What would be the two steps?

9. What delivers blood to the glomerulus? What receives blood from the glomerulus?

10. Describe the blood flow through the kidney.

11. Draw and label a detailed illustration of nephron and its related structures. Indicate what substances are being filtered, reabsorbed and secreted at each location. You do not need to indicate active or passive transport.

12. Fill in the table.

	Filtered	Reabsorbed	Secreted
Bowman's Capsule			
Proximal Tubule			
Descending Loop			
Ascending Loop			
Distal Tubule			
Collecting Duct			

13. If your blood pressure is low, how would your body respond to raise it?

14. If your blood pressure is high, how would your body respond to lower it?

15. How is pH regulated in the kidneys?

III. Inquiring minds want to know…

Challenge Questions

1. Individuals with compromised kidney function often undergo renal dialysis. What mechanisms are fundamental to this process? How is it carried out? What are some common causes of compromised kidney function?

2. Renal lithiasis that form inside the kidneys can cause significant pain. What is the biological basis for the formation of renal lithiasis? How can this problem be treated and prevented?

Chapter 12

Nutrition and Digestion

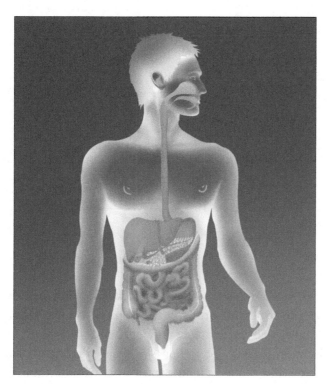

Figure 12-1 The digestive system.

Energy and nutrients

All animals utilize biochemical reactions to enable a cell or an organism to extract and use energy in order to maintain homeostasis, grow, and reproduce. These processes (that is, the body processes that convert or use energy) are collectively referred to as metabolism. Metabolism is composed of two components: catabolic reactions and anabolic reactions. Catabolism refers to the breakdown of organic (carbon containing) substances to obtain energy. Anabolism refers to reactions that build essential chemical substances (such as proteins) from smaller components and can facilitate organ and tissue development.

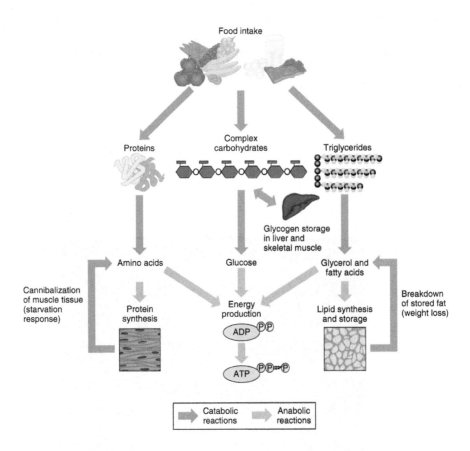

Figure 12-2 Metabolic processes.

Organic molecules are regularly used as fuels for oxidative reactions and often serve as building blocks for more complex molecules, in part because carbon is so very versatile. It can readily share its four electrons in its outer shell to form up to four covalent bonds, allowing it to bond with other carbons and form a virtually limitless diversity of carbon skeletons. Important classes of carbon-containing molecules include nucleic acids, proteins, lipids, and carbohydrates. Carbohydrates are composed of carbon, oxygen, and hydrogen (usually with a 2:1 hydrogen to oxygen ratio) and are major sources of nutrition. Classes of carbohydrates include monosaccharides, disaccharides, and polysaccharides. Monosaccharides are single monomer sugars, such as glucose and fructose ($C_6H_{12}O_6$). Disaccharides consists of two monosaccharides that can be linked by a dehydration synthesis reaction.

(a) Dehydration synthesis

Monomers are joined by removal of OH from one monomer and removal of H from the other at the site of bond formation.

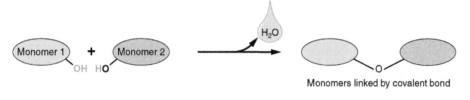

(b) Hydrolysis

Monomers are released by the addition of a water molecule, adding OH to one monomer and H to the other.

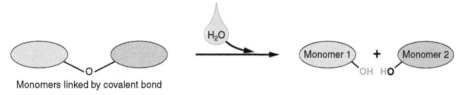

Figure 12-3 Dehydration synthesis and hydrolysis reactions.

Common disaccharides include sucrose (table sugar, composed of glucose + fructose), lactose (glucose + galactose), and maltose (glucose + glucose). Notable examples of polysaccharides include starch (composed of long chains of glucose and found in plants such as potatoes, wheat, rice), glycogen (composed of long chain of glucoses that branch and are found in animals), and cellulose (composed of long chain of glucoses with unique linkages that serve as the structural components of cell walls). Lipids include such common molecules as fats, steroids, and phospholipids. They consist mainly of carbon and hydrogen atoms linked by nonpolar, covalent bonds, and therefore, are mostly hydrophobic and, thus, insoluble in water. Primary functions of fats include insulation, cushioning, and energy storage. Dietary fat is composed mostly of triglycerides, which are themselves made up of a glycerol molecule linked to three fatty acids by dehydration synthesis.

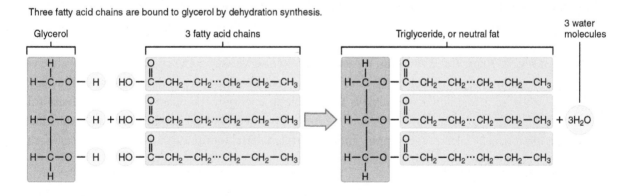

Figure 12-4 Triglycerides.

Triglycerides can be characterized as saturated or unsaturated. Saturated fatty acids have all the carbons of the fatty acid backbone bonded to the maximum number of hydrogens, whereas unsaturated fatty acids have fewer than the maximum number of hydrogens bonded to a given carbon atom, resulting in a double bond, which creates a bend in the fatty acid chain.

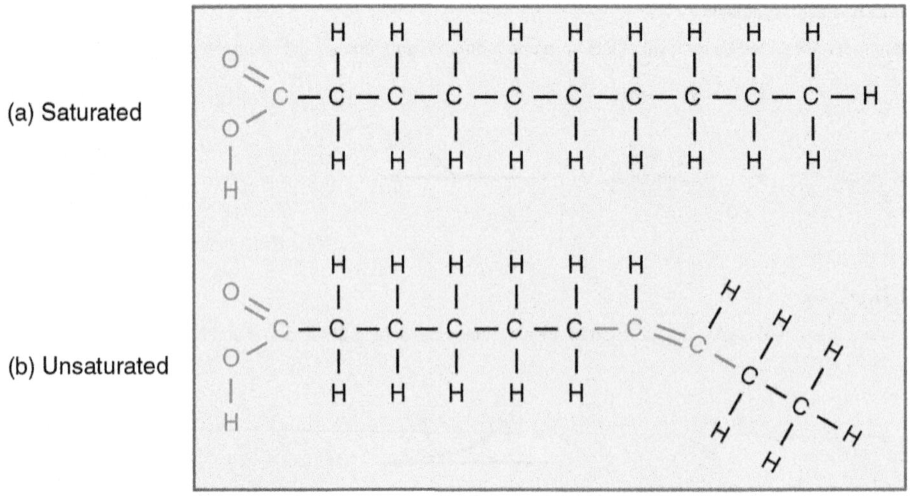

Figure 12-5 Saturated and unsaturated fatty acids.

Triglycerides with unsaturated fatty acids generally have a lower melting point than saturated fats, and tend to be liquid at room temperature (oils). This is because they cannot pack together tightly due to the bend in their structure that results from the double bond. Most plant triglycerides and some triglycerides found in fish are unsaturated. Triglycerides with saturated fatty acids that are linear can firmly pack together and tend to be solid at room temperature. Most animal triglycerides are saturated.

Animals can synthesize many organic molecules that are not directly obtained by diet. Carbohydrates, for example, can be synthesized from fatty acids and amino acids. However, there are a number of essential nutrients that are required in an animal's diet for normal body function that cannot be produced in sufficient quantities. These include essential fatty acids, essential amino acids, essential vitamins, and minerals. The essential nutrients can be different for each animal. For example, linoleic acid is an essential fatty acid for humans, because humans do not have the enzyme necessary for its synthesis. There are eight amino acids that are essential for humans: methione, tryptophan, leucine, phenylalanine, threonine, valine, isolelucine, and lysine. These can usually be easily obtained by eating a normal, healthy diet. Vitamin A (or retinol), vitamin C (ascorbic acid), and a number of B vitamins are also examples of essential nutrients for humans. Vitamins are necessary for numerous functions in the body, and have a variety of special roles. The B vitamins, for example, often serve as enzyme cofactors that associate with enzymes to aid in catalysis. Riboflavin (vitamin B_2) is a central component of flavin adenine dinucleotide (FAD, a redox cofactor) and as such, plays a vital role in energy metabolism. Minerals likewise fulfill a variety of vital roles in the body. Ions are important for neuronal excitability, cardiac conductance, osmoregulation, etc. Calcium is an important structural material for bones, and iron is necessary for the proper functioning of hemoglobin.

Animal digestion

Once an animal has obtained nutrients, it must digest them by processes involving the mechanical and chemical breakdown of the nutrients into molecular subunits that are small enough to be absorbed into the body fluids and cells. Digestion may be intracellular or extracellular. Intracellular digestion takes place within cells and can be found in organisms such as sponges. In the sponge, water containing organic matter and microorganisms enters a central cavity via pores. Specialized cells (choanocytes) that line body wall will trap endocytose and digest food particles, which are then transferred to the amoebocytes that deliver the nutrients to other body cells. Extracellular digestion occurs outside of the body cells in an internal pouch or tube (such as a stomach or intestine). In most cases, epithelial cells lining the tube secrete enzymes that digest food particles. Extracellular digestion has many benefits. In general, larger foods can be processed by extracellular digestion, and food can be eaten less frequently, and in larger quantities, because it can be stored and broken down while the animal carries out other activities.

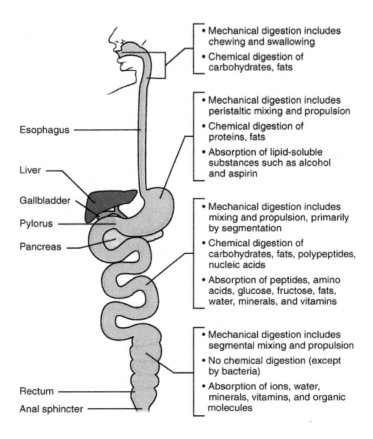

Figure 12-6 The digestive process.

The five main stages of extracellular digestion include: mechanical processing (the chewing and grinding of food), the secretion of enzymes and other digestive aids into the digestive tract, the enzymatic hydrolysis of food molecules into molecular subunits, the absorption of molecular subunits across cell membranes, and the elimination of undigested matter.

Although animal digestive systems share many common components, many animals have unique adaptations to optimize their digestive process for their own particular needs. For example, earthworms and some insects and birds have a structure known as a gizzard for grinding up food and a crop to store food for later consumption. Herbivores, such as rabbits, have a relatively long digestive tract with extensive storage regions to provide sufficient time for local microbes to aid in the digestion of plant cellulose.

Carnivores have relatively short digestive tracts with comparatively less storage space because animal material is rich in nutrients (e.g., proteins, fats), and is less fibrous. Thus, it can be more readily digested. Other examples of adaptive digestive structures can be found in the digestive systems of ruminants. Ruminants are animals (such as cows) that obtain nutrients from plants by initially directing food to a specialized digestive chamber (the omasum), where bacteria initiate digestion. Food is then regurgitated so it can be chewed again before it is ingested into the true stomach (abomasum) and further processed through the remainder of the digestive tract.

Human digestion

Digestion begins in the oral cavity (mouth) where food is broken down mechanically and encounters saliva. Saliva moistens and mixes food with lubricating mucus. It is also contains amylase, a starch-digesting enzyme; lysozyme, an enzyme that kills some forms of bacteria; and bicarbonate ions. Swallowing is accomplished by the muscular contractions of the pharynx (throat region at the posterior of the mouth), which involves the displacement of the epiglottis (a flap of elastic tissue) to prevent food from entering the trachea and to direct it to the esophagus. The esophagus is the muscular tube that connects the pharynx with the stomach. Food is moved through the esophagus by synchronized cycles of contraction and relaxation (known as peristalsis). Throughout the gastro-intestinal tract, there are several sphincters, or rings of smooth muscle that can constrict or relax to regulate the passage of digested material from one location to the next, as well as prohibit the backflow of substances. For example, the lower esophageal sphincter resides at the junction between the stomach and the esophagus. It functions to prohibit the contents of the stomach (such as stomach acids) from passing up into the esophagus.

The structure of the vertebrate gastrointestinal tract includes four major layers that are well de-signed for its function. The mucosa is the innermost layer of the gut. It is composed of epithelial cells that confine the digestive contents and absorb nutrients. The other specialized cells of the mucosa secrete mucus, enzymes, and factors for regulating pH. The next layer is the submucosa. It contains connective tissue, networks of neurons for the local control of digestive activity, and blood and lymph vessels. The third layer is the muscularis layer. In the stomach, it is composed of three layers of smooth muscle: oblique, circular, and longitudinal. These layers are important for the movement of digested material through the system. The circular layer and longitudinal layer, in particular, are important for the peristaltic movements that occur throughout the gut. The circular layer functions to constrict the gut and propel the digestive contents in the forward direction. The longitudinal layer contracts and relaxes regularly, which shortens and expands the gut, creating space for the digested material to move into. The outermost gut layer is the serosa. It is composed of connective tissue that is adjacent to the tissue (known as the mesentery) that supports the digestive organs in the abdominal cavity. Cells in the serosa secrete fluid that lubricates the tissue, reducing the friction between the digestive organs and flanking structures.

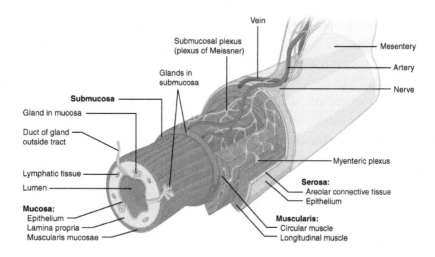

Figure 12-7 Layers of the gastrointestinal tract.

The mucosa lining the lumen of the stomach is composed of indentations known as gastric pits. These pits are formed from surface epithelial cells, glandular cells, chief cells, and parietal cells. Once in the stomach, the food material encounters gastric juice produced by specific types of these particular cells. Gastric juice is a general term for the mucus, hydrochloric acid (HCl), and pepsin (a protease-enzyme that breaks down protein to amino acids) found in the stomach. Glandular cells produce mucus, chief cells secrete pepsinogen (a precursor to pepsin), and parietal cells secrete HCl. When food enters the stomach, stretch receptors in the stomach wall are activated, which stimulate the release of mucus, HCl, and pepsinogen. HCl production facilitates the formation of pepsin from pepsinogen, which is further promoted by a positive feedback mechanism such that the initial production of pepsin stimulates the production of additional pepsin. The release of hydrochloric acid into the lumen maintains a pH=2. These acidic conditions are optimal for the enzymatic activity of pepsin, provide a hostile environment for unwanted bacteria, and help to unfold proteins to facilitate their breakdown. The stomach mucus protects the stomach wall from this high acidity, as well from the enzymatic activity of pepsin. In addition to the breakdown of proteins, limited absorption of some small molecules (such as water, certain medications, and amino acids) can occur through the stomach lining. In humans, the volume of an empty stomach can range from 45 ml to 75 ml, but can expand to hold up to approximately 1 liter. In general, it can take 1 to 6 hours for the stomach to empty after a meal.

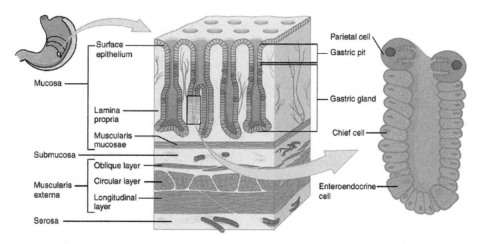

Figure 12-8 The anatomy of the stomach.

The action of the gastric juices, as well as the muscular churning of the stomach, help to breakdown food material into a substance referred to as chyme. The movement of chyme past the pyloric sphincter (which is located at the junction of the stomach and small intestine) into the small intestine is regulated such that it only occurs when the small intestine is available to carry out the next step in the digestive process. Dietary fat, for example, is digested relatively slowly in the small intestine, and chyme will be stored in the stomach until dietary fat is appropriately processed. In addition to fat digestion, the small intestine is also responsible for the chemical digestion of proteins and carbohydrate, as well as for nutrient absorption. As part of the gastrointestinal tract, its structure is also highly organized.

Anatomically, the small intestine is composed of three main sections: the duodenum (the first section, nearest to the stomach, where much of the breakdown of nutrient molecules occurs), the jejunum (the middle section, which is primarily involved in absorption), and the ileum (the final segment, which is also specialized for absorption).

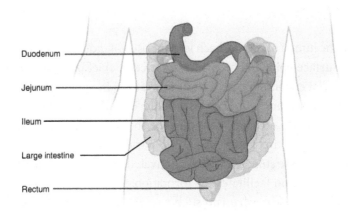

Figure 12-9 The intestines.

Together, these sections comprise an average total length of the small intestine of roughly 7 meters. The pancreas delivers digestive fluid to the duodenum via the pancreatic duct. This fluid contains proteolytic enzymes (such trypsin, chymotrypsin, carboxypeptidase, aminopeptidase, and dipeptidase), pancreatic lipase (for lipid digestion), pancreatic amylase (for carbohydrate digestion), and pancreatic nucleases (for DNA and RNA digestion). These enzymes are secreted by the exocrine cells of the pancreas. Duct cells of the pancreas secrete bicarbonate ions, which are also delivered to the duodenum, thereby neutralizing the pH of the chyme, which optimizes the enzymatic activity of the resident proteases, lipases, amylase, and nucleases. Specialized endocrine cells of the pancreas release major hormones that are involved in glucose regulation into the bloodstream. Pancreatic alpha cells release the hormone glucagon when blood glucose levels fall below normal levels. Glucagon stimulates the liver to convert stored glycogen into glucose and release it into the bloodstream, raising blood glucose levels. The beta cells of the pancreas release insulin when blood glucose levels rise. Insulin causes cells in the liver, muscle, and fat tissue to take up glucose from the blood where it can be used or stored as glycogen.

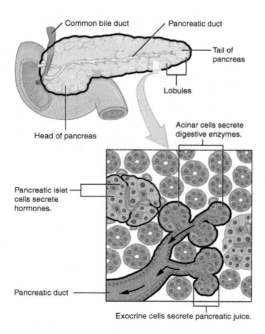

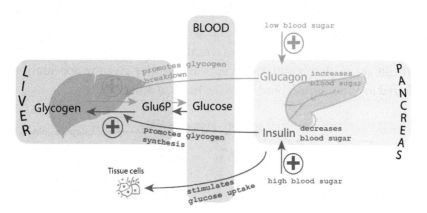

Figure 12-10A The pancreas.

Figure 12-10B Blood glucose control.

The liver also contributes to the digestive process in the duodenum. It produces bile, which consists of a mixture of substances that include water, bile salts, mucus, and pigments. Bile aids in fat digestion by helping to emulsify fats. Although it is made in the liver, bile is stored in the gallbladder and is delivered to the duodenum by the common bile duct from the gallbladder.

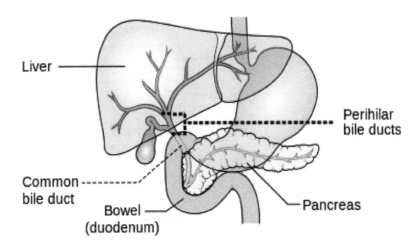

Figure 12-11 Organs that aid in the digestive process.

Once proteins, carbohydrates, and fats are broken down into smaller molecules, they are suitable for absorption. The small intestine has specialized structures, the intestinal villi and microvilli, which increase the surface area of the intestine and optimize the absorptive process. The lining of the small intestine has large circular folds that contain numerous intestinal villi, which are small projections lined by mucosal epithelial cells that contain capillaries and lacteals (lymph vessels). Microvilli are microscopic protrusions of the mucosa epithelial cell plasma membranes. The microvilli are positioned on the apical (top) side of the epithelial cells, which faces the lumen (or the inside) of the small intestine. Because the microvilli are so closely situated to each other, they give the appearance of bristles on a brush and are referred to as the "brush border" of the luminal lining.

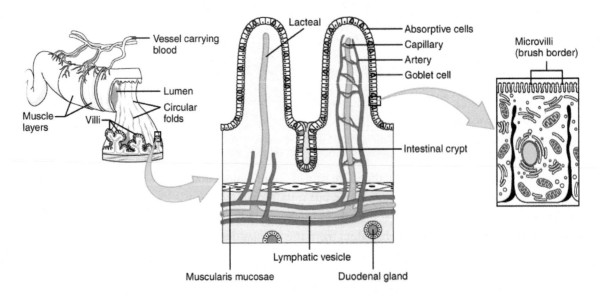

Figure 12-12 Histology of the small intestine.

Breakdown of molecules begins in the lumen of the small intestine. Here, pancreatic amylase converts polysaccharides to disaccharides, trypsin and chymotrypsin cleave proteins to peptides, carboxypeptidase cleaves large polypeptides to smaller ones, pancreatic nuclease breaks down DNA and RNA to nucleotides, and lipids and tryglycerides are cleaved to fatty acids and monoglycerides by lipase. However, most of these molecules are still too large to be transported from the intestinal lumen across the brush border into the cytoplasm of the mucosa cell. Thus, additional enzymes are present at the brush border. For example, disaccharidases at the brush border break down disaccharides (such as sucrose, lactose, and maltose) into monosaccharides (e.g., glucose). Aminopeptidases and dipetidases at the brush border cleave larger peptides to amino acids. Nucleotidases, nucelosidases, and phosphatases break down nucleotides to their primary components (nitrogeneous bases, five carbon sugars, and phosphates). These water soluble digestive products are capable of being transported into and across the mucosal epithelial cells. They are then transported across the basal side of the mucosal epithelial cell membrane and released into the extracellular fluid in the villi, where they are acquired by the bloodstream.

The digestion and absorption of fats requires a more complex mechanism. As mentioned previously, bile is produced in the liver and stored in the gallbladder. Bile enters the duodenum of the small intestine by way of the common bile duct from the gallbladder. The chemical make-up of a bile salt (such as glycocholic acid) is such that one side of the molecule is generally non-polar, while the other side is polar. This unique structure is vital to the ability of bile salts to emulsify fats, as it enables them to form "hydrophillic coats" around triglyceride fat molecules. Triglycerides coated with bile salts form micelles, which are structures that facilitate the mixing of the triglycerides with the fluid in the intestinal lumen. Lipase present in the intestinal lumen digests the triglycerides into monoglycerides and fatty acids. These can dissociate from the bile salts and diffuse from the intestinal lumen, across the brush border, and into the cytoplasm of the epithelial mucosal cells. Once inside the cell, the monoglycerides and fatty acids reassemble into fats and are incorporated into chylomicrons. Chylomicrons are lipoprotein particles consisting mostly of triglycerides, but also contain cholesterol and phospholipids. They are coated by proteins to provide a hydrophillic surface on their exterior.

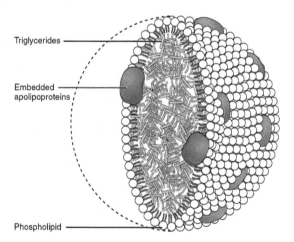

Triglycerides

Embedded
apolipoproteins

Phospholipid

Figure 12-13 A chylomicron.

Chylomicrons belong to a set of lipoproteins (which are complexes of lipids and proteins) that includes HDL (high density lipoprotein) and LDL (low density lipoprotein). They efficiently transport hydrophobic substances, such as fats and cholesterol, throughout the body via the aqueous blood and lymph systems. In the intestine, the chylomicrons are exocytosed from the basal side of the epithelial mucosal cell into the surrounding interstitial fluid of the villi, where they pass into lacteals and enter the lymph system en route to the bloodstream.

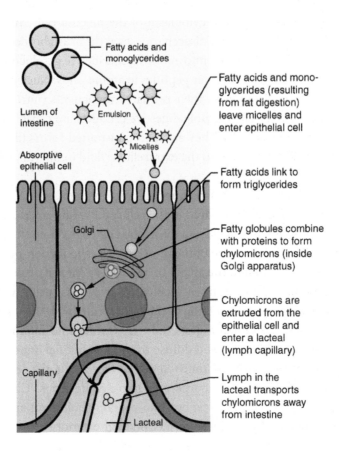

Figure 12-14 Lipid Absorption.

Many nutrients that are absorbed from the small intestine are delivered to the liver by way of the hepatic portal venous system where they are processed before returning to the heart to be distributed to the rest of the body. In this regard, the liver carries out a multitude of vital functions. For example, it is involved in glucose synthesis, glycogen formation and breakdown, cholesterol synthesis, the production of triglycerides, amino acid synthesis, and the modification of toxic substances. Interestingly, to date, there is no artificial device that is capable of carrying out all the functions of the liver. However, liver transplantation is feasible and effective. The liver is also capable of regenerating a large amount of its tissue when damaged or lost.

The remaining contents of the small intestine next pass into the large intestine (or colon), which is the final part of the digestive tract.

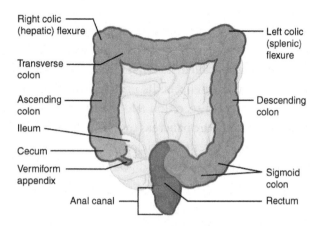

Figure 12-15 The large intestine.

Its main functions are to absorb water and pass wastes from the body, but it also partakes in the absorption of vitamins (such as vitamin K and some B vitamins) and secretes some ions (such as K+ and Cl). The large intestine is significantly wider than the small intestine and measures about 5 feet in length. The terminal portion of the large intestine is the rectum, which connects to the anus. Stretch receptors in the walls of the rectum signal the need for defecation. If defecation is delayed, the waste material in the rectum reenters the absorptive area of the colon and more water is absorbed, which can result in constipation.

Regulation of digestion and appetite

Digestion is controlled by a variety of mechanisms. These include signaling by the neural networks in the walls of the digestive tract, the action of specialized hormones, and signaling from the appetite and satiety centers in the brain. These regulatory mechanisms respond to action potentials from mechanical and chemical receptors that monitor the volume and the composition of digestive contents. For example, the lining of the gastrointestinal system houses afferent (sensory) neurons, efferent (motor) neurons, and interneurons, which comprise a subdivision of the peripheral nervous system known as the enteric nervous system (ENS). Stretch receptors in the ENS can be activated by an increase in stomach content. This leads to the activation of efferent neurons that control intestinal muscles, resulting in the peristaltic churning of the contents in the digestive tract. Other local neurons in the ENS regulate the secretion of digestive enzymes.

Initially, the digestive process begins when glands in the mouth increase the production of saliva in response to the presence of food. As food accumulates in the stomach, stretch receptors signal neuronal networks to increase stomach contractions. Chemoreceptors and stretch receptors respond to the food by signaling the G cells of the stomach (which are innervated by the vagus nerve) to secrete the peptide hormone gastrin. Gastrin initiates the secretion of pepsinogen and HCl in the stomach. The passage of the highly acidic, partially digested material (chyme) to the terminal portion of the stomach and into the duodenum stimulates the release of the hormone secretin. Secretin is produced in the S cells of the duodenum, and is released in response to low duodenal pH. It functions to inhibit acid secretion by the parietal cells of the stomach and stimulate bicarbonate production by pancreatic exocrine cells. A member of the secretin family of hormones, glucose dependent insulinotrophic peptide (GIP), is also secreted when the digestive contents reach the small intestine. GIP stimulates insulin release from the pancreas. Insulin facilitates the uptake and storage of glucose from the digested material. The peptide hormone, cholecystokinin (CCK) is likewise secreted when chyme enters the small intestine. It is released by mucosal epithelial cells (called "I" cells) of the small intestine, as well as by neurons in the brain and ENS. CCK has a number of effects. Its primary functions include inhibiting the gastric activity in the stomach by preventing acid secretion and the further emptying of the stomach contents into the small intestine. It also stimulates the pancreas to release digestive enzymes and the gall bladder to release bile. If the chyme in the small intestine is rich in fat, the high levels of secretin and CCK serve to inhibit peristalsis in the stomach, thereby slowing digestion.

GI Hormones

Hormone	Secreted By	Source & Stimulus	Target Organ	Respone
Gastrin	Stomach mucosa	Stomach in response to food	Stomach, small intestine	*release of HCL *Increase of intestine movement *release of pepsinogen
Secretin	Small Intestine	Duodenum in response to acidic chyme	Pancreas	*secrection of alkaline *digestive pro-enzyme *Inhibits intestine motility
Cholecystokinin (CCK)	Small Intestine	Intestinal cells in response to food	Pancreas, gallbladder	*Secretion of proenzymes and bile
Gastric Inhibitory Peptide (GIP)		Intestinal cells in response to fat	Stomach, Pancreas	*Insulin secretion *Inhibits gastric secretion and motality

Figure 12-16 Gastrointestinal hormones.

The hypothalamus plays a vital role in the highly complex processes that regulate appetite by responding to a number of hormones. In general, the reduction of the body's energy stores (such as carbohydrates and fats) results in a feeling of hunger. When adipose cells are low in fat, they produce a lower amount of the hormone leptin. When they have an abundance of fat, they produce increased levels of leptin. The binding of leptin to receptors in the hypothalamus stimulates the hypothalamic satiety center and reduces appetite. Peptide YY (PYY) also suppresses appetite. It is released by cells in the small intestine in response to the presence of a meal. CCK and insulin, as mentioned above, likewise suppress hunger. The hormone ghrelin, on the other hand, is believed to trigger hunger. It is produced by a variety of cells, including cells in the stomach and pancreas, and has receptors in a number of tissues. Although its exact mechanism of action is still being elucidated, it has been shown that circulating levels of ghrelin is highest directly prior to a meal and lowest immediately following a meal (Williams DL and Cummings, DE 2005).

It is clear that hormones play a crucial role in the regulation of the digestive process, appetite and satiety. Hormones also play a tremendous role in many other physiological processes. They are released by the specialized components of the endocrine system, which is the topic of our next chapter.

Chapter 12 Review

I. Helpful and Interesting Animations:

1. The role of insulin in the body:
   http://www.youtube.com/watch?v=OYH1deu7-4E&list=TLRpKwwZyBtvdvjd-gb0WGZ-VQz5NvqAyJS
2. The fate of fat:
   http://www.hhmi.org/biointeractive/fate-fat
3. Leptin feedback control system:
   http://www.hhmi.org/biointeractive/leptin-feedback-control-system

II. Active Testing: Do you know the facts?

A. List the words in this chapter you would have printed in bold type.
Can you define these words?

B. What are the main, "take home" messages of this chapter?
 Is your answer the same as your instructor's answer?

C. Some Questions:

1. What is an organic molecule and why are organic molecules important?

2. Compare and contrast: carbohydrates, lipids, proteins and nucleic acids.

3. Define: essential amino acid. What are the 8 essential amino acids in humans?

4. List 4 tasks of digestive systems.

5. What role does each of the following play in the digestive process: mouth, salivary glands, pharynx, esophagus, stomach, small intestine, liver, gallbladder, and pancreas.

6. What is a sphincter? Give some examples of where sphincters are located in the gastrointestinal tract.

7. Name the 4 layers of the gut and describe the function of each.

8. Describe gastric juice.

9. Describe the location and function of the chief and parietal cells.

10. Name the hormone that is released due to stomach distension. Describe its function.

11. Name 7 chemicals (that are not hormones) that enter the small intestine from the pancreas.

12. Name 2 primary pancreatic hormones and describe their function.

13. List the reactions that the following enzymes catalyze and where they are found in the body: salivary amylase, pancreatic amylase, pepsin, trypsin, chymotrypsin, carboxypeptidase, lipase, and nuclease

14. What is the function of bile? Where in the body does it originate and where does it function?

15. Draw, label and explain a diagram showing the absorption of fat soluble products of digestion by intestinal mucosa cells.

16. List 4 events that occur in the liver.

17. What are the functions of the large intestine?

18. Fill in the chart below

Hormone	Location	Stimulated by	Function
gastrin			
GIP			
CCK			
insulin			
glucagon			
leptin			
ghrelin			
PYY			

III. Inquiring minds want to know...

Challenge Questions

1. Could the body be "tricked" to burn more calories? Is there a way to convert white fat (which stores energy) to brown fat (which burns energy)? To explore these questions, see: Lee, S.D. and Tontonoz, P. (2014). Eosinophils in Fat: Pink is the New Brown. *Cell 157*: 1249-1250; and Qiu, Y. et al. (2014). Eosinophils and Type 2 Cytokine Signaling in Macrophages Orchestrate Development of Functional Beige Fat. *Cell 157*: 1292-1308.

2. A recent report by the Institute of Medicine states: "Two-thirds of adults and one-third of children are overweight or obese. Left unchecked, obesity's effects on health, health care costs, and our productivity as a nation could become catastrophic." The report can be accessed at:

http://www.iom.edu/Reports/2012/Accelerating-Progress-in-Obesity-Prevention.aspx

Do you agree with the recommendations in this report? Do you think the goals outlined in the report are attainable?

Reference

Williams, D.L., & Cummings, D.E. (2005). Regulation of Ghrelin in physiologic and pathophysiologic states. *The Journal of Nutrition, 135,* 1320-1325. Retrieved from http://www.ncbi.nlm.nih.gov/pubmed/15867333

Chapter 13

The Endocrine System

Figure 13-1 No Doping.

Endocrine signaling

Like the nervous system, the endocrine system regulates many of the other body systems. Specifically, it controls such physiological processes as metabolism, growth, development, sleep, mood, response to stress, and sexual development. Unlike the nervous system, endocrine regulation initiates more slowly and lasts longer (days to weeks). Endocrine hormones are usually released directly into the bloodstream, traveling to target tissues where they bind particular receptors to elicit a specific response. The endocrine system employs four major types of cell signaling processes. The first is classic endocrine signaling which entails the secretion of a hormone by an endocrine gland into the bloodstream for transport to a target cell over a significant distance. The second is neuroendocrine signaling, which utilizes neurosecretory neurons that release neurohormones into the circulation. For example, in the hypothalamus, there are two types of neurosecretory cells, the magnocellular cells, whose longer axons terminate in the posterior pituitary, and the parvocellular cells, whose shorter axons terminate at a group of capillaries at the base to the hypothalamus (known as the median eminence). (Refer to figure 13-7). The "releasing" hormones of the hypothalamus are generally termed neurosecretory. Thus, thyroid releasing hormone (TRH) is secreted from the parvocellular cells of the hypothalamus and binds to receptors in the anterior pituitary, which releases thyroid stimulating hormone (TSH) into the circulation. THS will travel to and bind to its receptors on the thyroid gland (and thus serves as an example of classic endocrine signaling).The third type of signaling is paracrine signaling, which involves the regulation of adjacent cells. Here, cells release regulators that do not travel long distances but rather diffuse through extracellular fluid to target nearby cells. Estradiol, which binds to estrogen receptors during mammary gland development, is an example of a paracrine regulator. The fourth major type of signaling is autocrine regulation. In this case, cells release local regulators that affect the same cells that produced it. Growth hormone (GH) is an example of an autocrine regulator that is involved in embryonic development.

Hormones

Hormones are the main chemical regulators of the endocrine system. Based on their chemical structure, hormones can be classified into 4 major categories: amines, peptides, proteins, and steroids. Examples of amine hormones include epinephrine, norepinephrine, and thyroxine. Their chemical structure is based on tyrosine. Peptide hormones contain short amino acid chains and include examples such as: oxytocin, PYY (peptide YY, an appetite suppressing hormone) and atrial natriuretic peptide (ANP), which acts to reduce blood pressure, in part by causing a decrease in sodium reabsorption in the kidney). By comparison, protein hormones, such as human growth hormone, have longer chains of amino acids. Steroid hormones are based on the canonical steroid structure, which is four cycloalkane rings. They are also usually synthesized from cholesterol. Because they are lipids, they can diffuse though cell membranes to react with intracellular receptors found in the cytoplasm of nucleus.

Hormone Class	Components	Example(s)
Amine Hormone	Amino acids with modified groups (e.g. norepinephrine's carboxyl group is replaced with a benzene ring)	Norepinephrine 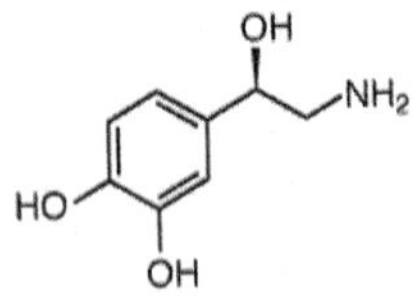
Peptide Hormone	Short chains of linked amino acids	Oxytocin 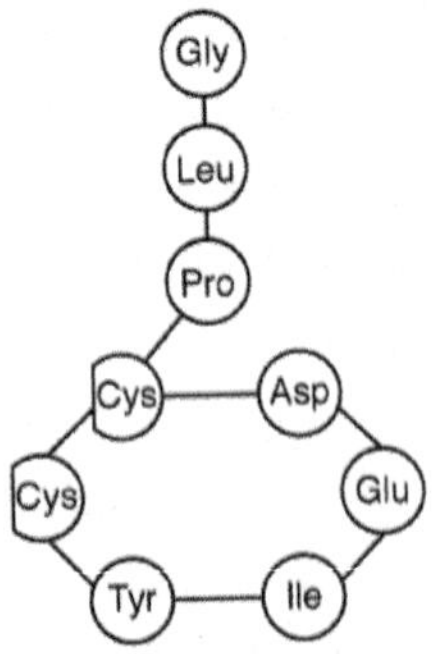
Protein Hormone	Long chains of linked amino acids	Human Growth Hormone 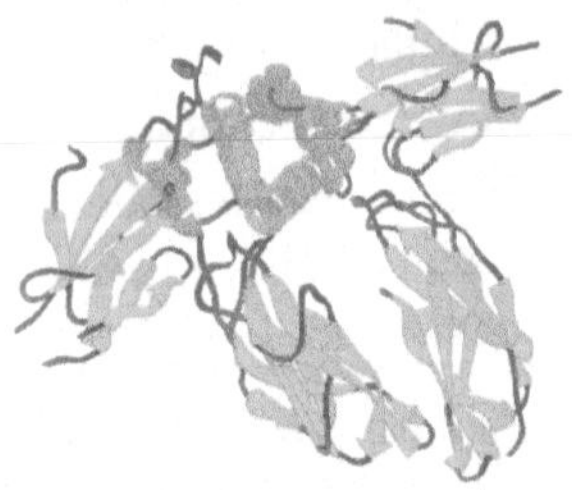
Steroid Hormones	Derived from the lipid cholesterol	Testosterone 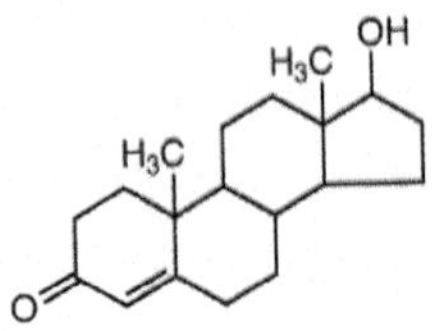 Progesterone 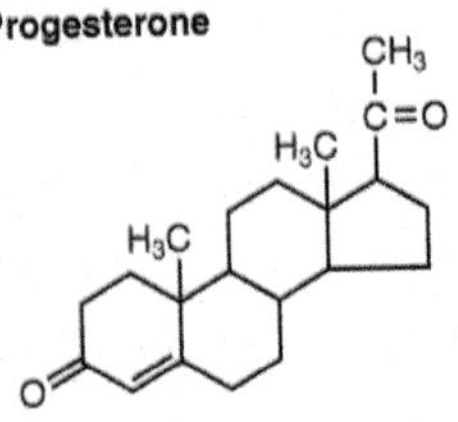

Figure 13.2 Structural classifications of hormones.

There are five major groups of steroid hormones that can be classified according to their specific receptor. These include: glucocorticoids, mineralocorticoids, androgens, estrogens, and progestogens. The glucocorticoids have roles in metabolism and immune function. The stress hormone cortisol, for example, is a type of glucocorticoid that acts to increases blood pressure and blood sugar as well as to reduce immune responses. Mineralocorticoids are involved in the regulation of electrolytes and water balance, which helps to control blood volume. The mineralocorticoid aldosterone, for example, is produced by the adrenal gland and acts on the kidney nephron to promote sodium reabsorption and potassium secretion. Androgenic hormones include hormones, such as testosterone, that control the development or maintenance of male characteristics. Natural estrogens are the primary female hormones responsible for the development of secondary sex characteristics in the female (such as breast development) as well as menstruations and reproduction. Progestogens, such as progesterone, are also important for the proper function of the menstrual cycle and for maintaining pregnancy. The fourth major category of hormones are those that are derived from fatty acids. They are referred to as eicosanoids, which are signaling molecules that can be made in all body cells (and are not usually produced in just one gland). They are generally autocrine or paracrine in nature (thus they act locally), often have a short half-life, and have a variety of functions. The prostaglandins are common eicosanoid sub-type. These signaling molecules are involved in such varied functions as blood clotting, inflammation, constriction or dilation of vascular smooth muscle, pain, fever, cell growth, and more. They are produced by the oxidation of a precursor molecule in a reaction catalyzed by cyclooxygenases (COX-1 and COX-2). Interestingly, non-steroidal anti-inflammatory drugs (NSAIDs), such as aspirin and ibuprofen, inhibit cyclooxygenase, which affects prostaglandin production, thereby reducing pain, fever, inflammation.

Hormones affect physiological systems at the cellular level by initiating changes in membrane permeability, stimulating gene expression, protein synthesis, or mitosis, promoting or inhibiting enzyme activity, or initiating the release of regulatory factors. Hormones generally function by one of two mechanisms: by binding to a specific receptor on a cell membrane, or by entering the target cell and binding to an intracellular receptor. Hormones that bind to a membrane bound receptor are classified as hydrophilic (or water soluble). These hormones include peptide/amino acid based hormones (except thyroid hormone) and usually function by activating second messenger pathways in the cell cytoplasm to elicit a cellular response.

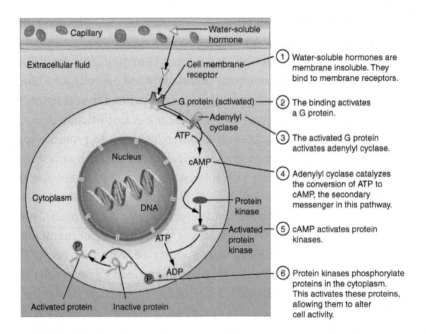

Figure 13-3 Hydrophilic hormones mechanism of action.

⌐ surface receptors

An example of a hydrophilic hormone is epinephrine. It can act on a liver cell to cause glucose release when necessary (such as during the "fight or flight" sympathetic response).

eg: aldosterone   Lipid soluble (or hydrophobic) hormones, such as steroids, have a different mechanism of action. They diffuse into the cell, and form a complex with an intracellular receptor. The receptor-hormone complex then enters the nucleus where it binds to target DNA, initiating the transcription of particular genes.

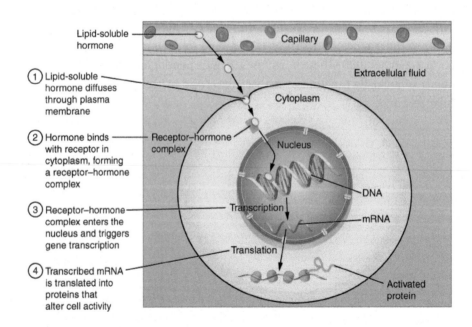

Figure 13-4 Hydrophobic hormones mechanism of action.

An example of a lipid soluble hormone is aldosterone, which is secreted into the blood by the adrenal glands when Na+ levels are low in the body fluids. Aldosterone can enter kidney cells where it binds to an aldosterone receptor. The resulting complex can enter the nucleus and activate target gene expression that results in the production of additional Na+ channels, which are then inserted into the kidney cell membrane to increase Na+ reabsorption.

Another key feature of hormones is that they are usually regulated by a negative feedback mechanism. For example, the release of thyrotopin releasing hormone (TRH) by the hypothalamus causes the release of thyroid stimulating hormone (TSH) from the pituitary, which acts on the thyroid gland to produce thyroid hormones (such as T3 and T4). Sufficient production of these hormones inhibits the further secretion of TSH by the pituitary.

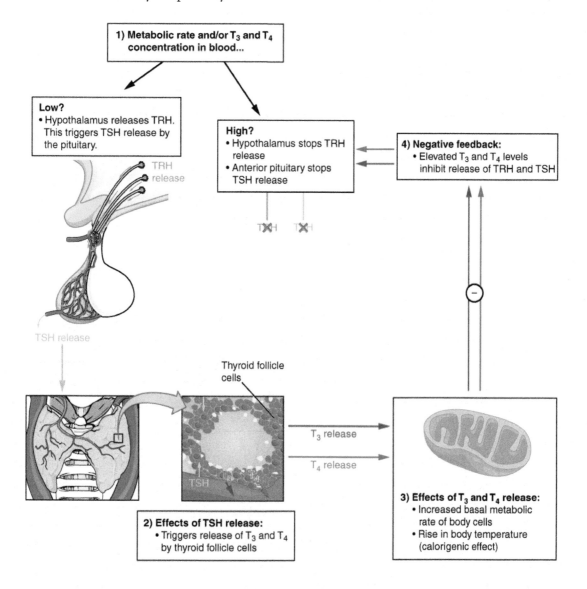

Figure 13-5 Negative feedback regulation.

TRH and TSH can also be classified as trophic hormones, hormones that regulate hormone secretion by another endocrine gland. Hormones can also be quite effective at low concentrations. In this regard, the effect of a single hormone molecule binding to a receptor can be greatly amplified by the activation of a large number of proteins via second messenger pathways.

The endocrine system is in contrast to the exocrine system, which includes glands found in the gastrointestinal tract, the sweat glands, and the salivary glands, and which use ducts for the secretion of chemical modifiers. Endocrine hormones are not usually released into ducts, but rather are often transported by vesicles from specialized glands. The specialized glands and cells of the endocrine system include: the pineal gland, hypothalamus, pituitary, thyroid, parathyroids, thymus, adrenals, the islet cells of the pancreas, the ovaries, and testes. Glands that signal the next gland in a series are referred to as an axis, such as the hypothalamic-pituitary-adrenal axis. In addition to specialized glands, the endocrine system also utilizes organs from other body systems (such as the kidney, which secretes the hormone, renin).

The endocrine glands

Figure 13-6 shows the location of each endocrine gland in the body. A description of each gland is included below.

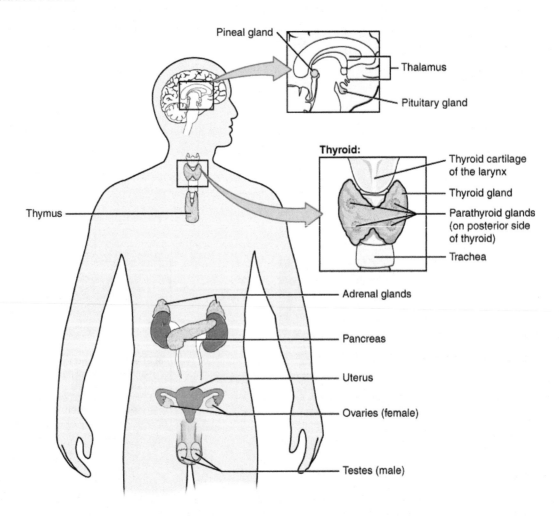

Figure 13-6 The endocrine system.

The pineal gland

The pineal gland is located towards the center of the brain, near the thalamus. Its name: "pineal" reflects its shape, which is similar to a small pine cone. It produces melatonin, a hormone derived from serotonin, which is involved in the regulation of wakefulness and sleep, and in seasonal patterns. For example, lower light levels are believed to stimulate the release of melatonin and produce sleepiness. Bright light causes the breakdown of melatonin, promoting wakefulness. Melatonin levels are also affected by the duration of the day and night, and are generally higher during the winter months.

The hypothalamus and pituitary gland

The hypothalamus is located in the medial part of the brain, just ventral to the thalamus. As mentioned previously, it is involved in a number of homeostatic mechanisms in the body, including the regulation of body temperature, thirst, hunger, circadian rhythms, etc. and is highly interconnected to components of the central and autonomic nervous system. It also has a very important role in endocrine function. It produces and releases a number of trophic hormones that can stimulate or inhibit the secretion of other hormones. Anatomically, is contains some distinct groups of neurons with specific functions (such as the paraventricular nucleus and the supraoptic nucleus) whereas other hypothalamic regions are less well defined. The hypothalamus connects to the anterior and posterior pituitary gland by a branch (or stalk) known as the infundibulum.

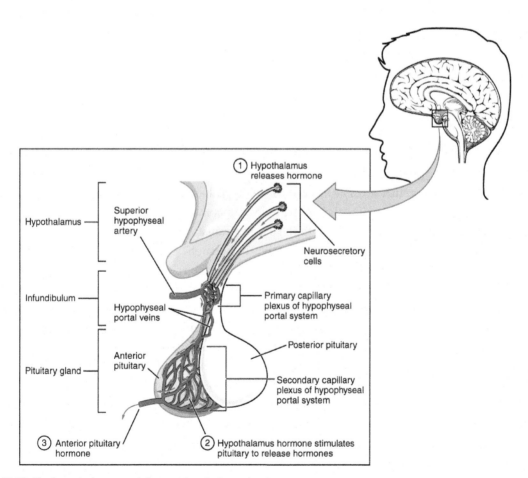

Figure 13-7A The hypothalamus and the anterior pituitary gland

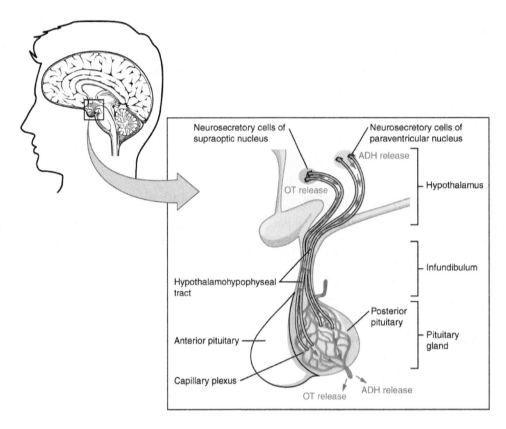

Figure 13-7B The hypothalamus and the posterior pituitary gland.

The pituitary gland is also known as the hypophysis. The anterior pituitary gland is called the adenohypophysis, while the posterior pituitary gland is known as the neurohypophysis. Hypothalamic neurons (known as magnocellular neurosecretory cells) found in the paraventricular and supraoptic nuclei produce oxytocin and antidiuretic hormone (ADH). Oxytocin is a hormone involved in uterine contractions during birth, maternal bonding, and the stimulation of lactation (breast milk release). ADH (also called vasopressin) is primarily involved with water retention and the constriction of blood vessels. These hormones, that are synthesized in the hypothalamus, pass to the posterior lobe of the pituitary gland by way of the hypothalamic-hypophyseal axonal tract. In the posterior lobe, they enter hypophyseal capillaries and are released into the blood circulation.

Hypothalamic neurons also synthesize a number of hormones that are transported to the anterior pituitary gland, where they function to inhibit or stimulate the release of additional hormones. These hypothalamic hormones include: growth hormone releasing hormone (GHRH), growth hormone inhibiting hormone, or somatostatin (GHIH), thyroid releasing hormone (TRH), corticotropin releasing hormone (CRH), gonadotropin releasing hormone (GnRH), and prolactin inhibiting hormone (PIH). These hormones follow a path to the anterior pituitary that is different from the path to the posterior pituitary. Vesicles containing these stimulatory or inhibitory hormones are transported from the axons of hypothalamic neurons to the primary capillary plexus located in the upper region of the pituitary gland. They then enter the hypophyseal portal system (which is composed of capillary beds adjoined to veins) and travel to the anterior pituitary lobe. The anterior pituitary secretes the appropriate hormones into the secondary capillary plexus, which drains into the bloodstream.

Hormones secreted by the anterior pituitary gland include: prolactin, which targets mammary glands and stimulates breast milk production; growth hormone (GH), which targets muscle bones and other tissues and fosters growth; thyroid stimulating hormone (TSH), which targets the thyroid gland and regulates metabolism; adrenocorticotropic hormone (ACTH), which targets the adrenal gland and is involved in the regulation of fluid balance and stress; endorphins, which regulate pain pathways in the peripheral nervous system and function to inhibit pain; and the gonadotropins (which include FSH-follicle stimulating hormone and LH-luteinizing hormone). FSH affects both the ovaries and testes. In females, it stimulates estrogen production and follicle maturation. In males, FSH stimulates the production of sperm. LH also affects both the ovaries and testes. In females, it stimulates the production of progesterone and estrogen, and initiates ovulation. In males, LH stimulates the production of testosterone. Cells located at the boundary of the anterior and posterior pituitary lobes produce melanocyte stimulating hormone (MSH). This hormone targets melanocytes and promotes pigmentation (skin darkening). The proper balance of each of these hormones is necessary for normal body functioning. For example, hyperproduction of growth hormone (GH) during childhood results in gigantism, whereas hypersecretion of GH results in dwarfism in children. See Figure 13-8 for a summary of the major pituitary hormones.

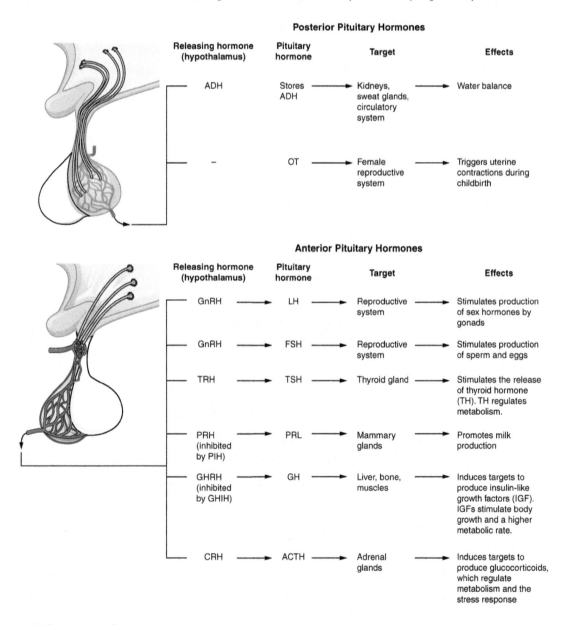

Figure 13-8 Major pituitary hormones.

The thyroid gland

The "shield shaped" thyroid gland, which is located in the neck, produces triiodthyronine (T3) and thyroxine (T4 or tetraiodthyronine).

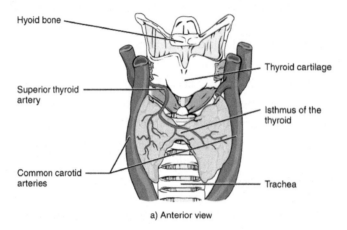

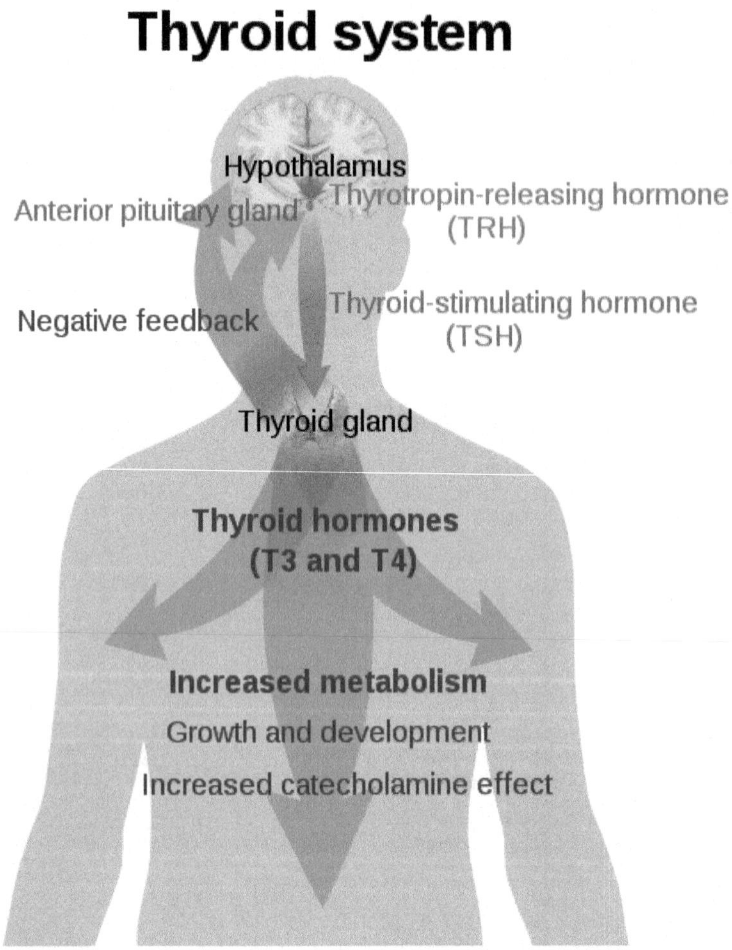

a) Anterior view

Figure 13-9A The thyroid gland

Figure 13-9B Thyroid hormone production

These hormones are synthesized from iodine and tyrosine, and regulate many functions, including the basal metabolic rate (BMR) and the production of body heat. The normal production of the thyroid hormones T3 and T4 results in numerous physiological effects, such as stimulating an increase in metabolism and promoting the normal growth, development, and functioning of the nervous, muscular, reproductive, cardiovascular, and gastrointestinal systems. Individuals who suffer from a low thyroid hormone output (or hypothryroidism) may feel lethargic, have a slower than normal heart rate, experience constipation, have pale skin, be predisposed to cold intolerance and weight gain, and have muscle aches (myalgia). Hypothyroidism can be caused by insufficient levels of TRH, TSH or dietary iodine, or can be due to the general dysfunction or inflammation of the thyroid gland (which can be caused by autoimmune disease known as Hashimoto's thyroiditis). Children with hypothyroidism may experience stunted growth. For example, cretinism is a syndrome caused by untreated congenital hypothyroidism and results in significantly reduced physical and mental growth.

Individuals who suffer from hyperthyroidism (or the over-production of thyroid hormones) may have a basal metabolic rate that is above normal, an increased body temperature, an intolerance to heat, a rapid heart rate, flushed skin and experience weight loss, irritability and insomnia. A common cause of hyperthyroidism is Grave's Disease. Grave's disease is an autoimmune disorder in which antibodies bind to TSH receptors promoting the constant release of thyroid hormones. In this case, the normal negative feedback mechanism by which excessive thyroid hormone production would inhibit the further secretion of TSH by the pituitary is blocked. Symptoms of Grave's disease include exophthalmos (or bulging of the eyes due to the abnormal accumulation of connective tissue) and an enlarged thyroid gland. An enlarged thyroid gland can also result in a swelled region of the neck known as a goiter.

Figure 13-10 Woman with a goiter.

A goiter can be produced from either the hypersecretion or hyposecretIon of thyroid hormones, or the lack of dietary iodine (which leads to hypothyroidism). Treatments of thyroid hormone diseases include iodine and/or thyroid hormone replacement. If necessary, the thyroid gland can be completely destroyed (or ablated) to ensure proper hormone supplementation.

Calcitonin, a hormone involved with calcium homeostasis, is also produced by specialized cells (the parafollicular or "C" cells) of the thyroid gland. Calcitonin secretion is stimulated when levels of calcium in the blood rise above normal (hypercalcemia). Calcitonin acts to reduce blood calcium levels by inhibiting Ca^{2+} uptake in the intestine, inhibiting the reabsorption of Ca^{2+} by the kidney (allowing it to be excreted in the urine), by stimulating the deposition of Ca^{2+} in the bones, and inhibiting bone reabsorption (see Figure 13-12). Bone reabsorption is the process by which specialized cells known as osteoclasts break down bone tissue to release essential minerals (such as Ca^{2+} and PO_4^{3+}) into the blood.

The parathyroid glands

In humans, the four small parathyroid glands are located on the surface of the thyroid gland.

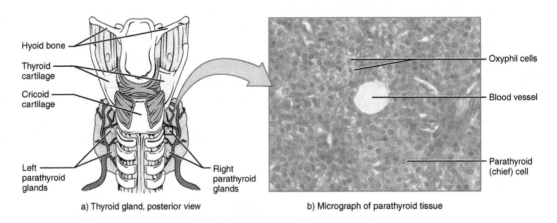

a) Thyroid gland, posterior view

b) Micrograph of parathyroid tissue

Figure 13-11 The parathyroid glands.

These endocrine glands secrete parathyroid hormone (PTH), which carries out the opposite function of calcitonin. PTH acts to increase the concentration of calcium in the blood by increasing the uptake up calcium in the intestines. It does this, in part, by activating vitamin D production, which promotes Ca^{2+} absorption into the blood from the food contents in the small intestine. It also stimulates calcium reabsorption in the kidneys and stimulates bone reabsorption, causing the release of Ca^{2+} into the general circulation.

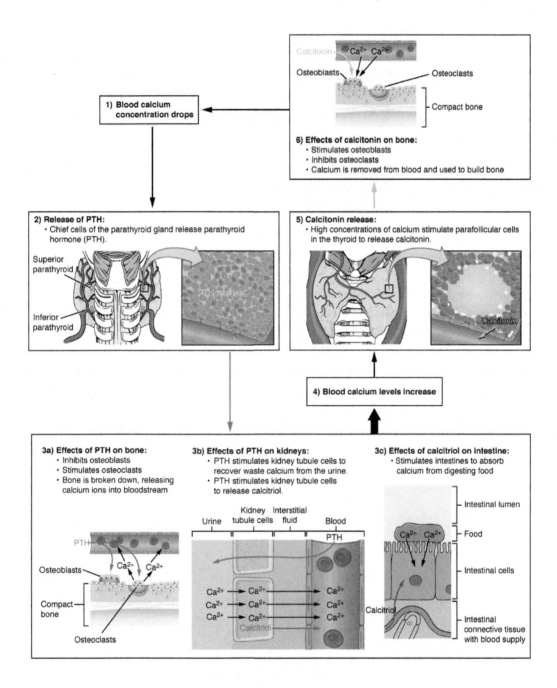

Figure 13-12 Blood calcium homeostasis.

The adrenal glands

The adrenal glands are located at the upper edge of the kidneys and are composed of an outer region (the adrenal cortex) and an inner region (the adrenal medulla). The hormones produced by the adrenal cortex are classified as corticosteroids and include the glucocorticoids, mineralcorticoids and gonadocorticoids.

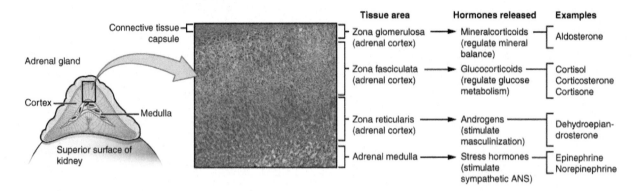

Tissue area	Hormones released	Examples
Zona glomerulosa (adrenal cortex)	Mineralcorticoids (regulate mineral balance)	Aldosterone
Zona fasciculata (adrenal cortex)	Glucocorticoids (regulate glucose metabolism)	Cortisol Corticosterone Cortisone
Zona reticularis (adrenal cortex)	Androgens (stimulate masculinization)	Dehydroepiandrosterone
Adrenal medulla	Stress hormones (stimulate sympathetic ANS)	Epinephrine Norepinephrine

Figure 13-13 The adrenal glands.

Glucocorticoids help maintain normal blood glucose levels by stimulating glucose synthesis from fats and proteins, inhibiting glucose uptake in muscle and adipose tissue (which is a mechanism to conserve glucose, sometimes called "glucose sparing"), and by stimulating the breakdown of fats and proteins to amino acids and fatty acids (which can be used as alternative energy sources when glucose is not readily available). A common example of a glucocorticoid is cortisol, which is released in response to stress by the action of corticotropin releasing hormone (CRH) from the hypothalamus. CRH triggers the secretion of adrenocorticotropic hormone (ACTH), from the anterior pituitary gland. ACTH stimulates the adrenal gland to increases cortisol production and promotes its release. This mechanism exemplifies the hypothalamic–pituitary–adrenal (HPA) axis.

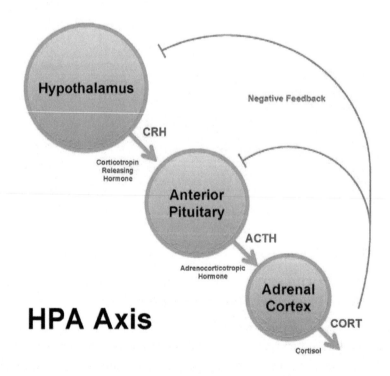

Figure 13-14 The HPA axis.

Cortisol is involved in a number of activities, such as increasing blood pressure and blood sugar levels, and reducing the immune response (thereby serving as an anti-inflammatory agent). An excess of glucocorticoids (such as cortisol) which can result from high levels of ACTH or an adrenal tumor, can cause Cushing's disease. Symptoms of Cushing's disease are numerous, but may include "moon face" due to swelling, increased adipose tissue at the back of the neck and around the abdomen, elevated blood glucose, and high blood pressure (hypertension). In contrast to Cushing's disease, where there is an overproduction of hormones of the adrenal cortex, Addison's disease results from an underproduction of glucocorticoids. This can be caused by adrenal dysfunction, which may result from a number of maladies, such as infection, autoimmune reactions, etc. Low blood pressure, weight loss and severe dehydration are common symptoms of Addison's disease. A conventional treatment for Addison's disease is cortisol supplementation.

Mineralcorticoids are also released by the adrenal cortex. A common mineralcorticoid is aldosterone, which is essential for the regulation of Na+ and K+ and is stimulated by ACTH, as well as the mechanisms of the Renin-Aldosterone-Angiotensin-System (RAAS), as described in Chapter 11. Recall that the increased secretion of aldosterone from the adrenal cortex causes kidney cells to increase the reabsorption of Na+ and water (as well as increase K+ excretion), which leads to a rise in blood volume and blood pressure. The gonadocorticoids, which are the third sub-type of hormones produced in the adrenal cortex consist primarily of androgens. They can be converted to testosterone and estrogen in the corresponding gonadal tissues.

The adrenal medulla secretes the catecholamines epinephrine and norepinephrine, which are synthesized from tyrosine. In response to such stresses as danger, fear, injury, or infection, neurons of the hypothalamus stimulate preganglionic neurons of the sympathetic nervous system that emerge from the spinal cord. These preganglionic sympathetic fibers travel to the adrenal medulla and release acetylcholine, which stimulates the synthesis and release of epinephrine and norepinephrine from the chromaffin cells of the adrenal medulla into the circulation. This produces the sympathetic effect, which includes an increase in heart rate and blood pressure, bronchiole dilation, an increase in metabolic rate, the conversion of glycogen to glucose in the liver for release into the bloodstream, and a reduction in the activity of the digestive system. These effects are determined by the type of receptors epinephrine and norepinephrine bind. For example, epinephrine can bind to α, β1, β2 type receptors. When epinephrine binds α receptors on the smooth muscle of particular blood vessels, the vessels primarily constrict, resulting in less blood flow to peripheral body regions (such as the skin). When epinephrine binds to β1 receptors on heart cells, contraction intensifies, resulting in an increase in blood flow. When it binds to β2 receptors on liver cells, glycogen is broken down to glucose. The end result of these processes is an increase in energy.

The pancreas

The pancreas produce both exocrine and endocrine factors.

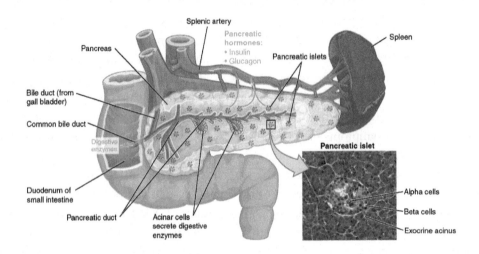

Figure 13-15 The pancreas.

The endocrine cells of the pancreas reside in the spherical shaped areas known as the Islets of Langerhans. These pancreatic islet cells are subdivided into the **α** cells, which produce the hormone glucagon, and the **β** cells, which produce the hormone insulin. Glucagon raises blood glucose levels by stimulating glycogen, fat, and protein degradation. Insulin functions to lower blood sugar levels by facilitating the uptake of glucose into body cells such as adipose cells, muscle cells, and liver cells. In muscle and liver cells, glucose can be stored as glycogen. In adipose cells, it can be converted to fatty acids. When insulin levels are low, glucose is not efficiently taken up by cells and the body begins to use fat and proteins as a primary energy sources.

Diabetes mellitus is a disease in which blood glucose levels are elevated due to either low (or no) insulin production or to inhibited insulin action (insulin insensitivity). Common symptoms of diabetes mellitus include frequent urination and excessive urine output (polyuria), increased thirst (polydipsia), and increased hunger (polyphagia). Polyuria results from the body's increase in the use of water to facilitate the excretion of the excess blood glucose. Polydipsia results from the need to replace this additional water loss, and polyphagia occurs because the body needs to replenish the energy sources (proteins and fats) that have been broken down as a result of the lack of cellular glucose uptake.

In Type 1 diabetes mellitus, pancreatic beta cells are destroyed by an autoimmune response. Those with Type 1 diabetes manage their disease by receiving regular insulin injections. In Type 2 diabetes mellitus, insulin is in fact produced, but target cells have insufficient quantities of insulin receptors. Because these cells are less responsive to insulin and cannot properly take up glucose, it is not available to the cells as energy source. As indicated above, to meet energy requirements, fats and proteins are utilized. However, extensive protein breakdown can weaken blood vessels and lead to poor blood circulation, which can result in the degeneration of body tissues. Left untreated, diabetes mellitus can result in complications such as kidney failure, blindness and peripheral neuropathies (nerve damage). Another type of diabetes, known as diabetes insipidus (DI), is characterized by excessive thirst and the excretion of large amounts of dilute urine. There are several sub-types of diabetes insipidus that result from specific causes. A common type is neurogenic DI, which is caused by a deficiency antidiuretic hormone (ADH).

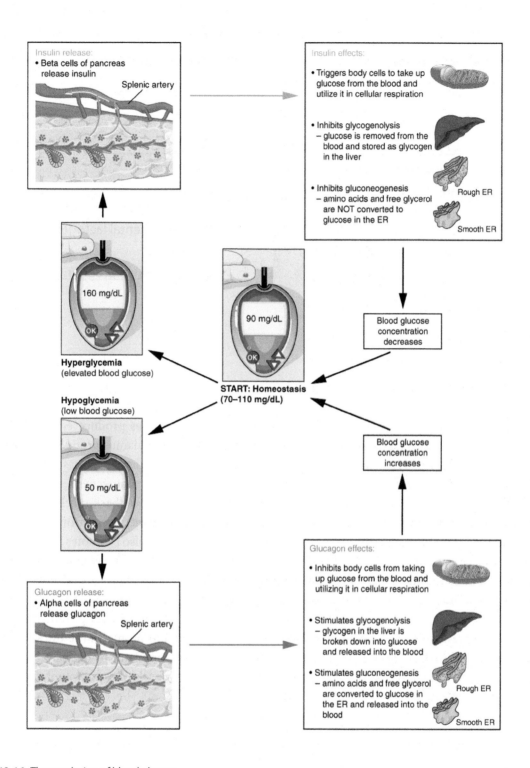

Insulin release:
- Beta cells of pancreas release insulin

Splenic artery

Insulin effects:
- Triggers body cells to take up glucose from the blood and utilize it in cellular respiration
- Inhibits glycogenolysis – glucose is removed from the blood and stored as glycogen in the liver
- Inhibits gluconeogenesis – amino acids and free glycerol are NOT converted to glucose in the ER

Rough ER

Smooth ER

160 mg/dL
OK

Hyperglycemia
(elevated blood glucose)

90 mg/dL
OK

Blood glucose concentration decreases

START: Homeostasis
(70–110 mg/dL)

Hypoglycemia
(low blood glucose)

50 mg/dL
OK

Blood glucose concentration increases

Glucagon release:
- Alpha cells of pancreas release glucagon

Splenic artery

Glucagon effects:
- Inhibits body cells from taking up glucose from the blood and utilizing it in cellular respiration
- Stimulates glycogenolysis – glycogen in the liver is broken down into glucose and released into the blood
- Stimulates gluconeogenesis – amino acids and free glycerol are converted to glucose in the ER and released into the blood

Rough ER

Smooth ER

Figure 13-16 The regulation of blood glucose.

The male and female gonads

The testes and the ovaries produce hormones that regulate the development of the reproductive systems, sexual characteristics (puberty), and mating behavior.

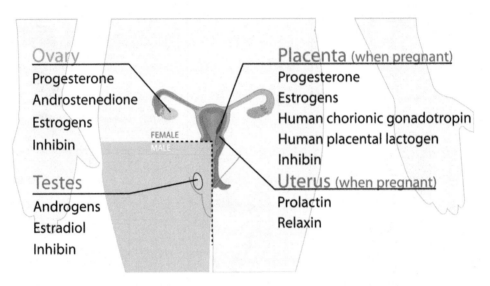

Figure 13-17 Hormones of the reproductive system.

The testes produce androgens (such as testosterone) and the ovaries produce estrogens (such as estradiol) and progestins (such as progesterone). Recall that the hypothalamus produces gonadotropin releasing hormone (GnRH), which acts on the anterior pituitary to stimulate the release of FSH and LH. In the male, FSH acts on the Sertoli cells of the testes, stimulating spermatogenesis. It also elicits the production of inhibin from Sertoli cells, which functions by a negative feedback mechanism to inhibit further FSH secretion by the anterior pituitary. The LH that is secreted by the anterior pituitary acts on the Leydig cells of the testes to stimulate testosterone production, which also promotes spermatogenesis. Testosterone can also inhibit further LH production from the anterior pituitary, as well as GnRH production from the hypothalamus via a negative feedback mechanism. In females, the release of FSH from the anterior pituitary into the blood circulation (which is triggered by GnRH from the hypothalalmus) facilitates the growth and development of a follicle in the ovaries. A surge in LH production results in ovulation. Progesterone and estradiol produced by the corpus luteum promotes the thickening of the endometrium. The release of GnRH from the hypothalamus can be stimulated by high levels of estradiol and inhibited by a combination of estradiol and progesterone. Low levels of estradiol inhibit the secretion of both FSH and LH from the anterior pituitary gland.

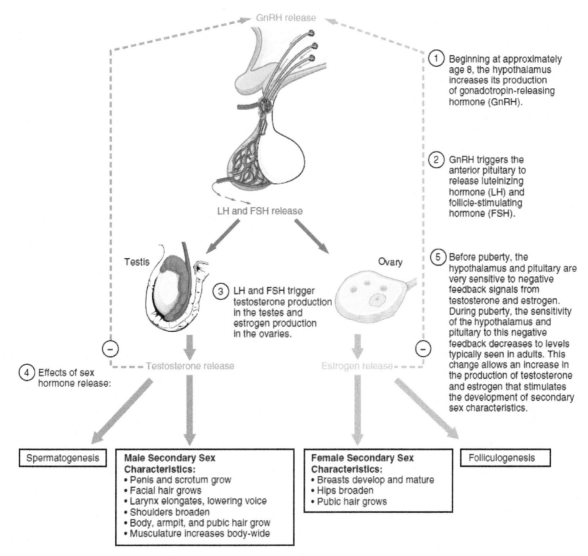

Figure 13-18 Sex hormone feedback mechanisms

Why is doping harmful?

Simply stated, a steroid is a general class of lipids that can easily cross the plasma membrane. Steroids are related by their structural features, such as a fused ring system (i.e., 3 cyclohexanes and 1 cyclopentane), and a large number of carbon-hydrogen bonds, with functional groups that can be highly diverse. Recall the classes of naturally occurring steroid hormones produced in the body: glucocorticoids, mineral corticoids, androgens, estrogens and progestins. However, in colloquial language, the term "steroid" often refers to synthetic compounds that can mimic the effects of natural steroids. In particular, anabolic steroids are a class of steroids that can bind to androgen receptors and initiate a number of molecular interactions that result in increased muscle and bone mass. Specifically, anabolic steroids stimulate the production of myosin and actin proteins, which can then be incorporated into muscle myofibrils, thereby increasing muscle mass and muscular strength. Anabolic steroids can also block some of the actions of the stress hormone cortisol. Cortisol is believed to inhibit protein synthesis and decrease amino acid uptake in muscle, which contribute to the breakdown of muscle tissue.

There are a number of serious and damaging side effects associated with steroid use. Some examples include: stroke, hypertension, heart disease, liver damage, joint pain, tendonitis, headaches, impotence, aggressive behavior, enlarged prostate and acne.

Chapter 13 Review

I. Helpful and Interesting Animations

1. Hormonal regulation:
   http://highered.mcgrawhill.com/sites/0072507470/student_view0/chapter18/animation__hormonal_communication.html

2. Steroid hormones:
   http://highered.mcgrawhill.com/sites/0072507470/student_view0/chapter18/animation__mechanism_of_steroid_hormone_action__quiz_1_.html

3. HPA:
   http://bcs.whfreeman.com/thelifewire/content/chp42/4202s.swf

4. Testosterone production:
   http://www.youtube.com/watch?v=djqqao2Uebo&list=TLRpKwwZyBtvdvjd-gb0WGZVQz5NvqAyJS&index=7

II. Active Testing: Do you know the facts?

A. List the words in this chapter you would have printed in bold type.
Can you define these words?

B. What are the main, "take home" messages of this chapter?
 Is your answer the same as your instructor's answer?

C. Some Questions:

1. Name 3 main features of the chemical structure of steroids. Give an example of a common steroid.

2. How are steroid hormones classified? List each classification and give an example of a steroid hormone that belongs to each group.

3. List 3 important facts about cholesterol

4. Identify the location of each endocrine gland in the human body.

5. Explain the 4 major types of cell signaling in the endocrine system. Give an example of each.

6. Hormones can be classified by the types of molecules they are derived from. List 4 classifications of hormones and give an example of each.

7. Explain the function of prostaglandins. What chemical factor can inhibit their production?

8. Distinguish between hydrophilic and hydrophobic hormones.

9. Explain the molecular mechanism of aldosterone.

10. Fill in the chart below:

Gland	Major Hormone(s)	**Function**
1.	melatonin	
2.	ADH	
	oxytocin	
	GnRH	
3. Posterior pituitary		
4.		Stress and fluid balance
		Metabolism
		Produce gametes, female hormones
		Ovulation, male sex hormones
		Milk production
		Growth of muscles, bone
		Skin darkening
		Inhibits pain perception
5.	T3	
	T4	
	calcitonin	
6. Parathyroid		
7. Adrenal (medulla)		
Adrenal (cortex)		
	aldosterone	
8. Pancreas		Facilitates glucose uptake from the blood into cells
		Raises blood glucose by stimulating glycogen, fat, and protein degradation
9.	estrogens (estradiol) progestins (progesterone)	
10.		Development of the male reproductive system secondary sex characteristics (male)

11. Describe the effects insulin-mediated glucose uptake (and amino acid uptake, when applicable) into muscle cells, adipocytes and the liver.

12. Compare and contrast diabetes mellitus with diabetes insipidus.

III. Inquiring minds want to know…

Challenge Questions

1. Thomas Beatie, a transgender female-to-male individual (See Figure 1-1) has given birth to three children. What type of hormone replacement therapy (HRT) did he likely receive to develop the secondary sex characteristics of a male? What type of hormone therapy did he likely receive to enable his pregnancies?

2. Osteoporosis is a widespread medical condition characterized by a significant decrease in bone density that can lead to bone fracture. Explain how estrogen, PTH and vitamin D can contribute to the pathology of osteoporosis.

Chapter 14

Specific and Non-Specific Responses of the Immune System to an Infection

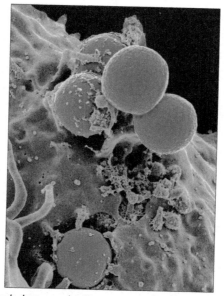

Figure 14-1 A scanning electron micrograph shows methicillin-resistant Staphylococcus aureus (MRSA) bacteria (purple) being ingested by a human neutrophil (green). MRSA causes many bacterial infections that are challenging to manage as they are resistant to a number of antiobiotics, such as the penicillins and the cephalosporins.

What is an infection?

Viruses

Simply stated, an infection is the condition that results when microorganisms that are capable of producing a disease (pathogenic) enter a host, multiply and challenge the host's defense system. Pathogenic microorganisms include viruses and bacteria. Viruses are infectious particles that are obligate intracellular parasites. They proliferate by controlling the host cell's genetic material and synthetic mechanisms in order to replicate themselves. Viruses are miniscule in size when compared to the cells they usually infect. In general, they have a very basic structure that usually includes a nucleic acid component (DNA or RNA) encapsulated by a protein shell (capsid). Some viruses also have a lipid component (an envelope) that surrounds the protein coat and may also have some additional structural proteins. Viruses usually have a small amount of genetic material, possessing only the genes that are needed to invade a host cell and redirect its activity in order to replicate themselves.

Viral infection typically begins by the binding of a viral capsid protein to a receptor on the host cell membrane. This pairing determines the specificity of the virus for particular host cells. For example, human immunodeficiency virus (HIV) has a protein (gp120) on its surface that binds to the CD4 receptor molecule found on specific cells of the immune system (CD4+ T cells). Once bound to a host cell, the virus next enters the cell via processes such as endocytosis. (Note that some bacteriophage viruses inject their genetic material into the cell, rather than enter by endocytosis). The virus is then uncoated as the capsid is separated from the genetic material. Enzyme degradation of the capsid often facilitates this process. The released genetic material from DNA viruses enters the nucleus, where it can utilize the host cell's DNA synthesizing and transcriptional apparatus, or inserts into the host DNA and remains as a dormant provirus until being activated at a later time. Translation of the viral mRNA provides the proteins necessary to reassemble numerous additional viruses. The newly made viruses are then released from the host cell and are fully competent to infect other cells. This release can be accompanied by lysis of the host cell, or may occur by budding. Enveloped viruses (such as HIV) are typically released by budding, which is the process by which they acquire their envelope from a portion of the host cell's membrane. RNA viruses can use specialized RNA replicase enzymes to copy their RNA or reverse transcriptase to generate complementary DNA. In addition to lysing a cell, viral infection of a cell can cause severe damage that is collectively referred to as cytopathogenic effects (CPEs). Viral infection can cause the termination of cellular metabolism and gene expression, as well as the destruction of organelles and membranes. Infected cells can fuse, forming multinucleated syncytia, enlarge, and harbor inclusion bodies (aggregates of cellular material) or round up. All of these effects will result in the deterioration of normal cell function which lead to the systemic effects of a viral infection.

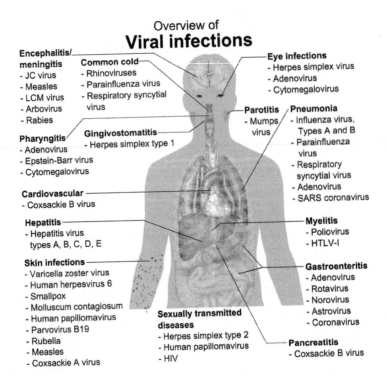

Figure 14-2 Viral Infections.

Bacteria

Bacteria comprise a wide variety of unicellular organisms. Pathogenic bacteria can cause infections by invading and colonizing body tissues and producing toxins that disrupt normal cell function. For example, Cholera toxin is secreted by the bacterium *Vibrio cholera*. This toxin is a protein complex that, through a number of intracellular steps, disrupts the functioning of chloride channels in the plasma membrane of intestinal cells, resulting in an efflux of Cl-. This leads to an increase in the secretion of water, HCO_3^-, K+ and Na+ into the intestinal lumen, resulting in diarrhea and dehydration. There are numerous types of bacterial infections. Figure 14-3 summarizes the effects of some common bacterial infections.

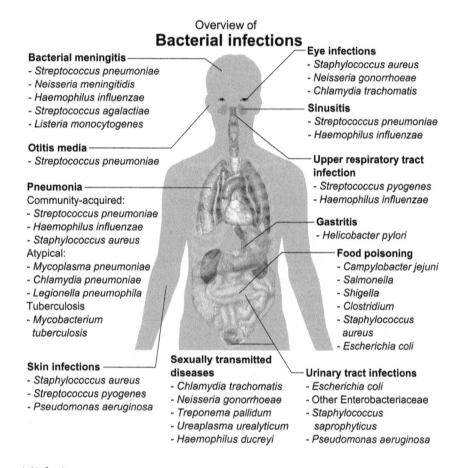

Overview of
Bacterial infections

Bacterial meningitis
- *Streptococcus pneumoniae*
- *Neisseria meningitidis*
- *Haemophilus influenzae*
- *Streptococcus agalactiae*
- *Listeria monocytogenes*

Otitis media
- *Streptococcus pneumoniae*

Pneumonia
Community-acquired:
- *Streptococcus pneumoniae*
- *Haemophilus influenzae*
- *Staphylococcus aureus*
Atypical:
- *Mycoplasma pneumoniae*
- *Chlamydia pneumoniae*
- *Legionella pneumophila*
Tuberculosis
- *Mycobacterium tuberculosis*

Skin infections
- *Staphylococcus aureus*
- *Streptococcus pyogenes*
- *Pseudomonas aeruginosa*

Eye infections
- *Staphylococcus aureus*
- *Neisseria gonorrhoeae*
- *Chlamydia trachomatis*

Sinusitis
- *Streptococcus pneumoniae*
- *Haemophilus influenzae*

Upper respiratory tract infection
- *Streptococcus pyogenes*
- *Haemophilus influenzae*

Gastritis
- *Helicobacter pylori*

Food poisoning
- *Campylobacter jejuni*
- *Salmonella*
- *Shigella*
- *Clostridium*
- *Staphylococcus aureus*
- *Escherichia coli*

Sexually transmitted diseases
- *Chlamydia trachomatis*
- *Neisseria gonorrhoeae*
- *Treponema pallidum*
- *Ureaplasma urealyticum*
- *Haemophilus ducreyi*

Urinary tract infections
- *Escherichia coli*
- Other Enterobacteriaceae
- *Staphylococcus saprophyticus*
- *Pseudomonas aeruginosa*

Figure 14-3 Bacterial Infections.

A common treatment for bacterial infections is antibiotics, which destroy bacteria by a variety of mechanisms that target the bacterial cells while sparing the organism's cells. For example, penicillin is a type of antibiotic that inhibits the formation of the bacteria cell wall. Another class of antibiotics, the tetracyclines, bind to a subunit of the bacterial ribosome, disrupting protein synthesis. Quinolones are antibiotics that inhibit bacterial DNA gyrase, which blocks DNA synthesis in the bacterium.

How to fight an infection-The immune response

The body's immune response is subdivided into two major categories: the non-specific, innate immune response and the specific, acquired (or adaptive) immune response. Key players in the innate immune response include: the inflammatory response, phagocytes, complement, and chemical mediators such as cytokines and interferon. Some of the key players of the adaptive immune response include: antibodies, antigens, and antigen presenting cells, as well as T and B lymphocytes. Certain components (such as complement, phagocytic cells, and various chemical factors) are active in both the innate and acquired immune response. The innate immune response acts sooner and does not have a high degree of specificity (that is, it responds to a broad range of pathogens). The acquired immune response recognizes features that are unique to particular pathogens, is less rapid (there is a delay between pathogen exposure and initial response) and has immunologic memory. Immunologic memory refers to the ability of immune cells to recognize aspects of a pathogen after the initial infection has been eradicated so that a more rapid and more potent immune reaction can be elicited each subsequent time the pathogen is encountered. Because of this, the adaptive immune response can confer long lasting immunity to a pathogen.

The first line of defense the body uses to fight an infection is elicited in response to a broad range of infectious agents and includes non-specific physical, chemical and genetic mechanisms. For example, the skin forms a physical barrier that resists penetration by infectious agents such as viruses and bacteria. Mucous membranes in the mouth and nasal passages contain inhibitors that can prevent viral attachment to cells or may even directly inactivate a virus. Lysozyme is an enzyme that is found in a number of secretions, such saliva, mucous, tears, and human breast milk. It breaks down essential components of bacterial cell walls (peptidoglycans, chitodextrins) which cause their demise. The acid environment of the stomach also kills many unwanted bacteria. Additionally, some viruses may only infect certain hosts due to the specificity of their surface proteins to host receptors. For example, the virus that causes distemper in dogs does not affect humans.

When a pathogen successfully penetrates the general protective mechanisms of the body, the non-specific, innate immune response is activated. This activation can occur in response to the recognition of general components shared by pathogens, or by factors released by damaged cells. For example, PRRs (pattern recognition receptors) on immune cells recognize pathogen associated molecular patterns (PAMPs) that are found in a number of microbes. A common example of a PPR are the Toll-like receptors, which are membrane spanning protein receptors found on particular immune cells (such as macrophages and dendritic cells; the so-called "sentinel" cells). There are a number of toll like receptors (at least 13) that bind to specific ligands (or PAMPs). Some examples of PAMPs include lipopolysaccharide (LLP), a large carbohydrate found on the outer membrane of bacteria, unique bacterial proteins (such as flagellin), and bacterial or viral RNA and DNA.

The innate immune response employs a number of mechanisms and factors to perform its activities. Some of these include: specialized immune cells, the inflammatory response, cytokines, complement, and interferon (IFN).

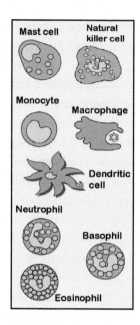

Figure 14-4 Cells of the innate immune system have characteristic morphologies and specialized functions.

An inflammatory response can be initiated by chemical factors that are released when cells infected by a pathogen become damaged. Inflammation serves to isolate the infected site, preventing the infection from spreading, as well as removing pathogen and damaged cells, which promotes healing. It is characterized by local vascular changes, such as vasodilation and increased circulation, redness, warmth, swelling and pain.

These changes are primarily initiated by the release of histamine by resident immune cells (such as mast cells and basophils). Histamine can dilate and increase the permeability of local blood vessels, which helps to rapidly deliver additional immune cells and chemical factors to the site of the infection. Cytokines are a broad category of chemical mediators that are involved in a number of roles in the inflammatory response. For example, chemokines are a class of cytokines that attract immune cells, such as phagocytic cells (neutrophils, macrophages) from the bloodstream to the infected area. Phagocytic cells are capable of engulfing large particles or cells into vesicles. Ingestion is usually followed by the formation of phagolysosomes, which are formed from the fusion of phagocytic vesicles with lysosomes. Lysosomes provide hydrolytic enzymes to digest the phagocytosed material.

The innate immune response also employs the complement system. Complement refers to a non-specific group of proteins that reside in the blood plasma as non-active precursors. They can become activated locally at a site of infection by a variety of mechanisms. For example, the presence of particular polysaccharides on the cell wall of bacteria can initiate a series of steps (the complement cascade) that generates a complex of proteins (the membrane attack complex) at the surface of a pathogen that effectively destroy the pathogen. Additionally, the activation of certain complement proteins can lead to increased phagocytosis and chemotaxis during the inflammatory response. Note that complement is also utilized by the adaptive immune response (and can be activated by the presence of antibodies).

Interferons (INF) are a class of cytokines that, like complement, can be used in both the innate and adaptive immune response. Their production in the host cell can be triggered by the interaction of PPRs and PAMPs when it is infected by a pathogen. Then name "interferon" derives from their ability to "interfere" with the production of a variety of viruses in host cells (thus, they do not have a specificity for a particular viruses). Once produced by a virally infected cell, interferons are secreted into the extracellular space, where they bind to other host cells and stimulate the production of proteins that can degrade viral nucleic acids or prevent the translation of viral proteins. They can also activate macrophages, enhance phagocytosis, and activate natural killer cells (NKs). Natural killer cells are lymphocytes involved both the innate and acquired immune response. They have the ability to detect virally infected or otherwise damaged cells and induce cellular apoptosis or cell lysis. Two important types of proteins that are secreted by NK cells are perforins and granzymes. These proteins are also secreted by the cytotoxic T cells of the acquired immune system (See Figure 14-17). Perforins create pores in targets cells that can either rupture the cells or provide a passage for granzymes and other molecules that can induce apoptosis or lysis. Note that cell death by lysis can result in the release of newly made virus particles that can infect other local cells. However, death by apoptosis destroys the viral particles inside the infected cell, thereby preventing the propagation of the infection.

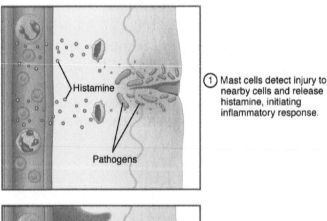

① Mast cells detect injury to nearby cells and release histamine, initiating inflammatory response.

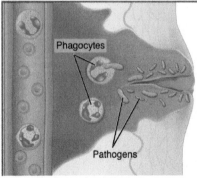

② Histamine increases blood flow to the wound sites, bringing in phagocytes and other immune cells that neutralize pathogens. The blood influx causes the wound to swell, redden, and become warm and painful.

Figure 14-5 The inflammatory response.

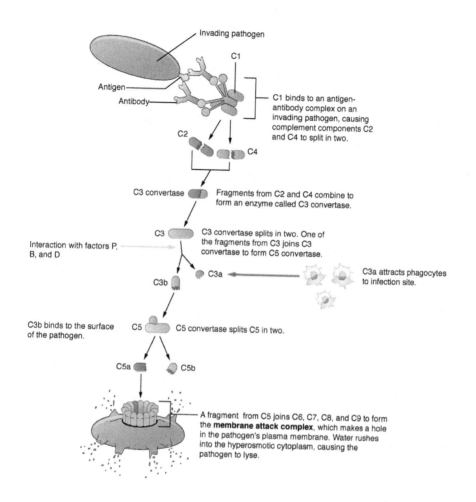

Figure 14-5 Complement activation.

A viral infection that results in the production of double stranded RNA (dsRNA) within a cell can similarly induce the production of interferon. Interestingly, the presence of dsRNA can also elicit the cellular mechanism of RNA interference (RNAi) which, by a series of steps, can efficiently degrade viral mRNA. In this process, an enzyme known as Dicer cleaves dsRNA into segments that are about 20 nucleotide pairs in length. These pieces are known as small interfering RNA (siRNA). A single strand of the siRNA is incorporated into a protein complex known as RNA induced silencing complex (RISC), where it binds to a complementary sequence of mRNA. Enzymatic proteins in the RISC complex, known as argonautes, cleave the viral mRNA, effectively disrupting the production of new viruses.

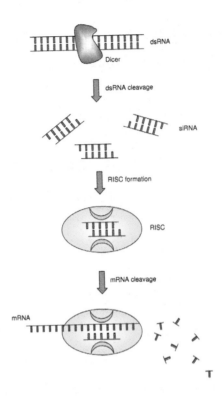

Figure 14-6 RNA interference.

The adaptive (acquired) immune response

To reiterate, the adaptive immune response has two major characteristics. First, it is specific. The components of the adaptive immune response identify and eliminate a particular antigen that is pathogenic. Second, it generates immunologic memory. A more rapid and stronger response will be mounted to subsequent infections by the same pathogen. To initiate an adaptive immune response, lymphocytes must be activated. This occurs by various mechanisms, such as the specific binding of the pathogen (or a component of the pathogen) to the receptor on a lymphocyte, the association of a lymphocyte with an antigen presenting cell, and stimulation by specialized molecules, such as cytokines, that can elicit a number of effects. Once activated, the lymphocytes will proliferate to produce two general classes of cells: effector cells and memory cells.

There are two types of adaptive immune responses: antibody mediated (which is also known as humoral immunity) and cell mediated immunity (CMI). Both mechanisms are stimulated by the exposure to antigen. An antigen is the term for something that is foreign to the body (such as a virus or bacteria) that is capable of triggering an immune response. An antigenic determinant (also known as an epitope) is the precise molecular group of an antigen that is identified by immune factors (such as antibodies, B cells, and antigen presenting cells). Antibodies and antigens are key players in the humoral immune response. Antibodies are secreted into the blood circulation by specialized types of immune effector cells, the plasma cells, which are derived from B lymphocytes. B lymphocytes, in turn, are one of many blood cell types that arise from the differentiation of hematopoietic stem cells found in the bone marrow.

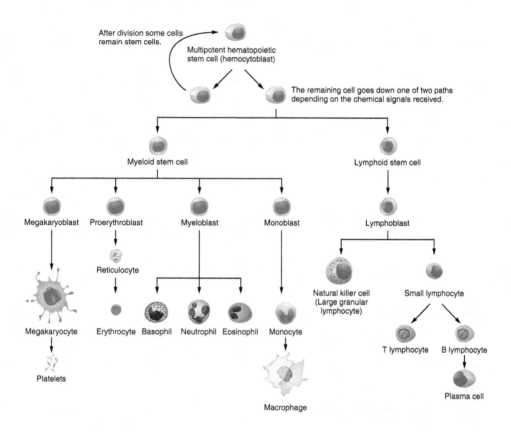

Figure 14-7 The hematopoetic system.

Specifically, antibodies are large glycoprotein molecules categorized as immunoglobins. In general, immunoglobins share similar structural components that are built upon to generate increased complexity and functionality, giving rise to different types of antibodies. The canonical four chain structure of one type of antibody, IgG2, is shown in Figure 14-8 below.

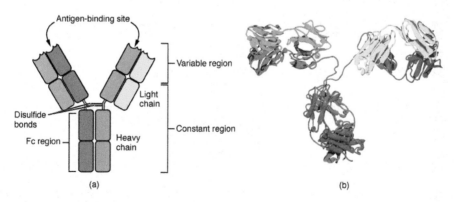

Figure 14-8 Antibody structure. The basic antibody structure consists of four polypeptide chains (two heavy, two light) connected by disulfide bridges. Each chain has a variable and a constant region termed Fc, "fragment that crystalizes" when stored at low temperatures. The Fc fragment determines the antibody class.

The general structure of an antibody is composed of two large heavy chains and two smaller light chains. Of great significance is the variable region located at the terminal portion of the heavy and light chains. This region serves as the antigen binding site. Because this structure, located at the tip of the immunoglobin protein, can vary so greatly between antibodies, a multitude of diverse antibodies are generated that can bind specifically to a multitude of unique antigens. The body is able to generate millions of different antibodies by combining different combinations of gene segments to produce a diversity of unique variable regions on the immunoglobin protein. It accomplishes this grand task by the process of somatic recombination (also called: V(D)J recombination). This process occurs in the bone marrow or thymus during the generation of B cells or T cells, respectively. Each heavy chain gene consists of a number of copies of 3 gene segments, referred to as V (variable), D (diversity) and J (joining). The light chains have V and J gene segments only. To generate a uniquely variable antigenic binding region on the heavy chain of an antibody, V, D or J gene segments that adjoin a "C" (or segment that encodes for the constant domain) are randomly selected and recombined. This new combination will be transcribed, processed and then translated into peptides that will comprise the antibody.

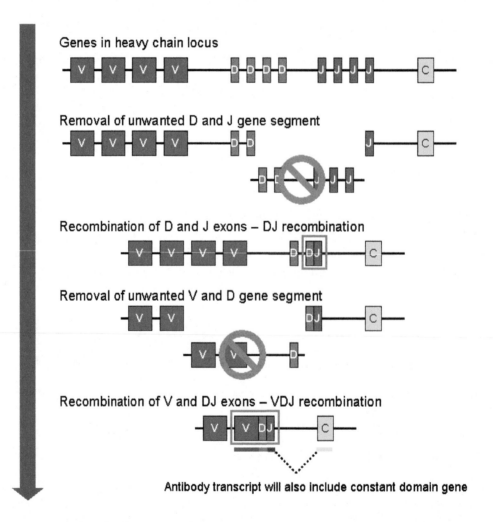

Figure 14-9 VDJ recombination.

The binding of antibody to antigen is very precise, allowing the antibody to neutralize a foreign pathogen or mark it for destruction by other immune system components. Specifically, antibodies can unite with and opsonize a pathogen (such as coating a virus), immobilize a pathogen by crosslinking and clumping the pathogen (agglutination), neutralize a pathogen by binding to its receptor sites thereby preventing its attachment to host cells, stimulating the complement system, and enhancing phagocytosis. There are 5 major antibody subclasses (or isotypes) found in humans. The 5 different classes of antibodies are categorized by their unique heavy chain structure and have specific functions in the body.

The Five Immunoglobulin (Ig) Classes					
	IgM pentamer	IgG monomer	Secretory IgA dimer	IgE monomer	IgD monomer
	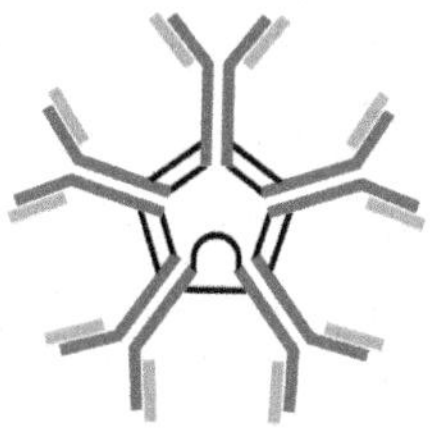	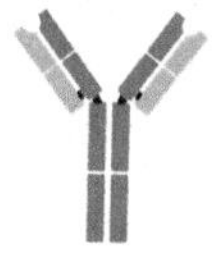	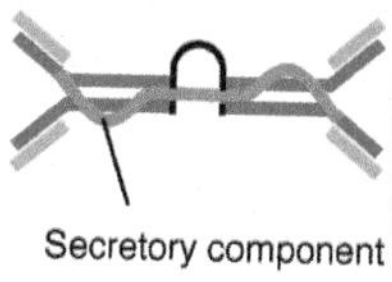 Secretory component	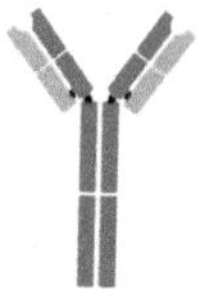	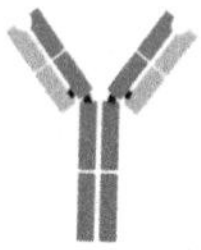
Heavy chains	μ	γ	α	ε	δ
Number of antigen binding sites	10	2	4	2	2
Molecular weight (Daltons)	900,000	150,000	385,000	200,000	180,000
Percentage of total antibody in serum	6%	80%	13%	0.002%	1%
Crosses placenta	no	yes	no	no	no
Fixes complement	yes	yes	no	no	no
Fc binds to		phagocytes		mast cells and basophils	
Function	Main antibody of primary responses, best at fixing complement; the monomer form of IgM serves as the B cell receptor	Main blood antibody of secondary responses, neutralizes toxins, opsonization	Secreted into mucus, tears, saliva, colostrum	Antibody of allergy and antiparasitic activity	B cell receptor

Figure 14-10 Antibody Classes.

In addition to functioning as secreted antibodies, immunoglobins also serve as membrane bound receptors on B cells. B cell receptors (BCRs) can bind to a variety antigens, such as proteins, glycoproteins, polysaccharides, viruses, and bacteria.

B-cell Receptor (BCR)

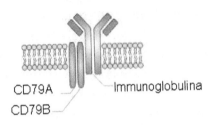

CD79A
CD79B ⌐Immunoglobulina

Figure 14-11 The B cell receptor.

With the aid of T helper (T_H) cells, the binding of antigen to B cell receptors stimulates B cells to differentiate into plasma cells (which produce soluble antibodies) or memory B cells, which will remain in the body after an initial infection to facilitate a more rapid immune response if the pathogen is encountered again. T_H cells are a sub-class of T lymphocytes. Unlike B cells, which develop into mature lymphocytes in the bone marrow, T cells differentiate and mature in the thymus (a lymphoid organ located in front of the heart). Both cell types will then migrate into other lymph tissue (such as the lymph nodes) for use in the body. T lymphocytes can be distinguished from other immune cells by the presence of characteristic T cell receptors (TCR) on their cell surface. Although T cell receptors are structurally different from B cell receptors, they too have a variable region that is generated by somatic recombination.

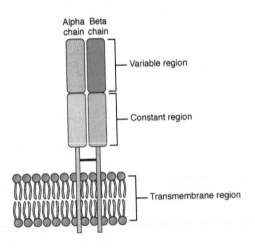

Figure 14-12 The T cell receptor.

The humoral immune response is implemented with the aid of both T and B lymphocytes. Initially, a pathogen is engulfed by an antigen presenting cell (APC). APCs, such as macrophages or dendritic cells, phagocytose and then display antigenic components on their cell surface in association with other specific molecules. These molecules are encoded by a large gene family called the major histocompatibility complex (MHC). Molecules of the MHC can be divided into three classes (I, II, III), each having primary roles in immune system function. Class II MHC molecules normally occur on antigen presenting cells. The displayed antigen/ MHC II complex on the APC is recognized by a specific type of T cell that harbors CD4 receptor molecules on its surface (and therefore is regarded as CD4+; CD stands for "cluster of differentiation"). In order for the CD4+ T cell to associate with the APC cell, its T cell receptor (TCR) must recognize and bind to the epitope displayed with the MHC II molecule on the antigen presenting cell. The CD4 molecule on the T cell facilitates the association between the APC and the T cell. This association triggers the production and secretion of cytokines (specifically, interleukins) from the antigen presenting cell, which activates the CD4+ T cell and stimulates it to produce cytokines. The cytokines act in an autocrine fashion to stimulate the proliferation of the CD4+ T cell. These activated CD4+ T cells can differentiate into a category of T cells known as helper T cells (T_H).

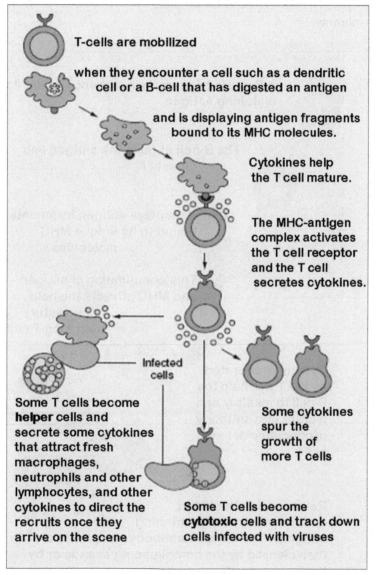

Figure 14-13 T cell activation.

In order for a B cell to elicit the assistance of a T_H cell and become activated to produce plasma or memory cells, it must display peptides from the antigen on its cell surface. To do so, much like an APC, it must ingest the antigen, degrade it into peptides and return the peptides to its surface in a complex with class II MHC proteins. The peptide/ MHC II complex on the B cell then associates with the T cell receptor (TCR) and the CD4 protein on the surface of the T_H cell. This association triggers the production of cytokines (such as interleukins) from the T_H cell, which in turn, stimulate B cell proliferation, producing a clone of B cells with the same B cell receptors, some of which differentiate into plasma cells, other into memory B cells. The plasma cells will secrete antibodies that are identical to the immunoglobin on the parental B cell's membrane.

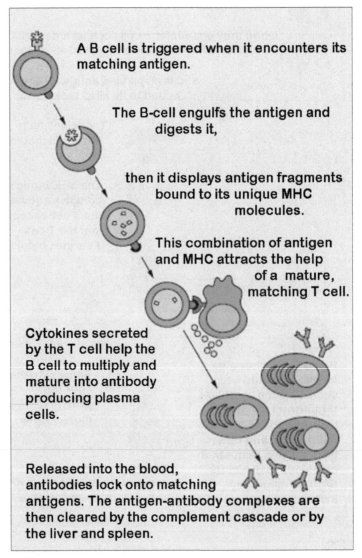

Figure 14-14 B cell activation.

In sum, a humoral response is triggered by activating B cells. However, B cell activation is best accomplished with the aid of T helper cells that have been activated by the association with an antigen presenting cell which displays the same antigen that will be encountered by the B cells.

Clonal selection

Recall that, as a consequence of V(D) J recombination, a multitude of unique variable regions are generated on the receptor molecules of B and T lymphocytes. Each particular receptor has the potential to recognize a particular antigen. By the process of clonal selection, a specific lymphocyte is chosen for clonal proliferation when it identifies an antigen. In this process, numerous immature lymphocytes are produced, each with unique antigen receptors. Any lymphocytes that bind to non-foreign molecules ("self") are destroyed. The remainder will mature, but may never come into contact with an equivalent antigen. However, those lymphocytes that do encounter a matching foreign antigen will be stimulated to proliferate, producing clones of themselves. All of these cells will have receptors for the same antigen.

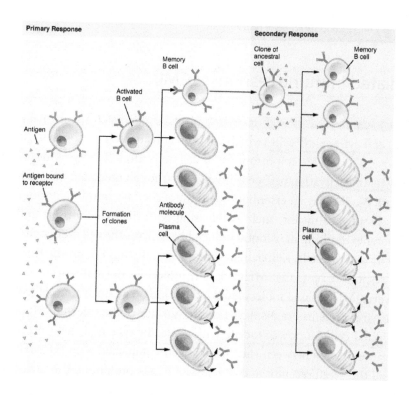

Figure 14-15 Clonal selection.

When a pathogen has been neutralized or destroyed and removed from the body, clonal proliferation of the selected lymphocytes ceases, and most of the remaining clonal cells are degraded. However, some inactive memory B cells and memory T_H cells remain in the lymph system. The persistence of these cells account for the secondary immune response. In general, the antibodies produced by the primary immune response can be detected within the first week of an infection. After the primary immune response subsides, a subsequent exposure to antigen previously encountered elicits a secondary immune response. Because memory B and T_H cells are already present, the clonal selection of new T and B cells is unnecessary, resulting in a more rapid response.

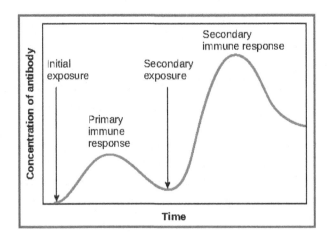

Figure 14-16 The primary and secondary immune response.

The cell mediated immune response (CMI)

T lymphocytes are key players in the cell mediated immune response. The primary types of T cells are T helper cells (T_H) and cytotoxic T cells (which are both considered effector cells), and memory T cells. As mentioned above, T_H cells are important for B cell activation. The cytokines they release are also beneficial for growth and activation of T cells involved in the cell mediated immune response. Memory T cells, like memory B cells, play an essential role in the secondary immune response. Cytotoxic T cells destroy infected cells various means, such as releasing perforins which insert and form pores in the infected cell membrane, resulting in osmotic induced lysis. Thus the cell mediated immune response is employed to directly destroy cells, rather than directly stimulating the production of antibodies (as is done by humoral response). Note that MHC class II molecules normally occur on antigen presenting cells (APCs). However, MHC class I molecules can be found on all nucleated cells. When a virus infects a cell, for example, viral proteins are displayed on the surface of the infected cell bound to MHC class I proteins. The infected cell can now associate with a specific type of T cell (in this case, it is a CD8+ T cell). The association occurs between the viral antigen complexed with the MHC class I protein on the infected cell and the T cell receptor and the adjacent CD8 protein on the surface of the T cell. This linkage stimulates the CD8+ T cell to proliferate and form a clone. Cells of this clone differentiate into cytotoxic T cells and memory T cells. The T cell receptor on the CD8+ cytotoxic T cell matches the antigen displayed with the MHC class I molecule on the virally infected cell, and the cells associate. This triggers the cytotoxic T cell to release perforins and granzymes, which ultimately lead to the demise of the infected cell. The destruction of an infected cell leads to the release of pathogen into the extracellular fluid, where it can be attacked by antibodies and phagocytosed by macrophages. The pores created by the perforins also provide a channel through which proteolytic factors (such as granzymes) from the cytotoxic T cells can enter, causing cell death by apoptosis.

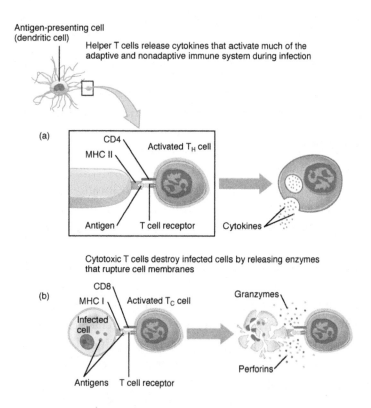

(a)

Antigen-presenting cell
(dendritic cell)

Helper T cells release cytokines that activate much of the adaptive and nonadaptive immune system during infection

CD4

MHC II

Activated T$_H$ cell

Antigen

T cell receptor

Cytokines

Cytotoxic T cells destroy infected cells by releasing enzymes that rupture cell membranes

(b)

CD8

MHC I

Activated T$_C$ cell

Infected cell

Antigens

T cell receptor

Granzymes

Perforins

Figure 14-17 Cytotoxic T cells.

The immune system, then, has an array of resources to defeat an infection by a pathogen. Its arsenal is replete with factors and mechanisms that are targeted to destroy infectious agents in both a non-specific and specific manner. For immediate action, the immune system employs innate mechanisms such as specialized cells, the inflammatory process, cytokines (INF), and the complement system to attack foreign pathogens in a non-specific manner. For action against distinct pathogens (and memory), it engages the adaptive immune system, which utilizes both humoral (antibody) and cell-mediated immune mechanisms. Both of these mechanisms enlist the assistance of antigen presentation and antigen binding to B or T cells via their unique receptors. This binding is facilitated by the association of accessory proteins (such as: CD4 and MHC Class II proteins, or CD8 and MCH Class I proteins). Both humoral and cell-mediated immune responses also rely on the assistance of helper T cells, which release cytokines to further activate the immune response in a number of ways, which include stimulating the growth of additional B and T cells. The B cells can then differentiate into the memory B cells or the antibody-producing plasma cells. Antibodies work to destroy pathogens by a variety of mechanisms (i.e., agglutination, neutralization, engagement of the complement system, induction of phagocytosis, etc.). T cells can differentiate into additional helper T cells, cytotoxic T cells, and memory T cells, which are all essential components of an effective immune response.

Microbes aren't all bad! The microbiota

In Chapter 12: The Digestive System, we learned that some types of bacteria actually facilitate the digestive process and thus are highly beneficial to animals. But the role bacteria play in the human body is much more widespread, as it is believed that for every one human cell, there are 10 bacterial cells that reside in the human body! (Savage DC, 1977). The microbiota is the name given to this population of "endogenous flora" and the term microbiome refers to the genetic material found within an individual microbe such as a bacterium, fungal cell or virus. (Lederberg J, McCray AT. 2001). The microbes that comprise the microbiota are generally considered to be non-pathogenic, co-existing symbiotically with their host. Because the microbiota constitutes such a large number of cells that inhabit the body, it is reasonable to suspect that they play a significant role in a number of normal physiological processes. Microbial colonies are most prevalent at 5 locations in the body: the gastrointestinal tract, the oral and nasal cavities, the skin, the airways, and the urogenital system (such as the vagina). A "healthy" cohort of microbes at these locations is believed to be necessary for proper functioning. Variant composition of microbes has been correlated to diseases such as inflammatory bowel disease, psoriasis, obesity, colorectal cancer, cardiovascular disease, asthma, and liver disease (Cho, S. and Blaser, MJ 2012).

But does correlation indicate cause? Do variations in microbial composition significantly contribute to diseases? The question is currently being explored by the endeavors of a well-funded research initiative of The National Institutes of Health (NIH) entitled "The Human Microbiome Project" (HMP). The goal of this initiative is to determine if there are relevant changes in the microbiomes of healthy and diseased individuals. The first phase of this initiative, the initial sequencing of the genomes of a reference collection of microbes is underway. Characterization of the genomic make-up and complexity of the microbiome at particular body sites, such as those listed above, will follow. The initiative will then focus on the changes in the microbiome in relationship to specific diseases. (See: The NIH Human Microbiome Project).

Chapter 14 Review

I. Helpful animations:

1. The immune response:
   https://highered.mcgrawhill.com/sites/0072507470/student_view0/chapter22/animation__the_immune_response.html

2. T cell activation:
   https://highered.mcgraw-hill.com/sites/0072507470/student_view0/chapter22/animation__t-cell_dependent_antigens__quiz_2_.html

3. Cytotoxic T cells:
   https://highered.mcgrawhill.com/sites/0072507470/student_view0/chapter22/animation__cytotoxic_t-cell_activity_against_target_cells__quiz_2_.html

4. Intracellular infection by salmonella bacteria:
   http://www.hhmi.org/biointeractive/intracellular-infection-salmonella

5. Antigen presentation and CTL:
   http://www.hhmi.org/biointeractive/antigen-presentation-and-ctl

6. HIV life cycle:
   http://www.hhmi.org/biointeractive/hiv-life-cycle

7. Cloning T cells:
   http://www.hhmi.org/biointeractive/cloning-army-t-cells-immune-defense

II. Active Testing: Do you know the facts?

A. List the words in this chapter you would have printed in bold type.
Can you define these words?

B. What are the main, "take home" messages of this chapter?
 Is your answer the same as your instructor's answer?

C. Some Questions:

1. Illustrate the process of viral multiplication.

2. Explain how antibiotics function.

3. Provide examples of the body's: non-specific first line of defense against an infection, nonspecific (innate) immune response and specific immune response (Adaptive/ Acquired).

4. List 4 stages of inflammation.

5. Identify three types of phagocytic cell types.

6. Describe how interferon functions.

7. Describe the role of complement proteins in the immune response.

8. Summarize the 2 main types of adaptive immune responses.

9. Describe how immunoglobin diversity is generated.

10. Describe the process of B cell activation.

11. Illustrate the structure of an antibody.

12. Describe the processes involved in the cell mediated immune response.

13. Compare and contrast non-specific and specific immune responses.

14. Are all microbes harmful? Why or why not?

III. Inquiring minds want to know...

Challenge Questions

1. RNA interference (RNAi), an innate response to viral infection, was initially accepted as an important immunological function in plants and invertebrates. But until recently, its existence in mammals was not uniformly agreed upon. How could a scientist prove that RNAi is a functional antiviral mechanism in mammals? [*Hint*-See: Sagan, S. & Sarnow, P. (2013). RNAi, Antiviral After All. Science 342:207-208; Li, Y. et al. (2013). RNA Interference Functions as an Antiviral Immunity Mechanism in Mammals. Science 342: 231-234; and Maillard, P.V. et al. (2013). Antiviral RNA Interference in Mammalian Cells. Science 342:235-238]

2. Bacteria are often thought of as pathogens. But the trillions of bacteria in the human gastrointestinal tract are important for normal function. How do bacteria actually assist in the normal function of the gut? An example of how Lactobacillus, a bacteria found in yogurt and cheese, aids digestive function is described at: http://www.embo.org/news/research-news/research-news-2013/the-benefits-of-bacteria-for-gut-health

References

Savage, D.C. (1977). Microbial ecology of the gastrointestinal tract. *Annual Review of Microbiology, 31.* doi: 10.1146/annurev.mi.31.100177.000543

Lederberg, M. & McCray, A.T. (2001). 'Ome sweet 'omics –A genealogical treasury of words. Scientist 15, 8. Retrieved from: http://www.the-scientist.com/?articles.view/articleNo/13313/title/-Ome-Sweet--Omics---A- Genealogical-Treasury-of-Words/

Cho, S., & Blaser, M.J. (2012). The human microbiome: At the interface of health and disease. Nature Reviews Genetics, 13. doi: 10.1038/nrg3182

Peterson, J., Garges, S., Giovanni, M., McInnes, P., Wang, L., Schloss, J., Bonazzi, V., McEwen, J., Wetterstrand, K., Deal, C., Baker, C., Di Francesco, V., Howcroft, K., Karp, R.W., Lunsford, R.D., Wellington, C., Tsesahiwot, B., Wright, M., Giblin, C., David, H., Mills, M., Salomon, R., Mullins, C., Akolkar, R., Begg, L., Davis, C., Grandison, L., Humble, M., Khalsa, J., Little, R., Peavy, H. , Pontzer, C., Portnoy, M, Sayre, M., Starke-Reed, P., Zakhari, S., Read, J., Watson, B., & Guyer, M. (2009). The NIH human microbiome project. Genome Research, 19 (12), 2317-23. Retrieved from: http://www.ncbi.nlm.nih.gov/pubmed/19819907

CPSIA information can be obtained
at www.ICGtesting.com
Printed in the USA
BVOW10s0346141016

464817BV00043B/85/P